# Exploring CHEMISTRY in Our World

**Author**
Charles Wolf

**Contributors**
Peter Au
Darryl Carpenter

**Reviewers and Consultants**
Herbert H. Gottlieb
Professor Harry Herzer III
Mark C. Via

**Components**
Exploring Chemistry in Our World
ISBN-10   0-920008-91-7
ISBN-13   978-0-920008-91
Teacher's Manual
Solution Manual
Computer Test Program

Reviewer: Lise Le Bel
Copy Editor: Erin Yount
Design: First Image
Illustrations: First Image
Researcher: Robyn B. Conant

## J.M. LeBel Publishers Inc.

1-800-882-0667
6420 Meadowcreek Drive, Dallas, Texas, 75254
10335-61 Avenue, Edmonton, Alberta, T6H 1K9
www.lebel.com
info@lebel.com

## TABLE OF CONTENTS

D1224085

# Unit A
# Matter, Energy and the Periodic Table

## A.1 What Is Chemistry?

You are surrounded by chemistry and things chemical. Your clothes, running shoes, cosmetics, toothpaste, the food you eat and the fuel burned in your car are all chemicals. You make use of many chemical reactions every day. Driving a car, racing downhill on fiberglass skis, washing the dishes, or playing a video game toy made of plastic are all possible because of chemistry. Chemical reactions power your body's physical activities and even your thoughts.

Environmental problems such as smog, toxic waste, industrial pollution and acid rain are chemicals found in the wrong places at the wrong time. *With a thorough knowledge of chemistry*, people who have the desire can solve most pollution problems by reducing the chemical processes which cause them.

Chemistry deals with matter (its composition), the properties of matter (its characteristics), how one kind of matter interacts with another kind of matter (chemical reactions), and energy changes that result when matter is transformed (energy released or absorbed by chemical reactions). When chemists look at matter, they consider the properties of that particular kind of matter and ask questions such as, "What is the makeup of that substance?", "What type of structure would cause those properties?", "How can the substance be changed or transformed?", and "How can the energy of a reaction be saved or used to do work?"

**Matter**—anything that has mass and takes up space (volume).

**Composition**—the "makeup" of the matter. That is, what kinds and numbers of particles (e.g., atoms) are present in that substance?

**Structure**—how particles are bonded together in a substance.

**Properties**—those characteristics of matter used to identify a substance. Both the composition (amount of each kind of atom) and structure (arrangement of the atoms) are responsible for the properties of a substance.

**Transformations**—changes in matter always involve changes in energy. There are three types:
- *Physical Change* — only the state (e.g., liquid, solid, or gas) or the appearance (e.g., texture) changes. The type of matter (e.g., basic makeup of atoms) is still the same as before (e.g., $H_2O$ [water] can be ice, liquid, or steam).
- *Chemical Change* — involves change to the makeup of a substance. The same atoms are arranged differently in the final substance. A chemical change is also called a chemical reaction (e.g., $H_2$ [hydrogen] and $O_2$ [oxygen] react together to form $H_2O$ [water].
- *Nuclear Change* — produces entirely different atoms.

**Energy**—whatever it takes to generate heat (e.g., burning, explosions, friction), produce electricity (e.g., alternator, battery), or move an object (e.g., push or pull—riding a bicycle).

# A.2 Scientific Methods

Observations are a vital part of science. They are generally of two types, qualitative and quantitative. **Qualitative observations** describe *what can be determined by the five senses* and include such properties as color, odor (must be done carefully), taste (not recommended in the chemistry lab), physical state of matter (e.g., solid, liquid or gas), texture and many others. **Quantitative observations** describe "how much" and *usually require tools for measuring*, such as a ruler, balances, graduated cylinders and other devices. Properties like mass, volume, density, percent composition, melting point and boiling point are considered quantitative properties derived by measuring. In other words, qualitative observations refer to identifiable qualities, while quantitative observations refer to measurable quantities.

Substances have physical or chemical properties. **Physical properties** are those characteristics of a substance that *do not involve a change in the internal makeup of the substance*. These properties include such things as color, crystalline or geometric shape, density, melting point, boiling point, conductivity (ability to conduct electricity) and solubility (ability to dissolve). **Chemical properties** require an *attempt to change the substance to something new*. For example, testing whether a substance is flammable does not necessarily mean the substance will actually burn (e.g., a metal or rock does not burn). Other chemical properties include their ability to react with an acid, water, air or some other gas; the changes that occur when electricity is passed through the substance; and their toxicity to humans and the environment.

Science is all about seeing and solving problems. Scientists are always looking for new and better ways of doing things. They are always looking for answers to questions like, "How can we make a better battery?", "When will a major earthquake hit the San Francisco area?", "What causes AIDS and is it possible to cure someone of HIV?", and many other questions. Scientists are detectives trying to unlock the hidden mysteries of the universe. Their careful observations of various properties of substances we come in contact with, and their skill in organizing and interpreting data, make it possible to solve these and many other problems.

There are many ways to solve scientific problems. Sometimes it is possible to simply look at the problem and come up with a possible answer. But these leaps of understanding are rare. Often scientists investigating one topic find themselves making new discoveries in a completely different area. Usually, though, a more step-by-step process occurs as seen in FIGURE A1:

An example comparing tap (fresh) water with salt water will show you how to use this flowchart.

1. **Observations**: When you swim in the ocean, you notice the water tastes salty; you also float more easily than in a freshwater swimming pool. Friends have told you about their experience floating in the Dead Sea in the Middle East and Great Salt Lake in Utah. Since these bodies of water are much saltier than the ocean, you float even higher in the water.

2. **Identify problems and patterns**: Can you draw a connection between the saltiness of the water and how easily a person floats?

3. **Hypothesis—Predict an answer to a problem**: The more salt dissolved in the water, the greater the "lifting power."

4. **Experiment**: Design an experiment to compare the lifting power of freshwater to different concentrations of salt water.

   Experimental Design:

   a. Obtain 5 jars large enough to float a golf ball.

FIGURE A1
Scientific Ways of Knowing

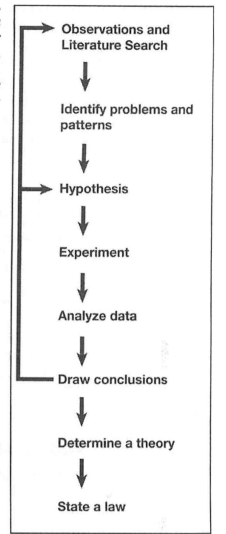

- Observations and Literature Search
- Identify problems and patterns
- Hypothesis
- Experiment
- Analyze data
- Draw conclusions
- Determine a theory
- State a law

Results from experiment

b. Pour 250 mL of water into each jar.

c. Do not put any table salt into the first jar, put 25 g of salt into the second, 50 g of salt into the third, 75 g of salt into the fourth, and 100 g of salt into the last jar.

d. Stir until dissolved.

e. Drop a golf ball into the first jar. Observe whether it floats and, if so, measure how high.

f. Repeat the process for jars 2 through 5.

5. **Evaluate data** (See results.):

a. The golf ball did not float in either the first or second jar.

b. The ball barely floated in the third jar. (It sinks slowly.)

c. The ball floated higher in jar 4 and highest of all in jar 5.

6. **Draw conclusions**: There is apparently a minimum amount of salt needed to float the ball. Once the ball is floating, the more salt added, the higher the ball floats.

7. **Determine a theory**: From other experiments we have done with objects that float, we know that whether or not something floats depends on its density. If the ball does not float in jar 1, then the density of the ball must be greater than the density of the plain water. Adding salt should increase the density of the water. The more salt added, the greater the density of the water solution and the better the ball floats.

Repeat the process:

a. Try the same experiment using Epsom salts instead of table salt.

b. Determine the density of the ball and each of the solutions to see if density is really a factor. If it is, then the densities of each should line up accordingly.

# A.3 Classification (Organization) of Matter

Scientists are always looking for ways to organize information to make it easier to understand. One way of classifying (organizing) matter into categories is shown in FIGURE A2. Let's look more closely at this classification system:

**PURE SUBSTANCES**—This is a category of only one type of matter (atom). Pure substances like Au (gold) cannot be separated or divided further by boiling, melting, spinning or filtering.

ELEMENTS—An element may be composed of a single atom or a group of atoms, but it is made up of only one type of atom. It cannot be broken down any further except by nuclear processes. Some elements are metals, some are nonmetals, some are metalloids (semi-metals), and some are noble gases (nonreactive, inert). The Periodic Table is used to classify the elements and will be studied in greater detail later. The stair-step line starting at the element B (boron) is the division between metals on the left side and nonmetals on the right. (See the Periodic Table on back cover.) There are currently 115 known elements.

*Examples*: Copper (Cu) metal, sodium (Na) metal, silicon (Si) metalloid, bromine ($Br_2$) nonmetal, sulfur ($S_8$) nonmetal and argon (Ar) noble gas.

COMPOUNDS—A compound is formed when two or more elements (atoms) have been chemically joined together to make a new substance. Its properties are entirely different from the elements used to make the new compound. Compounds may be broken down by *heating, reaction with acids, electric current* and other **chemical processes**. New compounds are always being discovered, leading to exciting research in chemistry. There are two general types of compounds:

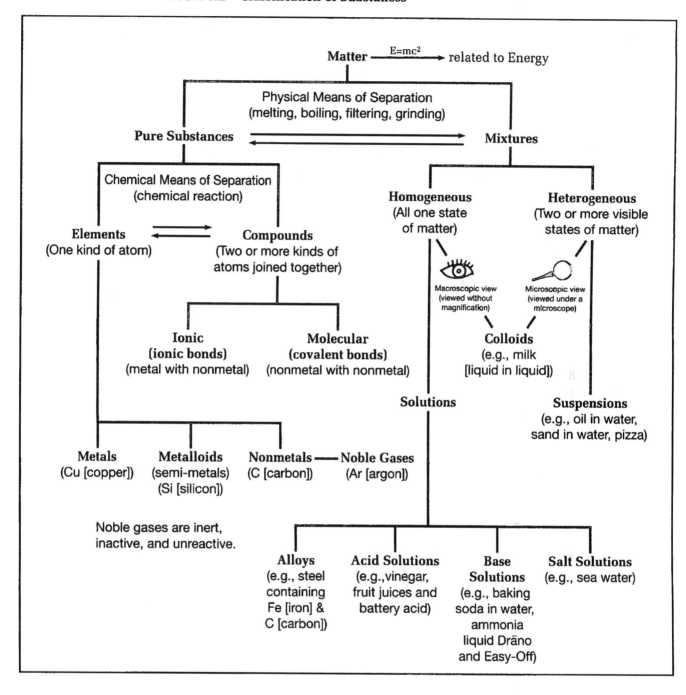

—*Ionic (ionic bonds)*—are formed by the combination of a metal with a nonmetal.

*Examples*: Table salt (NaCl), deicer salt ($CaCl_2$), Epsom salt ($MgSO_4$)

**Mineral** — any element (e.g., gold, copper) or compound (e.g., salt) that occurs naturally in the earth.  For example, table salt, NaCl, is known as halite when found in the earth; elements, like gold, are mined from the earth.

**Oxide** — a compound composed of oxygen and one other element.  For example, alumina is $Al_2O_3$, rust is $Fe_3O_4$, and carbon dioxide is $CO_2$.

**–Molecular (covalent bonds)**—are formed by the combination of a nonmetal with another nonmetal.  The result is called a molecule.

*Examples*: Carbon monoxide (CO), water ($H_2O$), ammonia ($NH_3$)

**MIXTURES (IMPURE SUBSTANCES)**—A mixture contains two or more pure substances that are not chemically joined together.  A mixture retains the properties of the original components.  These components may be mixed in any proportions and can be separated by *physical processes such as filtering, boiling and centrifuging* (spinning to separate an insoluble solid from a liquid).

HOMOGENEOUS MIXTURES—This kind of mixture is *completely uniform* in its composition.  That is, it looks the same everywhere in the mixture even under a microscope.  It has a uniform color and concentration.  There is only one solid, liquid or gas present.  Homogeneous mixtures are usually called solutions and may contains other solids or gases.

*Examples*: Sugar in water (solid in liquid), air (gas in gas), carbonated water—carbon dioxide in water (gas in liquid), brass (a copper-zinc solid in solid) or bronze (copper-zinc-tin solid in solid).

Alloy — a mixture of two or more elements, where at least one is a metal, that have been melted together to form a uniform compound.  Steel always contains iron and carbon.  Other elements are added to the steel to achieve desired effects, such as corrosion resistance.  (Stainless steel [corrosion-resistant metal] contains iron [Fe], carbon [C], chromium [Cr] and  nickel [Ni].)

HETEROGENEOUS MIXTURES—This kind of mixture is *not uniform* in its composition.  You can see different solids and liquids within the mixture.  This is the easiest type of mixture to separate. In fact, some may even separate by themselves.

*Examples*: Vinegar and oil salad dressing (liquid in liquid), chunky peanut butter (solids and liquid)

Ore — a rock containing a mineral or a mixture of minerals where an element can be obtained.  For example, iron ore may contain the mineral hematite, $Fe_2O_3$.  Processing this ore at a steel mill produces nearly pure iron, the main component of steel.

Plated Metal — one metal that has been covered with another metal.  This is typically done to prevent corrosion (e.g., rust) of an object or to make an item more attractive.  For example, car parts and roofing nails are coated with zinc—a process called galvanizing (to prevent rust); steel cans are coated with tin (to prevent corrosion); car bumpers and faucets are chrome-plated; and dinner utensils and bowls are silver-plated (to look more attractive); for the same reason, jewelry is often gold-filled or silver-plated.

COLLOID—This is a mixture that falls in between a homogeneous mixture and a heterogeneous mixture. It looks uniform without magnification, but liquids and solids can be seen under a microscope.

*Examples*: Milk (liquid in liquid), gelatin (liquid in solid), fog (liquid in gas), or smoke (solid in gas)

# A.4 <u>Exercises</u> Classification of Matter

For questions 1–15, use the classification system given in FIGURE A2, to put each type of matter (the substances present are in parentheses) into one of the following categories:

A. Pure Substance — Element      C. Homogeneous mixture
B. Pure Substance — Compound     D. Heterogeneous mixture

1. charcoal ($C_{(s)}$) _____

2. oxygen ($O_{2(g)}$) _____

3. sulfur dioxide ($SO_{2(g)}$) _____

4. tap water ($H_2O$, minerals) _____

5. quartz sand ($SiO_{2(s)}$) _____

6. hydrochloric acid ($HCl_{(aq)}$) _____

7. glass ($SiO_2$, $Na_2CO_3$, $CaCO_3$) _____

8. pizza (varies) _____

9. table salt ($NaCl_{(s)}$) _____

10. neon gas ($Ne_{(g)}$) _____

11. distilled water ($H_2O_{(l)}$) _____

12. salt water ($H_2O$, $NaCl$) _____

13. glucose ($C_6H_{12}O_{6(s)}$) _____

14. brass ($Cu - Zn$) _____

15. aluminum can ($Al_{(s)}$) _____

| |
|---|
| (s) = solid |
| (l) = liquid |
| (g) = gas |
| (aq) = aqueous solution (substance is dissolved in water) |

16. Classify each of the following mixtures and suggest how each could be separated into its components:

a. iron filings and powdered sulfur _____

_____

b. table salt and water _____

_____

c. sand, sugar, and water (well mixed) _____

_____

d. blood _____

_____

e. crude oil _____

_____

f. alcohol and water _____

_____

# A.5 Evidence for Chemical Reactions

**Purpose:**

✔ To become familiar with the types of evidence that verify a chemical reaction has occurred.

✔ To appreciate the everyday occurrence of chemical reactions.

✔ To practice observation skills and other laboratory related skills.

✔ To introduce precipitation, endothermic and exothermic reactions.

**Prelab Information:**

Chemical reactions involve a rearrangement of atoms or ions through the breaking and forming of bonds to create new and different substances. The rearrangement of atoms through the breaking and forming of bonds cannot be directly observed. Any evidence for a chemical reaction must come from observing the formation of new substances. Some of the easy-to-observe clues for recognizing a chemical reaction are:

1. **Formation of a precipitate** — a new substance is formed with a much lower solubility than the original substance. When a **precipitate** (*a new solid produced when solutions are mixed*) forms, new stronger bonds must have formed which cannot be broken by reactions with the other chemicals available.

2. **Formation of a gas** — a new substance is formed which is a gas at laboratory conditions of temperature and pressure (*visible bubbles without boiling*).

3. **Color change** — a new substance is formed which has a different color than the original substances. The forming of new bonds influences the energy of the electrons, which in turn influences the color of the substances.

4. **Energy change** (heat and/or light is released or absorbed) — new substances are formed which contain a different amount of chemical energy than the reactants. The new bond energies are either less or greater than the original energies. Energy is released or absorbed so as to obey the Law of Conservation of Energy.

**Lab Safety:**

• Wear your chemical splash goggles and apron.
• Observe all warnings and cautions.

**Procedure:**

In the experiments that follow, look for evidence of a chemical reaction. The description of the reaction will be important in the lab report and in the discussion of what was observed. Record your observations in the table provided.

1. There may be more than one piece of evidence for a chemical reaction. Write them all down.

2. Work quickly, only a few minutes are allowed at each station.

3. Most of the reactions are fairly practical; think about where they apply.

4. Put a check mark beside the evidence observed.

5. Write in any further descriptions of the reactants, the products and the reaction in the space provided to assist in describing what happened.

6. Clean up the station before going on.

7. Observe all safety precautions.

**Observations—Experiment Stations:**

1. *Baking soda and lemon juice (or sour milk) are commonly used in baking.* Place some baking soda in a beaker and add a small amount of lemon juice.

2. *Natural gas is burned in a home furnace or water heater.* Reduce the air supply to the Bunsen burner. Turn the gas on and light the Bunsen burner. Increase the air supply to the Bunsen burner in order to get more complete combustion (blue flame). After making the observations, turn the gas off.

3. *Drain cleaner is used to unplug a drain.* Add a scoopful of drain cleaner to approximately 10 mL of water and stir. (**Caution:** Drain cleaner can cause severe skin burns. Wash any drain cleaner off with lots of water.)

4. ***Demo:*** *Concrete should be etched with muriatic acid before painting.* Add a drop or two of muriatic acid to the concrete (or slaked lime) provided. (**Caution:** Muriatic acid is very dangerous. Wash any acid off with lots of water and baking soda.)(Wear gloves and goggles.)

5. *Objects may be plated with a more desirable metal.* Follow instructions at the station or otherwise just watch the copper-plating going on.

6. ***Demo:*** *Gunpowder is used to project a bullet from a rifle shell.* Light a small amount of gunpowder in an evaporating dish. (**Caution:** Use only 1 scoopula full as instructed.)

**Lab Safety:**
- Must have a safety shield in place.
- Stand back at least two meters and wear goggles.
- Alternatively, do this demo under a fume hood.

7. *The presence of lead compound may be detected by the following tests.* Test the given solution(s) for lead(II) ions by adding a few drops of aqueous sodium iodide together with a few drops of the given solution(s) to a test tube. Follow the directions for disposal as given at the station. (**Caution**: Lead compounds are TOXIC!)

8. *Chemicals are used to relieve an upset stomach.* Add a small amount of Alka Seltzer or equivalent to some water in a beaker.

9. *Cobalt(II) chloride is used to test for the presence of water, to detect high humidity and to indicate when a plant should be watered.* Add some dry cobalt(II) chloride solid or paper to water.

10. *Solutions may be tested for their aqueous ions, or fireplace logs with colored flames may be produced, as follows:*

    If atomizers are not present, soak a cotton swab (or nichrome wire loop) in one of the solutions provided and then hold the splint in a blue Bunsen burner flame. Repeat with another solution. Leave the Bunsen burner burning with a yellow flame when you leave the station.

11. *Hydrogen peroxide (known for its effect on hair and as an antiseptic) decomposes rapidly when a catalyst is added.* Add a small amount of hydrogen peroxide to a beaker and then sprinkle in a couple grains of manganese(IV) oxide.

12. *Sani-Flush is used as a disinfectant and a rust and stain remover.* Add a small amount of Sani-Flush (or equivalent) to a beaker full of water. (**Caution**: Sani-Flush is very corrosive. Read the first-aid instructions on the can.)

13. *Litmus paper may be used to test for the acidity of an aqueous solution.* Add a drop of vinegar to blue litmus paper. Then add another drop to red litmus paper. (Litmus turns red with an acid solution, blue with a base solution.)

14. *Foods may be tested for starch using iodine.* Add a few drops of iodine test solution to some potatoes and other foods to test for starch.

15. *Hard water may be softened by washing soda.* Put a few drops of (simulated) hard water in a small test tube. Add a few drops of aqueous washing soda to the water in the test tube. (This simulation exaggerates the actual process.)

| Station | Precipitate Formed | Color Change | Energy Change | Gas Formed | Observations |
|---|---|---|---|---|---|
| 1. Baking Soda | | | | | |
| 2. Natural Gas | | | | | |
| 3. Drain Cleaner | | | | | |
| 4. Etching concrete | | | | | |
| 5. Electroplating | | | | | |
| 6. Gunpowder | | | | | |
| 7. Lead compound | | | | | |
| 8. Upset stomach | | | | | |
| 9. Presence of Water | | | | | |
| 10. Flame test | | | | | |
| 11. Hydrogen peroxide | | | | | |
| 12. Sani-Flush | | | | | |
| 13. Litmus Paper | | | | | |
| 14. Starch Test | | | | | |
| 15. Hard water | | | | | |

**Questions:**

1. What is the difference between an observation and an interpretation?

_____

_____

_____

_____

2. Draw a sketch of a Bunsen burner. Label the gas and air adjustments. List the steps for lighting a Bunsen burner.

_____

_____

_____

_____

_____

3. What is used to test for the presence of starch? Describe the test.

_____

_____

4. What is used to test for the presence of water? Describe the test.

_____

_____

5. What is used to test for an acid/base solution? Describe the test.

_____

_____

_____

6. What is a precipitate?

_____

_____

_____

_____

7. How can you tell if a gas is produced?

_____

_____

_____

_____

8. What is an exothermic reaction? Give one example from this lab.

_____

_____

_____

_____

9. What is an endothermic reaction? Give one example from this lab.

_____

_____

_____

10. In terms of atoms and molecules, what is the difference between a chemical change and a phase change?

_____

_____

_____

_____

_____

_____

11. Use the observations from this lab and from everyday life to develop an argument for the value of chemistry to humans.

_____

_____

_____

_____

_____

_____

# A.6 Changes in Matter

Matter is constantly being changed. What kinds of changes can occur and what happens to matter during these changes?

**Physical Changes**—A physical change in matter is any change that alters the general shape or appearance of the substance, for example, water becomes ice under freezing conditions. In this case, the same kinds of molecules are present before and after the water freezes. *No new substance* has been produced. No chemical change has occurred.

*Examples of physical changes*: melting, freezing, boiling, condensing, subliming (solid to a gas; e.g., ice changing to water vapor, solid carbon dioxide [dry ice] to a gas), deposition (gas to a solid, e.g., water vapor to snow).

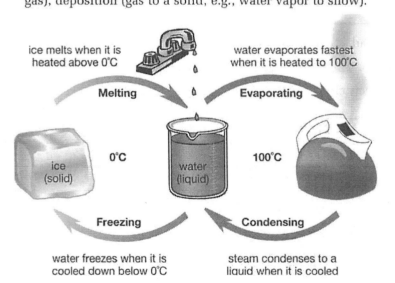

ice melts when it is heated above 0°C

**Melting**

water evaporates fastest when it is heated to 100°C

**Evaporating**

ice (solid)   0°C   water (liquid)   100°C

**Freezing**

water freezes when it is cooled down below 0°C

**Condensing**

steam condenses to a liquid when it is cooled

Increasing Temperature

Boiling Point — Boiling — **Gas** — Condensing —

**Liquid**

Melting Point — Melting — **Solid** — Freezing —

Examples of shape or appearance changes:
grinding, bending, breaking, cutting, pressurizing.

**Chemical Changes**—A chemical change in matter always results in the formation of one or more new substances. These new substances have a different composition and structure than the original substances. This means the color, solubility, density, melting point and other properties will be different from the original matter. In addition, a chemical change usually involves a greater amount of energy than a physical change (e.g., baking soda plus vinegar will produce much more energy than ice melting or water boiling). A chemical change can usually be identified by:

1. A color change

2. The formation of an insoluble solid (precipitate)

3. Bubbling (gas produced merely by mixing two different things)

4. An energy change

   *Examples*: tarnishing ($Ag_2S$), rusting (FeO), burning ($CO_2$) or respiring ($CO_2$)

Many times it is difficult to distinguish between a chemical change and a physical change because one often follows the other. It may be helpful to ask whether reversing the process will return the matter to the original substance. *Chemical processes are more difficult—sometimes impossible—to return to the original state than physical changes* (e.g., reversing the chemical reaction between vinegar and baking soda is more difficult than freezing water—a physical change).

**Nuclear Changes**—A nuclear change involves changing one atom to a different kind of atom. This nearly always means that a new element is formed. The amount of energy released during a nuclear change is thousands of times greater than the energy exchanged during a chemical reaction.

# A.7 <u>Exercises</u> Changes in Matter

Classify each of the following examples as a physical (P), chemical (C) or nuclear (N) change. State the evidence/reason for each decision.

1. Water freezes. _____

2. A cake is baked. _____

3. Air and gasoline are *mixed*. _____

4. Air and gasoline are *ignited*. _____

5. Latex paint dries. _____

6. Uranium changes to lead. _____

7. Dew forms on the grass. _____

8. Solar cells produce electricity. _____

9. An egg is fried. _____

10. Concrete sets. _____

11. Milk sours. _____

12. An apple ripens. _____

13. A light bulb is turned on. _____

14. Salt melts road ice. _____

15. Solar heat is produced in the sun. _____

# A.8 Energy and Matter

Energy is somewhat difficult to define, but it is always associated with an object moving. It is usually thought of in two different ways (see FIGURE A3):

**1. Potential Energy** — the possibility of causing matter to move. Potential energy, in general, is energy stored in matter due to its position relative to other objects (e.g., one object positioned above another).

*Examples*:
- A person standing at the top of a cliff has more gravitational potential energy than a person standing at the bottom of the same cliff.
- Water behind a dam has gravitational potential energy to turn a turbine to produce electrical kinetic energy that will produce other forms of energy.
- Matter is actually a very concentrated form of energy. During a nuclear change, a small amount of matter can be converted into a large amount of energy. In a nuclear reactor, such potential energy can be channeled to turn a steam turbine to produce electrical kinetic energy.

Formula: $E_k = \frac{1}{2}mv^2$

Legend: $E_p$ = potential energy
$E_k$ = kinetic energy
$m$ = mass
$v$ = velocity (speed)
$E$ = energy
$c$ = speed of light

**2. Kinetic Energy** — the movement of matter. Sometimes this movement can be observed directly while at other times this movement is on the microscopic level. The amount of kinetic energy depends on how big the object is and how fast it is moving.

*Examples*:
- A ball being thrown, a car moving down the street, or a tree falling all involve moving objects.
- Heat, sound, electricity and light are also forms of kinetic energy because they all involve the motion of particles or waves.

**FIGURE A3  Classification of Energy Types**

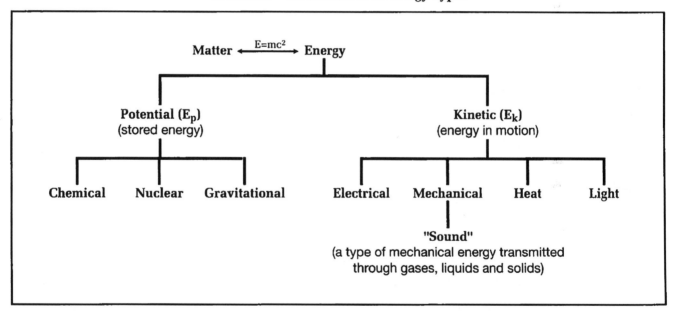

The Law of Conservation of Energy states that energy is never lost or gained, but is often converted from one form to another. Consider the transformation of energy as a battery is used to operate a flashlight.

All of the energy put out by the battery can be accounted for either by actual use of the energy (e.g., as light) or "lost heat" (e.g., from light bulb). (The Law of Conservation of Energy is also known as the First Law of Thermodynamics.)

## A.9 <u>Exercises</u> Energy and Matter

1. Determine whether the following situations represent primarily kinetic (K) or potential (P) energy.

    a. A moving car                           _____

    b. Water behind a dam                _____

    c. Food                                 _____

    d. Electricity                         _____

    e. Sunlight traveling from sun to earth   _____

    f. A wound clock spring              _____

    g. A stick of dynamite              _____

    h. A charged battery                _____

2. What two factors determine the kinetic energy of a moving object?

_____

3. Which has more kinetic energy?
    a. A bicycle moving 10 km/h or a car moving 10 km/h?  Explain.

_____

_____

    b. A 90-mph fastball or a barely rolling bowling ball?  Explain.

_____

_____

_____

# A.10 The Classification of Elements on the Basis of Chemical and Physical Properties

Now that the differences between elements, compounds and mixtures have been explained, elements and their properties will be dealt with in more detail.

Scientists are always searching for ways to organize information. *One of the best ways of organizing the elements* is to use the **Periodic Table**. Throughout the rest of this unit you will learn why the Periodic Table is organized the way it is and some of the useful information that can be obtained just by looking at where an element is positioned on the Periodic Table. (See FIGURE A4.)

The Periodic Table is made up of vertical columns and horizontal rows. The *vertical columns are called* **groups**. (A group is also called a **family**). All of the elements in the same group have similar chemical and physical properties. The groups have been identified by a number/letter designation (e.g., 2A) at the top of the column. Some of the groups have been given special names. An example of this would be that Group 1A is called the **alkali metals**. All other groups are named by the first element in the column. For example, Group 4A is also known as the carbon family.

Hydrogen appears in both Group 1A and Group 7A because it has properties similar to both groups, but does not actually fit into either group. Hydrogen is a "chemical orphan"—it doesn't belong to one particular family. Another method of labeling the groups is to number the columns from 1 to 18 where Group 1 is the same as Group 1A (alkali metals) and Group 18 is the same as Group 8A (noble gases). (See "Main Groups of Elements.")

The *horizontal part of the Periodic Table* is called a **period**. (A period is also known as a **row** or **series**.) A period is a sequence of elements that change their properties in a regular way. On the far left side of the Periodic Table are the very reactive (i.e., easily changed) metals. As you proceed from left to right across the period, the metals become less reactive. Examine a Periodic Table and you will notice a "stair-step line" on the right-hand side of the chart. This line separates the metals from the nonmetals. From this line the elements become increasingly nonmetallic in their characteristics. *The last element in the period (row)* on the right is always a **noble gas**. Noble gases do not react with other elements. This sequence of changes in properties repeats itself with each new period (row). A detailed Periodic Table appears on the back cover.

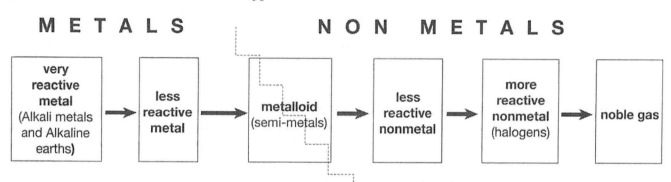

FIGURE A4    Main Groupings of the Periodic Table

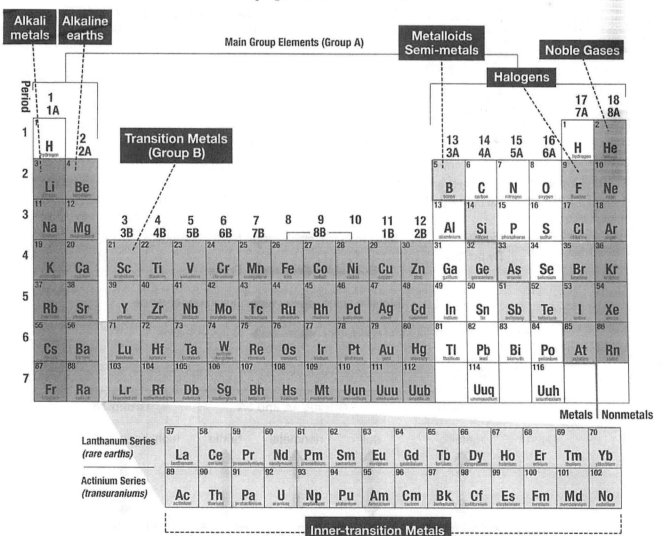

## Properties of the Elements at Room Temperature (25°C) and Standard Pressure

**Metals:**
1. Shiny (metallic **luster**).
2. Good conductors of heat and electricity.
3. Flexible: can be bent, pulled into wires (**ductile**), or rolled into sheets (**malleable**).
4. All are solids except for mercury.
5. All have a "silver" color except for gold and copper.

*Examples*: sodium (Na), iron (Fe), copper (Cu), aluminum (Al)

**Nonmetals:**
1. Solids may be dull in appearance or may have a glassy luster.
2. Poor conductors of heat and electricity.
3. Brittle.
4. Some are solid, some liquid, and some are gaseous.
5. Colors vary.

*Examples*: carbon (C), nitrogen (N), sulfur (S), iodine (I)

**Metalloids (Semi-Metals):**
1. Have some of the properties of both metals and nonmetals.
2. Semiconductors: conduct in some conditions, but not in others. This makes them useful for computer chips and transistors in calculators, personal computers and video games.
3. All are solids.

*Examples*: arsenic (As), silicon (Si), antimony (Sb), germanium (Ge)

**Noble Gases:**
1. Are the least reactive elements on the Periodic Table.
2. Do not conduct electricity.
3. Include 7 gases: He (helium), Ne (neon), Ar (argon), Kr (krypton), Xe (xenon), Rn (radon) and Uuo (ununoctium).

**Trends:**
By period:

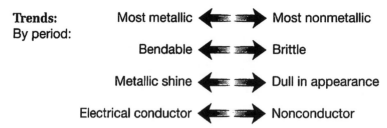

**Trends:**
By group:

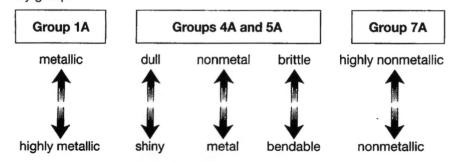

# A.11 Relationship of Chemical Symbols to Chemical Names

Jöns Jakob Berzelius suggested the chemical symbols that everybody uses today. Berzelius used letters to represent the atoms of each element.

Thus:

| | | | |
|---|---|---|---|
| C – carbon | P – phosphorus | H – hydrogen | S – sulfur |
| I – iodine | N – nitrogen | O – oxygen | F – fluorine |

With over 100 elements and only 26 letters in the alphabet, it became necessary to include a second letter with the first. The second letter of the symbol is usually the second letter in the name of the element or a main consonant in the name (i.e., Ca, not CA nor $C_A$). The full name of the element is written with lower case (noncapital) letters only.

Thus:

| | | | |
|---|---|---|---|
| Al – aluminum | As – arsenic | Ba – barium | Br – bromine |
| Ca – calcium | Cl – chlorine | Mg – magnesium | Zn – zinc |

In addition, symbols are not all derived from the common English name. Many come from the Latin name. The table below gives a summary of these exceptions. The important Latin names are italicized. The Classical System uses the root word portion of the Latin names to name the ions.

| Common Names | Symbol | Latin Names |
|---|---|---|
| antimony | Sb | *stib*num |
| copper ( ♀ ) | Cu | *cu*prum |
| gold ( ✿ ) | Au | *au*rum |
| iron ( ♂ ) | Fe | *ferr*um |
| lead ( ♄ ) | Pb | *plumb*um |
| mercury ( ☿ ) | Hg | *hydra*gyrum |
| potassium | K | *kal*ium |
| silver ( ☾ ) | Ag | *arg*entum |
| sodium | Na | *na*trium |
| tin ( ♃ ) | Sn | *stann*um |
| tungsten | W | *wolfram* |

The name and symbol for all new elements is now established by IUPAC (The International Union of Pure and Applied Chemistry). IUPAC generally respects the recommendations of the scientists who discovered the element. IUPAC now requires two letters for any new element symbol.

## A.12 <u>Exercises</u> Relationship of Chemical Symbols to Chemical Names

Complete the following table. (Use the Periodic Table on the back cover.)

| Element | Symbol | Group and Element Number | Period | Element Category* |
|---|---|---|---|---|
| 1. bromine | | | | |
| 2. | Co | | | |
| 3. | | 2A/2 | 4 | |
| 4. | | | 2 | noble gas |
| 5. | B | | | |
| 6. sodium | | | | |

\* halogen, noble gas, alkali metal, alkaline earth metal, transition metal, or none of these

7. Which two elements in the following set would be expected to have similar properties?

$_{37}$Rb $\qquad$ $_{38}$Sr $\qquad$ $_{54}$Xe $\qquad$ $_{56}$Ba

8. What element is in Period 4, Group 5A? (Give both name and symbol.)

9. How many elements could be classified as metals in Group 4A?

10. Which element in Period 5 cannot be found occurring naturally in the universe?

11. What is the total number of elements in the Periodic Table that are gases at room temperature?

12. How many elements are alkali metals?

13. How do the boiling points of the halogens change from the top to the bottom of the group?

14. Give the name and symbol for all the elements in Period 2 that are gases at room temperature.

15. In what year was bismuth discovered?

16. Fluorine belongs to what group? (Give group name and group number.)

_____

17. Which noble gas is the least likely to change to a solid?

_____

For questions 18–19, gadolinium is an element that is magnetic at some temperatures, but not magnetic at other temperatures.

18. To what period does it belong?

_____

19. To what special classification of elements does it belong, i.e., what kind of metal is it?

_____

For questions 20–21, radon gas is a radioactive element produced naturally in the earth's crust as certain elements decay to form new elements.

20. What is the name of the group to which it belongs? _____

21. In what year was radon discovered? _____

For questions 22–23, identify two important characteristics of phosphorus:

22. Is it shiny or dull? _____

_____

23. Would it be brittle or malleable? _____

For questions 24–25, silver is considered to be a precious metal.

24. Identify three major characteristics of silver.

_____

_____

25. To what special classification of elements does silver belong?

_____

For questions 26–32, the symbols of the following groups of elements spell out the names of various beverages. Using the chemical symbols, decipher and spell out these "Atomic Beverages."

26. Tantalum, Phosphorus; Tungsten, Astatine, Erbium. _____

27. Iodine, Cerium; Tellurium, Arsenic. _____

28. Cobalt, Fluorine, Iron, Einsteinium. _____

29. Cobalt, Calcium – Cobalt, Lanthanum. _____

30. Sulfur, Hydrogen, Arsenic, Tantalum. _____

31. Plutonium, Nitrogen, Carbon, Hydrogen. _____

32. Phosphorus, Oxygen, Phosphorus. _____

# Unit B
# Structure of the Atom

## B.1 A Look Inside Matter

So far the emphasis on matter has been on observation and classification. The elements have been observed and classified as metals and nonmetals and as families of elements. The classifications of elements based on chemical and physical properties led to the development of the Periodic Table. The value of this classification system was proven through its usefulness in predicting the existence and the properties of as-yet-undiscovered elements.

Since the days of the ancient Greeks, people have wondered about the makeup of atoms (matter). At that time, the Greeks had two ideas: either matter was continuous, and you could break it down — dividing it in half — forever; or you could break it down until you arrived at a basic building block or indivisible unit of matter. In fact, the word *atom* comes from the Greek word ***atomos***, which means "indivisible." **Atoms** are the *basic building blocks of all substances* and cannot be broken down further by chemical means.

John Dalton proposed the existence of an indivisible atom in 1804. This was well before Mendeleev published his periodic table in 1869. However, it was not until 1912 that Niels Bohr developed a model of the atom which could explain the periodic repetition of properties of the elements. (See FIGURE B18.)

In this unit, a theory of atomic structure will be presented which helps to explain **why** elements have the properties that were observed in Unit A. In this unit, elements will be defined in terms of their atomic structures. You will discover the two main parts of an atom: the nucleus and the electrons outside the nucleus.

Remember that for a theory to be considered accurate, it must agree with and make predictions consistent with the facts (i.e., *observations*). If a **theory** (*explanation*) and its **model** (*picture* or *diagram to help understand the theory*) do not agree with the observations, then the theory must be revised or a new theory must be developed. (See FIGURE A1)

Over the last 200 years, different and gradually more complex models of the atom have been proposed. Each model was based on a theory that tried to explain then-current observations and predict future observations. Mendeleev's periodic table is an example of a good model.

## B.2 Models of the Atom

How do scientists know that matter is made up of particles called atoms? What evidence is available to indicate the existence of atoms? By about 1800, a number of important generalizations existed as a result of hundreds of experimental observations. These are:

- The combined mass of all the substances involved in a physical or chemical change remains constant. This is known as the **Law of Conservation of Mass.**

  *Examples*: 23 g sodium + 35 g chlorine → 58 g sodium chloride
  2 g hydrogen + 16 g oxygen → 18 g water
  2 g hydrogen + 32 g oxygen → 34 g hydrogen peroxide

- Elements react in specific mass ratios.

*Examples*: Sodium Chloride:  23 g sodium

                              35 g chlorine

Water:   $\dfrac{2 \text{ g hydrogen}}{16 \text{ g oxygen}} = \dfrac{1 \text{ g hydrogen}}{8 \text{ g oxygen}}$

Hydrogen Peroxide:  $\dfrac{2 \text{ g hydrogen}}{32 \text{ g oxygen}} = \dfrac{1 \text{ g hydrogen}}{16 \text{ g oxygen}}$

- Compounds have a specific composition, no matter how they are prepared.
  *Example*:  Sodium Chloride: NaCL     Water: $H_2O$     Hydrogen Peroxide: $H_2O_2$

## Dalton Model ("Billiard Ball" Model)

In 1804 John Dalton, using known observations and a table of element masses, proposed the theory that elements are actually made up of indivisible, spherical particles called atoms similar to the billiard ball shown in FIGURE B1. He further suggested that:

- Atoms of one substance are chemically alike and have the same mass.
- Only atoms can work together in a reaction.
- Chemical reactions consist of rearranging atoms.
- Elements are made of "simple atoms" while compounds contain "compounded atoms," that is, two or more atoms joined together (now called molecules).

This model satisfied known observations as follows:

- The mass stays constant because there are the same number and kind of atoms before and after a reaction. The only difference is that the atoms have been rearranged to form a new substance.

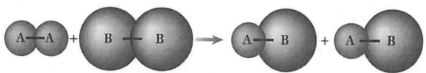

- Elements react in specific proportions by mass because only whole atoms can be involved in a reaction and each kind of atom has its own mass.

Dalton's model was amazingly successful and parts of the model are still used today. However, the model was not able to explain how atoms joined together. In addition, particles smaller than the atom were soon discovered. The atom was no longer the smallest particle possible. The model had to be revised.

## New Evidence is Gathered

Around the 1900s, new evidence was discovered about the atom that Dalton's model of the atom did not address:

- The atom is made up of both positive and negative parts.
- The heaviest part of the atom has a positive charge.
- The atom contains equal numbers of positive and negative charges.
- Opposite charges (+ and –) attract; like charges (+ and +, or – and –) repel.
- Some substances are radioactive.

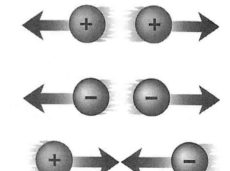

In keeping with scientific methods, it was necessary to modify Dalton's theory or discard it completely.

**FIGURE B1
"Billiard Ball"
Model**

### Thomson Model ("Raisin Bun" Model)

J. J. Thomson revised the Dalton model in 1898 by proposing that the atom be considered a sphere of positive electricity in which negative electrons are embedded like raisins in a bun (see FIGURE B2). The "dough" part of the bun represented the positive part of the atom. It certainly would not make sense to put all the positive charge in the middle of the atom and the electrons outside, because the atom would repel itself apart or collapse into the center.

It should be noted that the Thomson model did not alter the main points of Dalton's theory concerning elements and their reactions to form compounds.

---

**MINI DEMO**

# B.3 Static Electricity

**Purpose:**
✔ To use an electroscope to show how electrical charges behave.

**Materials:**
- black plastic strip
- electroscope (optional)
- pith balls on a string
- glass rod
- fur
- ring stand & clamp
- clear plastic strip
- silk

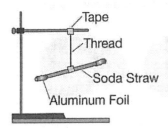
Tape
Thread
Soda Straw
Aluminum Foil

**Procedure:**
1. Rub clear plastic strip with fur (makes strip negatively charged). Touch pith ball(s).
2. Charge strip again using fur. Bring strip close to pith ball. This time ball is repelled.
3. Rub dark plastic strip with silk (makes strip positively charged). Bring strip close to pith ball. Now ball is attracted.

**Note:** This demo does NOT work well in humid weather!

**Conclusions:**
What did you learn during each part of the experiment?

_____

_____

_____

_____

---

### Rutherford Model ("Empty-Space" Model or Nuclear Model)

In 1911, Ernest Rutherford performed an experiment involving tiny alpha particles (*positively charged*) and very thin gold foil (*only a few atoms thick*). He reasoned that if the atom was constructed like Thomson's model, then the alpha particles should slow down somewhat and might "fan out" slightly like a spray nozzle. What he found instead was that 99% of the alpha particles went straight through the foil, some were deflected (pushed aside) at large angles, and a few were actually deflected back along their path (see FIGURE B3). This evidence did not agree with a uniform distribution of mass and charge as shown in the Thomson model.

Rutherford proposed a model of the atom with a nucleus or core, containing all of the positive charge and nearly all of the mass. Almost the whole volume of the atom would be empty space occupied only by the moving negatively charged **electrons** (see FIGURE B4). The relatively massive alpha particles fired at the gold foil would generally pass through the very low mass region of electrons without being affected. Any alpha particles passing near the heavy, positive core would be repelled away. The closer the alpha particle was to the nucleus, the greater the deflection would be.

## FIGURE B3
### Gold Foil Experiment

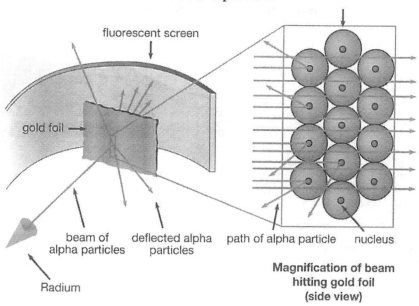

Magnification of beam hitting gold foil (side view)

## FIGURE B4
### "Empty Space" Model
A close-up on the nucleus shows attraction between protons and neutrons.

This nuclear model agreed with Rutherford's experimental findings. It also supported what was known about radioactivity at that time. Rutherford suggested that the core of the atom contains positively-charged particles called protons, but could not explain why the nucleus did not repel itself apart.

Later, in 1932, James Chadwick discovered the neutron, an uncharged particle located in the nucleus with a mass slightly larger than the proton, which helped to prevent the nucleus from repelling itself apart.

During the time of Rutherford's work, many advances were made in physics dealing with charged particles and radiation. This research pointed out a number of problems with the Rutherford model. If the electrons are not moving, then the attraction of the negative electrons for the positive nucleus should collapse the atom. However, if they are in motion (to counteract the pull of the nucleus), then the electrons should radiate energy and spiral down to the nucleus. *It is obvious that electrons must not collapse or spiral into the nucleus since atoms are, for the most part, very stable.*

### Bohr Atom (Orbit Model)

About 1913, several scientists, including Niels Bohr, studied *atomic spectra* of the elements. To see this effect, view a *spectral discharge tube* such as neon or helium through a *diffraction grating*. Many lines of color—the "line spectrum"—will be visible. Each color corresponds to one and only one energy. This was the opposite of the Rutherford model, which predicted a whole *rainbow of colors rather than discrete lines*. To explain this observation and why atoms do not collapse, Bohr assembled a revised model of the atom.

Bohr proposed that electrons of specific energy moved in circular orbits around the center of the nucleus and that the electrons could not exist between the rings (see FIGURE B5). That is, he made the radical suggestion that the electron is **quantized**—*the electron can only have certain energy values*—instead of the possibility of existing anywhere within the atom (see FIGURE B6). This would require that any change in the energy of the electron must be accompanied by the gain or loss of a specific amount of energy. Line spectra, as seen in FIGURE B7, could only be produced if specific amounts of energy, as shown by only certain colors of light, are given off by the atoms. This theory of electron motion may

FIGURE B5    "Orbit" Model

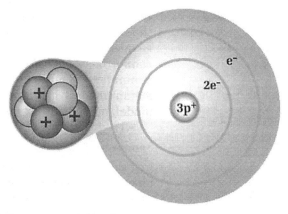

Structure of the Atom    **UNIT B**    **23**

## FIGURE B6
## Quantized vs Continuous

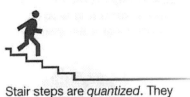

Stair steps are *quantized*. They only have certain places where a person may stand.

On the other hand, a wheelchair ramp is *continuous*. It has an infinite number of possible positions.

## FIGURE B7
## Simple Spectroscope — Hydrogen gas only produces certain colors when energized — a line spectrum.

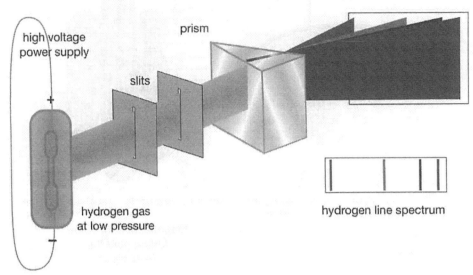

be compared, in a simplistic way, to the motion of the planets around the sun. The atomic spectrum of hydrogen and the periodic repetition of the properties of the elements are two examples of experimental observations supporting the Bohr model.

Even though the Bohr model was a tremendous step forward and still is a useful model, it was soon realized that only the properties of hydrogen could be satisfactorily explained by this model. The model needed further revision.

### Quantum Mechanical Model ("Cloud Model")

Advances in theoretical physics in the 1920s led to the development of the Quantum Mechanical Model. Electrons are still thought to be located in specific energy levels. But, instead of thinking of electrons as particles, it is often more useful to think of them as having "cloud-like" behavior. In this way, electrons can exist anywhere within the energy level. (See FIGURE B8, "Cloud" Model.) The electron cloud is attracted toward the nucleus until the cloud gets too close to itself and is repelled away. In this way, the electron can only be found in certain probable locations (rings or orbitals) outside the nucleus.

The quantum mechanical model is the most recent model and has, to a large extent, overcome the pitfalls of the Bohr model. The drawback is that it is too complex — most mathematical equations arising from this model cannot be solved exactly by even the most powerful computers. Thus, the progressive development of atomic models has now brought us to, not a physical model, but a complex mathematical one.

### FIGURE B8
### "Cloud" Model, Lithium Atom

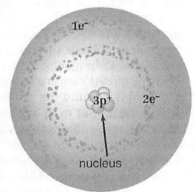

### Summary of Models

In the development of models of the atom, from the Dalton model to the quantum mechanical model, we have seen a progression where each successive model is a further refinement of an existing model. It should be noted that most of the chemistry we do in high school chemistry is and/or could be done using the Dalton model.

# B.4 <u>Exercises</u>  Models of the Atom

1. What are the features of a good theory?

   _____

   _____

2. Should a theory be discarded if conflicting evidence is gathered? Explain.

   _____

   _____

3. Describe briefly how the Dalton Model would explain the Law of Conservation of Mass in a chemical reaction. Include a simple diagram with your explanation.

   _____

   _____

   _____

   _____

For each of the Atomic Models listed in questions #4-8, give a supporting observation and a conflicting observation to each theory:

| Model | Supporting Observations | Conflicting Observations |
|---|---|---|
| 4.  Dalton | | |
| 5.  Thomson | | |
| 6.  Rutherford | | |
| 7.  Bohr | | |
| 8.  Quantum Mechanical | | |

# B.5  Subatomic Particles and the Structure of the Atom

As you have seen, a great deal of evidence supports the concept of atoms. Let's summarize the main ideas:

**Atoms** are the *basic building blocks of all substances* and cannot be broken down further by chemical means. The atom is composed of two main parts: the nucleus and the electrons around the nucleus. Atoms are electrically neutral, because they contain equal amounts of positive and negative charges.

The **nucleus** (core of the atom) is a small structure located at the center of the atom. The nucleus contains all of the positive charge and nearly all of the mass, but occupies only about one quadrillionth ($10^{-15}$) of the volume of the atom.

**Proton**—*a particle found in the nucleus carrying one unit of positive charge*. It has the symbol $p^+$ or just $p$. It is the number of protons that determines the identity of an element.

**Atomic Number**—*the number of protons in the nucleus of an atom.* Look at your Periodic Table to locate the atomic number for each element. For example, the atomic number of bromine is 35. Each atom of bromine has 35 protons.

**Neutron**—*an uncharged (neutral) particle found in the nucleus* with a mass slightly larger than that of the proton. It has the symbol $n^o$ or just $n$. It helps hold the nucleus together.

**Nucleons**—*any particle in the nucleus (both protons and neutrons).*

**Nucleon Number (mass number)**—*the total number of protons and neutrons* in the nucleus of an atom. More will be said about atomic number and nucleon number in section B.7 on isotopes.

**Atomic Symbol Notation**—used to indicate the number of particles in the nucleus of an atom.

FIGURE B9
Atomic Symbol
Notation

○ p=proton
○ n=neutron

Helium
Nucleus

Nucleon Number (# of protons + neutrons)
Atomic Number (# of protons)

$^4_2$He ← Element Symbol

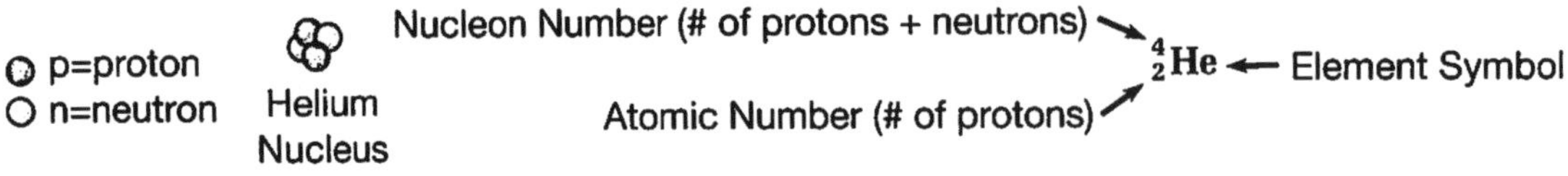

**Extranuclear Region**—*the part of the atom that is outside the nucleus.*
This part of the atom is mostly "empty space." It is responsible for the volume of the atom. If an atom were the size of a baseball stadium with an ant in center field representing the nucleus, the entire stadium would represent the electron cloud.

**Electron**—*a particle having one unit of negative charge.* It has the symbol $e^-$. The electrons determine the chemical behavior of the elements.

- The electrons of an atom are found in certain energy levels.
- The electrons move around the nucleus. These electrons can be compared to the way a spinning propeller appears to occupy a full circle. Keep in mind, however, that an atom is three-dimensional and the pattern of electron distribution is highly complex.
- The electrons are attracted by the positively charged nucleus.
- Atoms are electrically neutral. The total negative charge of the electrons is balanced by the total positive charge of protons in the nucleus.
- All electrons have the same mass and charge regardless of their position or from which element they come.

FIGURE B10   Basic Subatomic Particles

| Particle | Symbol | Charge | Actual Mass (g) | Mass Relative to Proton | Mass Relative to Electron |
|----------|--------|--------|-----------------|-------------------------|---------------------------|
| proton | $p^+$ | 1+ | $1.672 \times 10^{-24}$ | 1 | 1836 |
| neutron | $n^o$ | 0 | $1.675 \times 10^{-24}$ | 1 (1.002) | 1839 |
| electron | $e^-$ | 1- | $9.11 \times 10^{-28}$ | 0 (0.0005) | 1 |

# B.6 Exercises Subatomic Particles and the Structure of the Atom

Answer the following questions:

1. In 1804, who revived a theory that all matter was composed of unbelievably small particles called atoms as proposed by the Greek philosophers?

2. In 1898, who suggested a theory that an atom was a positively charged mass in which negatively charged electrons were embedded like raisins in a bun or plums in plum pudding? _____

3. In 1911, who suggested the nuclear model for atoms where electrons surround a small nucleus? _____

4. In 1913, who proposed a theory that electrons move around the nucleus of an atom in specific energy levels and that the atom could be pictured as a miniature solar system? _____

5. What is the name of the present model of the atom in which electrons occupy certain probable regions called orbitals? _____

6. Who discovered the neutron? _____

7. A neutral atom contains equal numbers of what particles? _____

8. What is the small structure in the center of an atom, and what does it consist of?

_____

9. What occupies the extranuclear region of the atom, which makes up most of the volume of the atom? _____

10. What makes up nearly all of the mass of any atom? _____

11. How are the elements in the Periodic Table arranged, i.e., what is increasing left to right across a period? _____

12. Which family starts each period, except the first, of the Periodic Table? Which family ends each period?

_____

13. What does the heavy "staircase" line on the Periodic Table divide (i.e., what from what)? _____

14. By what two names are vertical arrangements of elements in the Periodic Table called? _____

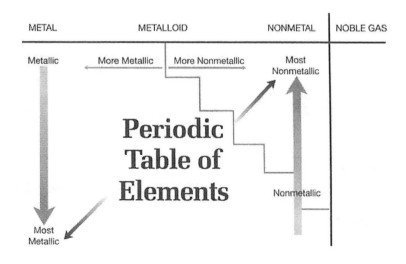

15. What is the most metallic element and the most nonmetallic element?

_____

16. Elements 4, 12 and 20 are closely related chemically. What is the *name* of this family, and the *name* of one other element from this family?

_____

17. An unknown element is a colorless gas at room temperature. Upon heating with lithium, no reaction occurs. What is the family of elements to which this unknown element belongs? _____

18. A soft metal reacts vigorously with water to produce hydrogen gas, $H_2$. What family does this metal probably belong to? _____

19. Which is the most reactive metal? The most reactive nonmetal?

_____

20. What are the elements that make up the **B groups** on the Periodic Table called?

_____

# B.7 Isotopes

Let's look at different nuclear arrangements that atoms have.

When Dalton first suggested that all matter is made up of atoms, he proposed that all atoms of the same element have the same mass. As it turns out, this is not quite true. Scientists have since learned that atoms of the same element will always have the same number of protons, but may have a different number of neutrons. Anytime atoms have the same atomic number (*number of protons*) but a different nucleon number (*therefore a different number of neutrons*), these atoms are called **isotopes**. For example, hydrogen is known to have three isotopes (See FIGURE B12).

FIGURE B11
Some Nuclear Particles and Their Symbols

| proton (hydrogen-1) | $p^+$ | $_1^1H$ |
|---|---|---|
| neutron | $n°$ | $_0^1n$ |
| electron or beta particle | $e-$ or $\beta-$ | $_{-1}^0e$ |
| alpha particle (helium-4) | $\alpha$ | $_2^4He$ |

FIGURE B12
Comparing Isotopes of Hydrogen

| protium (ordinary hydrogen) | deuterium (heavy hydrogen) | tritium (radioactive hydrogen) |
|---|---|---|
| $_1^1H$ | $_1^2H$ | $_1^3H$ |
| $p^+ = 1$ $n° = 0$ | $p^+ = 1$ $n° = 1$ | $p^+ = 1$ $n° = 2$ |

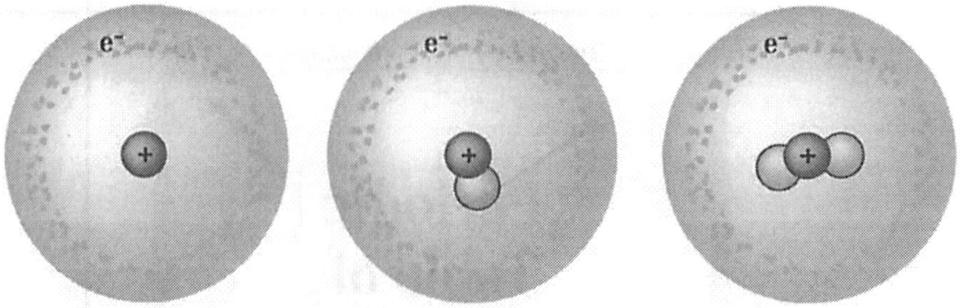

99.985% abundance     0.015% abundance     negligible abundance

*Legend:*
⊕ p=proton    ◯ n=neutron

As you can see, the number of protons in the atom is given by the atomic number (bottom number on the atomic symbol notation) and the number of neutrons can be found by subtracting the atomic number from the mass number (top number on the atomic symbol notation). All three of these hydrogen isotopes behave the same chemically since the chemical properties depend only on the number of protons and electrons. However, some of the physical properties vary slightly.

Each element has several different kinds of isotopes. Some of the isotopes are nonradioactive while other isotopes are radioactive. Many of the radioactive isotopes, or **radioisotopes**, are used in research as **tracers** which *follow the progress of molecules through a system*. For example, carbon-14 and phosphorus-32 are radioisotopes that are very useful in biological research.

# B.8 Atomic Mass

Since atoms have different numbers of protons, neutrons and electrons, it follows that each different kind of atom will have a different mass. It is also true that most elements consist of several kinds of isotopes. Chemists rarely consider only one kind of isotope, but rather the normal mix of isotopes as they naturally occur in the element. So the term **atomic mass** may refer to two different things:

- *The actual mass of a single type of isotope* (which could also be called the *isotope mass*). Since atoms are so small and it's too difficult to calculate their mass individually, it was decided to choose one isotope as a standard and assign a certain mass value to it. Carbon-12 was chosen as the standard and was given a value of 12.00000 amu (*atomic mass units*). The isotope magnesium-24 has an atomic mass of 23.98504 amu, which means it is slightly less than twice the mass of carbon-12. (1 amu has been determined to have a mass of $1.66 \times 10^{-24}$ g.)

- *The relative average mass of all the naturally occurring isotopes of that element.* This is normally what is meant when someone refers to the atomic mass of an element. The following problem will serve as an example of how atomic masses may be calculated for an element:

Carbon is known to have seven different isotopes ranging from mass number 10–16. Only two of the isotopes occur naturally in any appreciable amount. Carbon-12 has an isotope mass of 12.00000 amu and accounts for 98.89% of the carbon. Carbon-13 has an isotope mass of 13.00335 amu and accounts for 1.11% in natural abundance. Calculate the atomic mass of carbon. (Carbon-14, used in radioactive dating, exists in such a small amount that it is not included in these calculations.)

| carbon-12 | (0.9889) (12.00000) = | 11.87 amu |
|---|---|---|
| carbon-13 | (0.0111) (13.00335) = | 0.14 amu |
| carbon (*naturally occurring mix*) | | 12.01 amu |

This value agrees with the number given on the periodic table. (Check for yourself!)

| Living | 5770 Yr | 11 540 Yr | 17 310 Yr |
|---|---|---|---|
| | | | |
| Radioactive Material Remaining: | 1/2 | 1/4 | 1/8 |

X Carbon-14 Still Present
X Carbon-14 Decayed
O Other Atoms

The decay of carbon-14 tells us the age of an object that was once living. If the object has 1/8 of the carbon-14 found in a living object, it is 17,310 years old.

# B.9 Using Pennies to Represent Isotopes

**Purpose:**

✔ To use pennies to better understand the concept of what the atomic mass given on the periodic table actually represents.

✔ To understand that many conclusions about the atom can actually be determined without directly observing the inside of the atom itself.

**Background Information:**

Prior to 1982, pennies were made of an alloy composed of 95% copper and 5% zinc. In 1982, the composition of pennies was changed to a solid zinc core with a thin copper coating, a total composition of 97.6% zinc and 2.4% copper. Zinc is less dense than copper so the new pennies are considerably lighter than the old pennies.

Alloy: 95% copper, 5% zinc

Pure zinc inside, pure copper outside
(97.6% Zn, 2.4% Cu overall)

**Materials:**

- 35 mm film canister
- 10 pennies (a mix of pre-1982 and post-1982 pennies)
- balance
- one pre-1982 penny
- one post-1982 penny

**Procedure:**

1. Record the identifying code of the container with the pennies.

2. a. Determine and record the mass of the pre-1982 penny.

   _____

   b. Determine and record the mass of the post-1982 penny.

   _____

   c. Record the mass of the empty container as given on the container label. (Do not open the container!)

   _____

   d. Determine and record the total mass of the container with the 10 pennies inside.

   _____

**Calculations/Questions:**

1. Calculate the number of pre- and post-1982 pennies inside the container. This is a rather simple algebraic exercise.

   a. First, determine the total mass of pennies.

   b. Second, let x = number of pre-1982 pennies. Then (10 – x) = number of post-1982 pennies.

   c. Finally, solve for the equation below:

   *total mass of pennies*

   *= mass of pre-1982 pennies + mass of post-1982 pennies*

   *= (x) (mass of pre-1982 penny) + (10 – x)(mass of post-1982 penny)*

2. Knowing the number of each type of penny and knowing the total number of pennies, calculate the percent abundance of each type of penny. Also determine the average mass of the ten pennies.

3. Boron has an atomic mass of 10.81 amu. It is known that naturally occurring boron is composed of two isotopes, boron-10 (isotope mass = 10.01 amu) and boron-11 (isotope mass = 11.01 amu). Estimate the approximate percent of each isotope of boron.

4. Pennies have different masses because of different amounts of zinc in the penny. Explain what is the same and what is not in the different isotopes of an element.

   _____

   _____

   _____

5. Naturally occurring chlorine consists of Cl-35 and Cl-37. Look up the atomic mass of chlorine on the periodic table and decide which isotope is the most abundant. Explain your answer.

_____

_____

_____

_____

## B.10 <u>Exercises</u> Isotopes and Atomic Mass

1. Isotopes of an element have an equal number of _____ and _____, but a different number of _____.

2. The _____ _____ of an element is equal to the number of protons located in its nucleus or the number of electrons surrounding the nucleus in a natural atom.

3. The protons and neutrons in an atom contribute most to the _____ _____ of that particular element.

4. The number of _____ in the nucleus of chlorine atoms may vary.

5. Atoms with the same number of protons but with a different number of neutrons in the nucleus are called _____.

6. The relative average mass of all the naturally occurring isotopes of a particular element is called the _____ _____.

7. Identify the following elements:

   a. Atom A has 50 electrons. _____

   b. Atom B has a charge of 33+ on its nucleus. _____

   c. Atom C has 123 neutrons and 80 electrons. _____

   d. Atom D has 28 protons and 31 neutrons. _____

8. Fill out the chart below.

| Symbol | Name | Atomic Number | Mass Number | Protons | Neutrons | Electrons |
|--------|------|---------------|-------------|---------|----------|-----------|
| $^{31}_{15}P$ | | | | | | |
| | carbon-14 | | | | | |
| | | 35 | | | 44 | 35 |
| | | | | 29 | 34 | 29 |
| | | | | 92 | 143 | |

## B.11 Changes in Atoms During Chemical Reactions

In chemical reactions, only a rearrangement of the electrons takes place—the nucleus is not affected. Understanding chemistry depends on understanding how electrons of atoms are arranged around their nuclei and on how the electrons of atoms interact with the electrons of other atoms.

When atoms approach each other closely, their electrons become simultaneously attracted by the positive nuclei of other atoms. The simultaneous attraction for the same electrons by the nuclei of two or more atoms causes electron rearrangements among atoms. The electron rearrangements may be considered to be of two distinct types:

- The loss and gain of electrons, which ultimately results in **ionic bonding** of metals and nonmetals (e.g., NaCl).
- The sharing of electrons, which results in **covalent bonding** between nonmetals (e.g., $H_2O$).

The loss and gain of electrons will be discussed in the next few sections, and sharing electrons will be discussed in Unit C.

# B.12 The Wave Nature of Light

Previously, you learned that the presence of line spectra gave evidence that electrons in atoms can only exist in certain energy levels outside the nucleus (extranuclear region). How did Bohr know that spectral lines proved the existence of energy levels? To understand this we need to look at a kind of energy known as electromagnetic radiation.

**Electromagnetic radiation** *is any kind of energy that is transferred in the form of waves.* Usually when you think of waves you might think of an object in the water being pushed along by the motion of the water. With electromagnetic waves, however, *no matter is needed to move the energy along.* This kind of energy is transferred because of changes in electric fields and magnetic fields that need no particles. Consider that two magnets can have an effect on each other without actually touching.

It is useful to describe electromagnetic waves in terms of wavelength, frequency and speed (See FIGURE B13):

- **Wavelength**—this is the distance traveled by one complete cycle of a wave. Often it is measured as the distance from "peak to peak" or "crest to crest" on a wave pattern.
- **Frequency**—this is the number of complete waves that pass a given point in one second.
- **Speed**—this is how fast the waves are actually moving. All electromagnetic waves travel at the same speed: $3.00 \times 10^8$ m/s (also known as the *speed of light*).

FIGURE B13    **Differences Among Electromagnetic Waves**

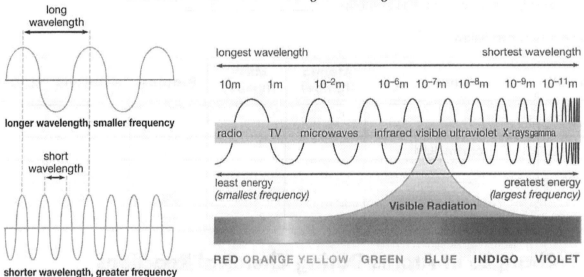

Electromagnetic (E-M) Radiation has the following properties:

- Has no mass.
- Travels at the speed of light.
- Can travel through a vacuum. (It does not need matter to vibrate or move to carry the energy.)
- Exists in "packets" or "bundles" of energy called **photons** (*i.e., it behaves similar to particles*).

FIGURE B13 shows a table that includes all the forms of electromagnetic radiation in order from the longest wavelength to the shortest wavelength (and from the smallest energy to the greatest energy).

As you can see, there are many kinds of electromagnetic radiation—visible light is only one small part of the entire spectrum. Visible radiation can be spread into a *rainbow of colors* known as the **visible spectrum** by using either a **prism** or a **diffraction grating**. The colors of the visible spectrum, in order from longest wavelength to the shortest wavelength, are:

Red, Orange, Yellow, Green, Blue, Indigo and Violet
(ROY G. BIV, or "Richard Of York Gave Battle In Vain!").

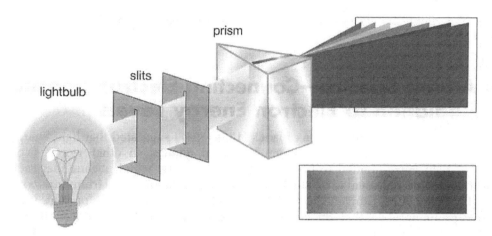

**FIGURE B14
Separating White Light into
the Visible Spectrum**

Even if you have never heard of electromagnetic radiation, it is a vital part of your life. It constantly surrounds you and is responsible for a great many everyday activities:

- **Radio Waves**—These are chiefly used in the communications field to transmit signals from a broadcasting station to a radio receiver. You may be familiar with Amplitude Modulated (AM) and Frequency Modulated (FM) radio waves.

- **Microwaves**—This type of radiation is used to send communication signals although it is more commonly known for cooking food. Microwave ovens work because they operate at the resonance frequency needed to make the water molecules in the food vibrate, which produces the heat necessary to cook the food.

- **Infrared**—This kind of radiation is more commonly known as "heat" or thermal energy. It is what causes the sun to feel warm on your body. Infrared is sometimes abbreviated "IR."

- **Visible**—Visible radiation is usually called "light." It is the energy responsible for allowing us to see with our eyes. It is also the kind of energy responsible for photosynthesis.

- **Ultraviolet (UV)**—This is sometimes called "black light." This type of radiation causes certain substances to glow in the dark. UV is also responsible for suntans, sunburns and some skin cancer.

- **X-rays**—The most common use for x-rays is to allow doctors to take "pictures" of your bones for medical diagnosis.

- **Gamma**—Doctors use gamma radiation (Cobalt-60) in the treatment of cancer to destroy a tumor. It is also one type of radioactivity used to irradiate foods to retard spoilage.

# B.13 Exercises  Electromagnetic Radiation

1. What do scientists call energy that is capable of traveling through empty space?

   _____

2. Which color of light has a longer wavelength, yellow or blue? _____

3. Which type of radiation has more energy, infrared or ultraviolet? _____

4. How does the speed of microwaves compare with the speed of x-rays? _____

5. What kind of energy is also known as thermal energy? _____

6. Name the two types of devices used to separate visible light into a rainbow of colors. _____

# B.14 Atomic Spectra—Connecting Electromagnetic Radiation to Electron Energy Levels

In 1901, a scientist by the name of Max Planck (1858–1947) suggested that light energy could only be given off in packets, which he called **quanta**. In other words, each frequency of light corresponded to one and only one energy, which means that each wavelength of color represented a single energy. A continuous spectrum (*rainbow*) contains all of the colors. (Review FIGURE B13) Therefore, all energies are present. If all electron jumps are possible, then the entire visible spectrum would be produced. If only a line spectrum is visible, then only *certain energies* are present. (Review FIGURE B7)

Bohr reasoned that the spectral lines must be caused by specific changes in the position of the electron. If only certain colors are present, then only certain energies are permitted. This means only certain electron jumps are possible. Therefore, electrons could only exist in specific energy levels rather than anywhere outside the nucleus. The process is summarized below:

FIGURE B15
**Electron Energy Levels and EMR**

When the atom absorbs energy, the lightest particle in the atom, the electron, moves away from the nucleus to another energy level farther away from the nucleus. Because of the attraction that the nucleus of an atom has for the electrons within the atom, the electron is brought back to one of the lower electron energy levels in the atom.

Think of neon light: When the electricity is turned on, the electrical energy is absorbed by the neon atoms. Since the electrons are on the outside of the atom AND are nearly 2000 times lighter than the lightest particle in the nucleus, the electron is easily elevated to a higher energy level. In fact, a large percentage of the population of the atoms is raised to higher energy levels. The nucleus exerts a "restoring force" to the atom causing the electron to "fall" to a lower energy level.

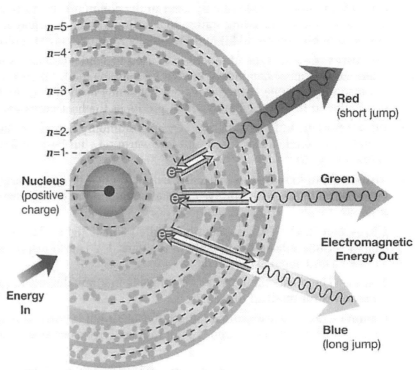

*Energy Levels*, Atom Being Energized

With each different distance the electron travels, there is a different energy produced as shown by the different lines of light in the spectrum.

1. *An atom absorbs energy.* This energy could be mechanical, electrical, chemical or thermal.

2. *One electron is raised to a higher energy level (by absorbing energy).* The nucleus is too massive compared to an electron to move significantly. In addition, once a single electron is moved away from the nucleus, the other electrons move closer to the nucleus and are therefore held more tightly.

3. *When the electron "falls back" to a lower energy level, it simultaneously gives off a single color of light (a specific E-M radiation frequency) corresponding to the distance that the electron traveled.* Remember that Planck determined that each color line of light has a certain energy. Also, according to physics, energy equals force times distance (E = F × d). Therefore, each line of color represents a specific distance traveled by the electron.

- **Ground State**—When all the electrons are in the lowest possible energy levels, the atom is said to be in the ground state.

- **Excited State**—After an atom absorbs energy, one electron is in a higher than normal energy level. The atom is now said to be in the excited state.

**Lithium Atom**

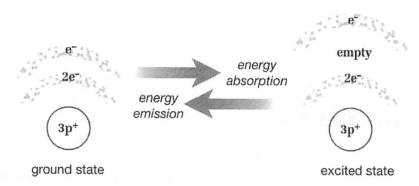

ground state          excited state

# B.15 Exercises Atomic Spectra

1. Electomagnetic radiation is produced when an electron moves from a higher

   _____ to a lower one.

2. An atom is put into the _____ when the atom absorbs energy to raise an electron to a higher energy level.

3. _____ is the process whereby atoms lose energy and give off electromagnetic radiation.

4. Electron energy levels that are further from the nucleus are considered to be of (*higher/lower*) energy than those closer to the nucleus.

5. Is an electron in the second energy level at a higher or lower energy level than an electron in the fourth energy level? Explain.

   _____

   _____

6. When an electron moves from n = 5 to n = 3, is energy absorbed or released? Explain.

   _____

   _____

7. Explain the difference between an atom in the ground state and an atom in the excited state.

_____

_____

_____

8. In your own words, describe the process where atoms absorb energy and give off electromagnetic radiation.

_____

_____

_____

_____

_____

_____

_____

_____

_____

**LAB**

# B.16 Elements and Line Spectra

**Purpose:**
✔ To view the spectra produced when a high voltage is used to energize several different gaseous elements.

**Materials:**
- diffraction grating (grating glasses are preferable)
- discharge tubes
- high-voltage source

**Procedure:**
1. Obtain a diffraction grating and view "white light" through the grating. Record the colors from left to right as seen through the grating. (Colored pencils should be used.)
2. Your teacher has several discharge tubes (e.g., for $H_2$, He, Ne, Ar, N, $O_2$, and Hg) set up for you to view. Prepare a chart to record your observations.

   a. Identify the element being viewed.
   b. Record the color of the energized gas as seen with the naked eye.
   c. Sketch the lines seen through the diffraction grating with the colors in the proper positions relative to the visible spectrum viewed in step 1.

3. Now, using only your observation sheet, identify several unknown elements provided to you by your teacher.

**Questions:**
1. A line spectrum is sometimes called the "fingerprint" of an element. What do you think is meant by that term?

_____

_____

_____

_____

_____

_____

_____

2. How might astronomers use a method similar to this to determine the composition of stars?

_____

_____

_____

_____

_____

# B.17 Electron Energy Level Representations for Atoms

As pointed out by the Bohr model, electrons are located in specific energy levels around the nucleus. Scientists have discovered where the electrons are most often found in the three-dimensional space around the nucleus, but no one knows what path, if any, the electrons are following. (*The electron is not traveling around the nucleus like planets around the sun. Atomic diagrams should not show a complete circle around the nucleus to represent an energy level.*) However, experimental evidence and theoretical calculations have provided a strongly supported theory outlining a scheme of electron energy levels.

The electron energy level theory did not come from the development of the Periodic Table (see Bohr model). However, the energy level theory, in order to gain acceptance, had to agree with or lend support to the Periodic Table. In fact, scientists very quickly saw the very close relationship between the energy levels of an atom and that atom's position in the Periodic Table.

- *The number of electrons and protons in an atom are equal.* The number of protons in an atom equals the atomic number (e.g., copper has 29 protons and 29 electrons, and its atomic number is 29). (The atomic number was originally related only to the element's position in the Periodic Table. Now the atomic number is most often used in relation to the number of electrons and protons in an atom.)

- *The maximum number of electrons in each successive energy level equals the number of elements in each successive period.* For example, the first period has 2 atoms and the first energy level can contain no more than 2 electrons; the second period has 8 elements and the second energy level has a maximum of 8 electrons; the same is true for the third period.

- *The number of energy levels occupied by electrons equals the period number* (i.e., if an element is in Period 3, its atoms will have electrons in three energy levels).

- *The number of valence electrons (i.e., those in the outermost energy level) equals the group number for the Group A elements (main group).* That is, if an element is in Group 2A, all the atoms in this group will have two valence electrons.

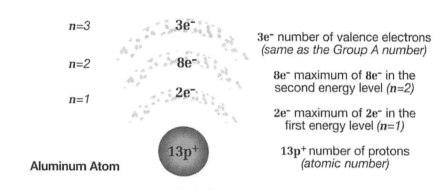

$n=3$    $3e^-$

$n=2$    $8e^-$

$n=1$    $2e^-$

$13p^+$

**Aluminum Atom**

$3e^-$ number of valence electrons *(same as the Group A number)*

$8e^-$ maximum of $8e^-$ in the second energy level *(n=2)*

$2e^-$ maximum of $2e^-$ in the first energy level *(n=1)*

$13p^+$ number of protons *(atomic number)*

**Note:** The energy level diagram is a modified Bohr model of the atom. The diagram represents energy levels in which the electrons exist. Electrons cannot exist in-between these levels: lower levels are filled first, and there are a certain maximum number of electrons which occupy each energy level. These energy levels do not represent orbits (what the electron is doing).

# B.18 Exercises Electron Energy-Level Representation for Atoms

Complete the following abbreviated periodic table for atoms as shown in the example:

Example:
Representative of the number of electrons in each energy level.

$\left.\begin{array}{l} 3\,e^- \\ 8\,e^- \\ 2\,e^- \end{array}\right\}$
Valence electrons (outer energy level)
Second energy level
First energy level

(13 p+)        Number of protons in nucleus

aluminum atom        Name of atom

| Group 1A | | Group 2A | Group 3A | Group 4A | Group 5A | Group 6A | Group 7A | Group 8A |
|---|---|---|---|---|---|---|---|---|
| | | | | | | | | |
| | | | | | | | | |
| | | | | | | | | |

1. What is the relationship between the group number and the number of valence electrons?

_____

2. What is the relationship between the period number and the number of energy levels in which electrons are accommodated?

_____

3. What is the relationship between the maximum number of electrons in each energy level and the number of atoms in each period of the periodic table?

_____

4. According to the above abbreviated periodic table, how many electrons can be accommodated before a new energy level is started in each of the first three energy levels?

First energy level_____     Second energy level_____     Third energy level_____

5. Do the diagrams drawn above represent what the electron is doing? Explain.

_____

_____

_____

# B.19 Electron Energy Level Representation for Simple Ions

In chemical reactions involving ionic bonds, atoms may lose or gain electrons to acquire the more stable electron structure of the nearest noble gas. After the atoms lose or gain electrons, their outermost energy level will have the same number of electrons as the nearest noble gas (usually 8). See FIGURE B16.

**FIGURE B16**

**Oxidation**—the process of losing electrons; the charge increases.

**Reduction**—the process of gaining electrons; the charge decreases.

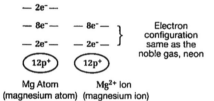

**Example #1 – Metal**
(loses electrons)

Li Atom (lithium atom)   Li⁺ Ion (lithium ion)

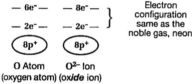

**Example #3 – Nonmetal**
(gains electrons)

O Atom (oxygen atom)   O²⁻ Ion (ox*ide* ion)

**Example #2 – Metal**
(loses electrons)

Mg Atom (magnesium atom)   Mg²⁺ Ion (magnesium ion)

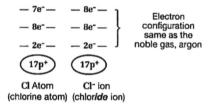

**Example #4 – Nonmetal**
(gains electrons)

Cl Atom (chlorine atom)   Cl⁻ ion (chlor*ide* ion)

Metal ions are smaller than metal atoms because they lose the entire outer energy level.

Nonmetal ions are larger than their atoms because the nucleus is holding a larger number of electrons.

The loss or gain of electrons results in a more stable electron energy level structure, but also unbalances the number of positive (*proton*) and negative (*electron*) charges. Atoms are neutral (*zero net charge*) because of an equal number of positive and negative charges. But ions are positively or negatively charged because of a different number of protons and electrons. The difference in the number of protons and electrons results from a loss or gain of *electrons*; the number of *protons* will never change in a chemical reaction.

**Simple ions** are charged particles formed when *atoms* (neutral) *gain or lose electrons and achieve a noble-gas-like electron-energy-level structure.* Metals lose electrons to achieve a noble gas structure and form positively charged ions, also called **cations**. Nonmetals gain electrons to achieve a noble gas structure and form negatively charged ions, also called **anions**. Losing one electron will result in an ion with a 1⁺ charge (*positive one*). Gaining two electrons will result in a 2⁻ charge (*negative two*). The energy level diagrams for simple ions in the first three periods are identical to the energy level diagrams for the closest noble gases. Atoms with 1, 2 and 3 valence electrons will lose their valence electrons to form ions with charges of 1⁺, 2⁺, and 3⁺. Atoms with 5, 6, and 7 valence electrons will gain 3, 2 and 1 electrons to form ions with charges of 3⁻, 2⁻ and 1⁻ , respectively. Atoms with 4 valence electrons in their second and third energy levels (i.e., carbon and silicon) do not form simple ions. These atoms generally share their four valence electrons with other atoms and form covalent bonds.

# B.20 Exercises Electron Energy-Level Representation for Ions

Complete the following abbreviated periodic table for simple ions as shown in the example. Use the *Periodic Table of Ions* found in the Appendix, if necessary. Do not write a diagram for the shaded areas.

Example:
Representation of the number of electrons in each energy level.

$$\left\{ \begin{array}{l} 8\,e^- \\ 2\,e^- \end{array} \right\}$$ Energy level structure characteristic of nearest noble gas

(13 p+)   # of protons in nucleus

aluminum ion   Name of ion

Al   Ion symbol

| Group 1A | Group 2A | Group 3A | Group 4A | Group 5A | Group 6A | Group 7A | Group 8A |
|---|---|---|---|---|---|---|---|

1. What is the relationship between the electron structure of a Group A ion and the electron structure of the nearest noble gas?

_____

2. How do boron, carbon and silicon satisfy their electron requirements?

3. What charge do the ions from the following groups assume? (Include the magnitude of the charge.)

Group 1A _____     Group 2A _____     Group 3A _____

Group 5A _____     Group 6A _____     Group 7A _____

4. What **_experimental evidence_** is there that a noble-gas-like electron structure is stable?

5. What are the differences in the chemical properties of a sodium atom and a sodium ion? *(Hint: In what substances are the sodium atom and sodium ion found?)*

# B.21 Exercises  Simple Ions

Complete the following table. Note that the name of a nonmetallic ion ends in –*ide* while the name for a metallic ion uses the full name of the metal. The first ion is given as an example.

| Ion Name | Ion Symbol | Number of Protons | Number of Electrons | Number of Electons Lost or Gained | Same Electrons as What Noble Gas? |
|---|---|---|---|---|---|
| Fluoride | $F^-$ | 9 | 10 | gained one | neon |
| 1. | | 53 | 54 | | |
| 2. | | 16 | | gained two | |
| 3. potassium | | | | lost one | |
| 4. | $Ca^{2+}$ | | | | |
| 5. | | 35 | 36 | | |
| 6. | $Sr^{2+}$ | | | | |
| 7. | $H^+$ | | | | (none) |
| 8. | | 8 | | gained two | |
| 9. | | 12 | | lost two | |
| 10. aluminum | | | 10 | | |
| 11. | | 34 | 36 | | |
| 12. | $H^-$ | | | | |
| 13. lithium | | | | lost one | |
| 14. | $Rb^+$ | | | | |
| 15. | | 17 | 18 | | |

**LAB ...**

# B.22 The Periodicity of the Elements—Properties of Atoms

**Purpose:**
✔ To investigate the periodic nature of several physical properties.

**Materials:**
- *Periodic Table*
- graph paper (or graphing program)

**Background:**
The periodicity (repeating nature) of the elements' properties will be illustrated by plotting some fundamental property against increasing atomic number. The properties studied in this experiment are:

**Atomic Radius** – the distance from the center of the atom to the outside "edge."

**Melting Point** – the temperature at which the element melts (changes from solid to liquid).

**Boiling Point** – the temperature at which the element boils (changes from liquid to gas).

**Electronegativity** – the attraction that an atom has for a shared electron pair (will be discussed further in Unit C).

**Ionization Energy** – the amount of energy required to completely remove an electron from a gaseous atom:

$$Atom(g) + energy \rightarrow ion(g)^+ + e^-$$

| 1A | | | | | | | 8A |
|---|---|---|---|---|---|---|---|
| H 1311 | 2A | (kJ/mol) | | 3A 4A 5A 6A 7A | | | He 2372 |

| 1A | | | | | | | | 8A |
|---|---|---|---|---|---|---|---|---|
| **H** 1311 | | | | | | | | **He** 2372 |
| **Li** 520 | **Be** 899 | **B** 800 | **C** 1086 | **N** 1402 | **O** 1314 | **F** 1681 | | **Ne** 2080 |
| **Na** 496 | **Mg** 738 | **Al** 577 | **Si** 786 | **P** 1012 | **S** 999 | **Cl** 1256 | | **Ar** 1520 |
| **K** 419 | **Ca** 590 | **Ga** 579 | **Ge** 761 | **As** 947 | **Se** 941 | **Br** 1143 | | **Kr** 1351 |
| **Rb** 403 | **Sr** 549 | **In** 558 | **Sn** 708 | **Sb** 834 | **Te** 869 | **I** 1009 | | **Xe** 1170 |
| **Cs** 376 | **Ba** 503 | **Tl** 589 | **Pb** 715 | **Bi** 703 | **Po** 813 | **At** (926) | | **Rn** 1037 |

**Electron Affinity** – the energy change that occurs when an electron is *added* to an atom:

$$Atom(g) + e^- \rightarrow ion^-(g)$$

| 1A | | | | | | | | 8A |
|---|---|---|---|---|---|---|---|---|
| **H** -72.8 | **2A** | **(kJ/mol)** | | **3A** **4A** **5A** **6A** **7A** | | | | **He** (0.0) |

| 1A | | (kJ/mol) | | | | | | 8A |
|---|---|---|---|---|---|---|---|---|
| **H**<br>-72.8 | **2A** | | 3A | 4A | 5A | 6A | 7A | **He**<br>(0.0) |
| **Li**<br>-59.6 | **Be**<br>(+18) | | **B**<br>-26.7 | **C**<br>-122 | **N**<br>+7 | **O**<br>-141 | **F**<br>-328 | **Ne**<br>(+29) |
| **Na**<br>-52.9 | **Mg**<br>(+21) | | **Al**<br>-42.5 | **Si**<br>-134 | **P**<br>-72.0 | **S**<br>-200 | **Cl**<br>-349 | **Ar**<br>(+35) |
| **K**<br>-48.4 | **Ca**<br>(+186) | | **Ga**<br>-28.9 | **Ge**<br>-119 | **As**<br>-78.2 | **Se**<br>-195 | **Br**<br>-325 | **Kr**<br>(+39) |
| **Rb**<br>-46.9 | **Sr**<br>(+146) | | **In**<br>-28.9 | **Sn**<br>-107 | **Sb**<br>-103 | **Te**<br>-190 | **I**<br>-295 | **Xe**<br>(+41) |
| **Cs**<br>-45.5 | **Ba**<br>(+46) | | **Tl**<br>-19.3 | **Pb**<br>-35.1 | **Bi**<br>-91.3 | **Po**<br>-183 | **At**<br>-270 | **Rn**<br>(+41) |

**Procedure:**

1. Your teacher may put you into groups of six.

2. Each member of the team will prepare a graph of his/her property versus atomic number for the first 20 elements.

   a. Put property values on the y axis and the atomic number on the x axis.

   b. Connect consecutive values with a straight line. Where data are missing for an element, connect consecutive points with a straight dashed line.

   c. Place a bold-colored vertical line through the value of each noble gas element to separate the periods.

3. Each member of the team will prepare a graph of his/her property versus atomic number for the Group 1A elements (alkali metals).

4. Each member of the team will prepare a graph of his/her property versus atomic number for the Group 7A elements (halogens).

5. Using the graphs assembled by all members of the group, complete the following questions.

**Questions:**

1. Answer the following questions regarding trends on the Periodic Table:

   a. What happens to the atomic radius...
      left to right across a period?

      _____

      _____

   top to bottom down a group?

   _____

   _____

   b. What happens to the electronegativity...
      left to right across a period?

      _____

      _____

   top to bottom down a group?

   _____

   _____

   c. What happens to the melting and boiling points...
      left to right across a period?

      _____

   top to bottom down Group 1A?

   _____

   top to bottom down Group 7A?

   _____

   _____

   d. What happens to the ionization energy...
      left to right across a period?

      _____

   top to bottom down a group?

   _____

   _____

   e. What happens to the electron affinity...
      left to right across a period?

      _____

   top to bottom down a group?

   _____

2. The word "periodic" means repeating. In what way do your graphs show that the properties of the elements change in a regular way?

_____

_____

3. Element 116 was recently discovered. Estimate its melting point, boiling point and atomic radius.

_____

_____

_____

**Conclusion:**
State at least two things you learned in this lab.

_____

_____

_____

_____

_____

_____

_____

_____

_____

## Atomic and Ionic Radii of Elements

- ● represents atomic radius
- ● represents ionic radius
- □ background is for metals
- ■ background is for nonmetals

**Note:** no radii are given for the noble gases

Atomic Radius Decreases — Metallic Properties Decrease

Metallic Properties Increase

Atomic Radius Increases — Metallic Properties Increase

Atomic Number Increase — Electronegativity Decrease

Atomic Number Increase — Electronegativity Increase

# Unit C
# Chemical Bonding

## C.1 Electrons in Atoms

Atoms are the basic building blocks of matter. They are everywhere. They make up pure elements, compounds and mixtures. Atoms gain or lose electrons to form ions. Molecules are formed when atoms share electrons. *The resulting bond is called a* **covalent bond**. Molecules and compounds are *combinations* of two or more atoms. But why do atoms combine at all? What is responsible for the attraction between atoms that results in a chemical bond?

### Atomic Models and the Periodic Table

In the previous unit, information was presented on several theories of atomic structure. A modified Bohr model of the atom was chosen as a simple, but useful model to explain observations encountered at this level of chemistry. The modified Bohr model explained the periodic pattern of the elements by suggesting energy level diagrams for the electrons. It was also able to suggest that atoms lose or gain electrons to form ions with a stable noble-gas electron configuration. But this model does not easily illustrate why covalent bonds form.

### Occupancy of Atomic Orbitals

Although the energy of electrons can be determined and is known, the actual manner in which electrons move around the nucleus is unknown. The likelihood of finding an electron at certain points in space is understood and has been calculated using quantum mechanics. *The three-dimensional space in which an electron is most often found* is called its **orbital**. An orbital is said to be the region in space occupied by the electron. This is similar to how the disc of a spinning fan is the region occupied by the fan blades as the fan spins (see FIGURE C1):

FIGURE C1
**Different Types of Orbitals**

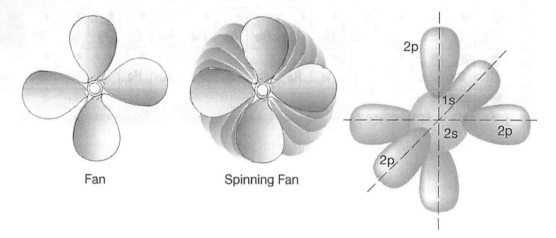

Fan          Spinning Fan

## Lewis Diagrams for Atoms

In 1916, Gilbert N. Lewis proposed a simple means of electron bookkeeping that has become a widely accepted *method of showing the organization of the valence electrons in an atom*. This method is known as a **Lewis diagram** or **electron-dot diagram** and allows for an easy understanding of covalent bonding between atoms. Lewis diagrams use:

**The atomic symbol**—generically symbolized below as element "X"—to represent both the nucleus and the electrons in the filled innermost energy levels of the atom not participating in the bonding.

**Four orbital regions around the atomic symbol**—initially symbolized below as a dotted oval—to represent the four possible locations around an atom where an electron may be found.

X

**Dots**—one per electron—arranged around the atomic symbol to represent the valence electrons. *Element with 6 valence electrons*:

- Half-filled orbitals with unpaired electrons—often called **bonding electrons**—are shown as individual dots.
- Filled orbitals with paired electrons—often called **nonbonding electrons** or **lone pairs**—are shown as two dots close together on the same side of the symbol.
- These dots do not signify actual positions of the electrons. However, they do signify how electrons occupy orbitals.

**Uniform distribution of valence electrons**—before any electron pairing occurs, one electron is placed in each of the four available orbitals. This distribution is more stable than doubling the electrons since electrons naturally try to repel each other. *For example, an element with 4 valence electrons would look like this*:

If there are more than 4 valence electrons (5 to 8), the half-filled orbitals will accept a second electron. This will result in some, or all, of the orbitals being filled. (Three electrons in an orbital would result in large repulsive forces and an unstable state.

**A maximum of eight electrons**—when the four valence (outer energy level) orbitals are completely filled with electrons ($8\ e^-$), the atom assumes the stable electron configuration of a noble gas. This is known as the **rule of eight**, or the **octet rule**. In this unit, Lewis diagrams will be limited to atoms and molecules following the octet rule (with the exception of hydrogen).

° °<br>° Ne °<br>° °

($2\ e^- \times 4$ orbitals $= 8\ e^-$ maximum)

The noble gas neon (shown above) has all its valence orbitals filled with electrons. Since there are no bonding electrons remaining in this atom, it should not be able to form compounds with other atoms. This is in agreement with what was previously observed regarding noble gases in Unit A.

| Atom | Group | # Valence Electrons | Lewis Diagram | # Valence Orbitals | # Bonding Electrons | # Lone Pairs |
|------|-------|---------------------|---------------|--------------------|--------------------|--------------|
| H | 1A | 1 | H ° | 1 | 1 | 0 |
| Ca | 2A | 2 | Ca° | 4 | 2 | 0 |
| Ga | 3A | 3 | °Ga° | 4 | 3 | 0 |
| C | 4A | 4 | °C° | 4 | 4 | 0 |
| N | 5A | 5 | °N° | 4 | 3 | 1 |
| O | 6A | 6 | °O° | 4 | 2 | 2 |
| F | 7A | 7 | °F° | 4 | 1 | 3 |
| Ar | 8A | 8 | °Ar° | 4 | 0 | 4 |

## C.2 <u>Exercises</u> Electrons in Atoms

Complete the following table.

| Atom | Group | # Valence Electrons | Lewis Diagram | # Valence Orbitals | # Bonding Electrons | # Lone Pairs |
|------|-------|---------------------|---------------|--------------------|--------------------|--------------|
| 1. S | | | | | | |
| 2. Si | | | | | | |
| 3. P | | | | | | |
| 4. Cl | | | | | | |
| 5. Br | | | | | | |
| 6. Se | | | | | | |
| 7. K | | | | | | |
| 8. Mg | | | | | | |
| 9. Al | | | | | | |

# C.3 Scientific Ways of Knowing

There are several ways of "knowing" something that is applicable to the science classroom. These include:

**Empirical knowledge:** an experiment was done. The experimenter either directly observed the information first-hand, or interpreted and organized data so a conclusion could be drawn. For example, to prove that the formula of water is $H_2O$, an electrolysis experiment could be performed that would show that twice as much hydrogen is produced as oxygen when water is decomposed.

**Theoretical knowledge:** understanding the phenomenon based on explanations and predictions. For example, atoms produce *line spectra* based on the theory by Bohr that electrons are raised to higher energy levels when atoms absorb energy, but electromagnetic energy of a specific energy amount (in the form of line spectra) is released as the electrons return to their lower energy levels.

**Given/memorized knowledge:** the information is found on the periodic table, data sheet, or other reference which has been memorized. For instance, copper (Cu) is a transition metal located in Period 4, Group 1B on the Periodic Table.

For example, Mendeleev's periodic table was a classification scheme he developed based on *empirical* data obtained from many sources (e.g., atomic masses and properties of various elements). The Dalton, Bohr and quantum-mechanical atomic *theories* were developed to explain the newly discovered data and observations related to the atom, and predict properties yet to be observed.

## Scientific Theories

In Unit B, a theory on atomic energy levels was presented. Then, at the beginning of this unit, an atomic orbital theory was given. These theories are acceptable to the scientific community because they

- *Explain* the known observations of chemical bonding (valence electrons, bonding capacity, etc.),
- Are able to *predict* new chemical formulas (as will be seen in the next few sections), and
- Are *simple* enough to understand and use.

To *explain* past or predicted observations, a theory must logically relate the cause and effect of a phenomenon. If the theory cannot make acceptable predictions, then it is a false theory and is either discarded or retained as a useful, but restricted theory. Acceptable scientific theories are said to be *simple* in two senses. First, there is the scientific belief that the laws of nature are simple, so if a theory is overly complex, then it cannot be "right." Secondly, *the simplest theory that explains and predicts the phenomenon observed is considered to be the "best" theory.* This is referred to as **scientific reductionism.** An example is given with Lewis' molecular theory, below.

## Molecular Theories

Over the years there have been a number of molecular theories developed to explain and predict the chemical formulas of molecular substances. John Dalton, for example, used his atomic theory around 1805 to draw pictures, now considered to be incorrect, of molecules whose formulas had been determined empirically by measuring percent composition. However, Dalton was not able to explain why the formula was what it was, nor was he able to accurately predict chemical formulas not previously determined empirically (experimentally). It was not until after J. J. Thomson provided evidence for the existence of the electron that acceptable explanations for chemical formulas were developed. Initially, explanations for ionic formulas were developed in terms of ion formation and attraction. Later, molecular theories were developed to explain and predict molecular formulas. One of the simplest molecular theories was developed by Gilbert N. Lewis between 1916 and 1923.

There are other, more complex molecular theories, but the Lewis molecular theory is very adequate for this course. Actually, a restricted version of Lewis' molecular theory, rather than the complete theory, is presented in Section C.5. This demonstrates the idea of *scientific reductionism* — the simplest version of a theory that adequately explains the data is the most useful.

## C.4 <u>Exercises</u> Scientific Ways of Knowing

1. What three scientific ways of knowing can be used for determining a molecular formula?

   _____

   _____

2. What scientific way of knowing will be used in the next section for determining a molecular formula?

   _____

3. List the attributes of an acceptable theory.

   _____

   _____

   _____

## C.5 Bonding Theory and Electronegativity

Nonmetal atoms not possessing a noble-gas-like electron structure (i.e., a stable octet) will share electrons with other nonmetal atoms with which they combine. The electron sharing will likely occur if both atoms involved in the combination achieve a stable octet of electrons. The transfer of electrons from metal to nonmetal atoms will result in the formation of ions, and the subsequent formation of a geometric grouping of the ions, held together by ionic bonding (see ionic bonding at Section C.9).

Experimental evidence indicates that atoms forming covalent bonds usually exhibit unequal attractions for shared electrons. In fact, different atoms have different electron-attracting abilities. *The relative attraction that an atom has for shared electrons in a covalent bond* is known as its **electronegativity**. A scale of electronegativities, developed by Linus Pauling (1901–1994), arbitrarily assigns fluorine, the most electronegative atom, a value of 4.0. Pauling's electronegativities are given on the *Periodic Table*.

Examination of the electronegativities of elements given in the *Periodic Table* will indicate the following trends:

- Electronegativities increase from left to right within a period; e.g., in the $3^{rd}$ period, we have

|  | Na | Mg | Al | Si | P | S | Cl | 3rd |
|---|---|---|---|---|---|---|---|---|
|  | 0.9 | 1.2 | 1.5 | 1.8 | 2.1 | 2.5 | 3.0 | **Period** |

- Electronegativities decrease from top to bottom within a group; e.g., in Group 6A, there are

| Gp | 6A |
|---|---|
| O | 3.5 |
| S | 2.5 |
| Se | 2.4 |
| Te | 2.1 |
| Po | 2.0 |

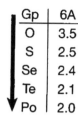

- Electronegativities of the nonmetals are generally higher than those of the metals (e.g., there are 14 metals between atomic numbers 19 and 32 whose average electronegativity is 1.5, ranging from 0.8 through 1.9; but the 15 nonmetals covering Groups 3A – 7A and Periods 2 – 6 have an average electronegativity of 2.6, ranging from 1.8 through 4.0).

The electronegativity scale is a composite of experimental evidence and, as such, reflects the fact that the metals on the left side of the Periodic Table and the nonmetals on the right side of the Periodic Table are the most reactive elements:

- the lowest electronegativity (0.7) belongs to the most reactive metals, Cs (cesium) and Fr (francium), and

- the highest electronegativity (4.0) belongs to the most reactive nonmetal, F (fluorine).

*Atomic Radius Decreases — Metallic Properties Decrease*

*Metallic Properties Increase — Atomic Radius Increases*

*Atomic Number Increases — Electronegativity Decreases*

☐ gray background is for metals
☐ white background is for nonmetals

| H | | | | | | | | | | | | | | | | H | He |
|---|---|---|---|---|---|---|---|---|---|---|---|---|---|---|---|---|---|
| Li | Be | | | | | | | | | | | B | C | N | O | F | Ne |
| Na | Mg | | | | | | | | | | | Al | Si | P | S | Cl | Ar |
| K | Ca | Sc | Ti | V | Cr | Mn | Fe | Co | Ni | Cu | Zn | Ga | Ge | As | Se | Br | Kr |
| Rb | Sr | Y | Zr | Nb | Mo | Tc | Ru | Rh | Pd | Ag | Cd | In | Sn | Sb | Te | I | Xe |
| Cs | Ba | La | Hf | Ta | W | Re | Os | Ir | Pt | Au | Hg | Tl | Pb | Bi | Po | At | Rn |
| Fr | Ra | Ac | | | | | | | | | | | | | | | |

*Atomic Number Increases — Electronegativity Increases*

# C.6 <u>Exercises</u> Comparing Electronegativities of Atoms

Write the electronegativity for each element under the symbol for that element. Draw an arrow toward the atom with the greater electronegativity. (These diagrams represent bonds only, not molecules. The question here really is, "Which atom in a chemical bond has the strongest attraction for the shared electrons?")

**Example:**  H – F⃗  The arrow indicates the shared electron pair is attracted more
2.1  4.0  strongly by the fluorine atom.

1. N – H        2. B – F        3. S – O        4. P – H

5. Si – Cl      6. Cu – Br      7. N – I        8. Br – Cl

9. C – H    10. O – H    11. C – Cl    12. C – O

13. List the elements of Period 2 and their respective Pauling electronegativities.

| | | | | | | | |
|---|---|---|---|---|---|---|---|
| | | | | | | | |

14. List the elements of Group 7A and their respective Pauling electronegativities.

| | | | | |
|---|---|---|---|---|
| | | | | |

15. Explain why cesium and francium are the most reactive metals. (*Hint: Do metals tend to gain or lose electrons? What is the electronegativity of these two metals compared with other metals?*)

_____

_____

_____

_____

_____

_____

_____

16. Explain why fluorine is the most reactive nonmetal. (*Hint: Do nonmetals tend to gain or lose electrons? What is the electronegativity of fluorine compared to other nonmetals?*)

_____

_____

_____

_____

_____

_____

# C.7 Determining Bond Types

When atoms bond together, what happens to the bonding electrons between the atoms? Consider the following possibilities:

FIGURE C3
**Electron Shift of Bonding Electrons Is Due to Differences in Electronegativity**

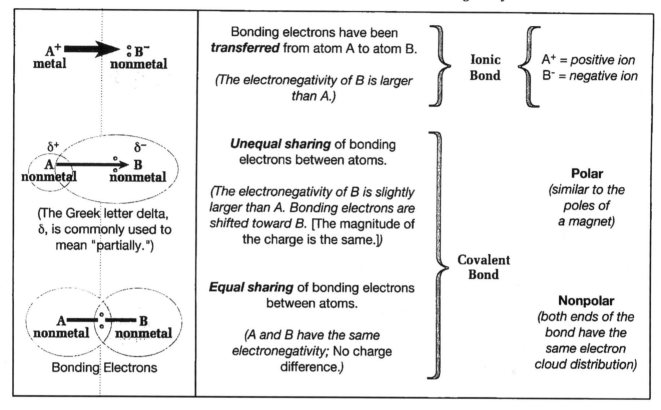

The type of bond between atoms will be determined as follows:

FIGURE C4
**Bond Determination**

| Type of Atoms Bonding | Type of Bond |
|---|---|
| Metal bonded to Nonmetal | Ionic bond |
| Nonmetal bonded to Nonmetal with different electronegativity | Polar Covalent bond |
| Nonmetal bonded to Nonmetal with same electronegativity | Nonpolar Covalent bond |

# C.8 <u>Exercises</u> Determining Bond Types

Classify the following compounds as predominantly covalent or predominantly ionic, using the "staircase" line separating metals from nonmetals on the Periodic Table as the basis for classification:

1. KCl _____

2. LiBr _____

3. CaS _____

4. HI _____

5. $CH_4$ _____

6. $H_2S$ _____

Identify the bond types (*ionic, nonpolar covalent* or *polar covalent*) for each of the following substances, using the Periodic Table and each element's electronegativities:

7. BrCl _____

8. $P_4$ _____

9. CsF _____

10. $CO_2$ _____

11. $CCl_4$ _____

12. $FeCl_3$ _____

13. $K_2S$ _____

14. $SiF_4$ _____

# C.9 Theory of Ionic Bonding

There are varying degrees of **charge separation** (see FIGURE C3) depending on the difference between electronegativities of the bonded atoms. As the difference between electronegativities of bonded atoms increases, charge separation can reach a condition at which the shared electron can be regarded as becoming the exclusive property of the more electronegative atom. At this point, we can assume an electron transfer has taken place. The more electronegative atom has become a negatively charged ion and the less electronegative atom a positively charged ion. Thus, the transfer of one or more electrons from one atom to another forms ions, the structural units of ionic compounds. Metallic elements, having relatively low electronegativities, lose one or more electrons to become positively charged ions. Nonmetallic elements, with high electronegativities, tend to gain one or more electrons to form negative ions.

FIGURE C5
**Ionic Bonding**
The formation of sodium chloride from sodium atoms and chlorine atoms can be thought of in two separate steps: first, the formation of ions by losing electrons (sodium) and gaining electrons (chlorine); second, the attraction between those ions.

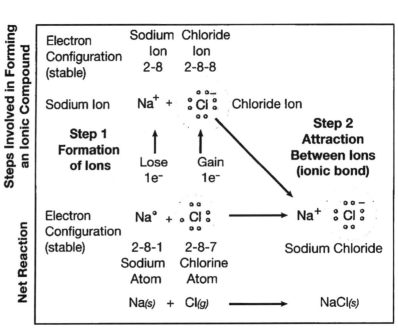

The process of electron transfer from a metallic atom to a nonmetallic atom involves a fixed number of electrons. Atoms lose or gain an appropriate number of electrons to acquire the electron configuration of the nearest noble gas, which, except for He (helium), is an octet structure. As a general rule, atoms of Groups 1A, 2A and 3A metallic elements lose one, two and three electrons, respectively, and atoms from Groups 5A, 6A and 7A nonmetallic elements gain three, two and one electron(s), respectively. In the case of transition metals (to which no simplifying general rule can be applied), ionic charges can be obtained from the Periodic Table.

# C.10 Exercises Theory of Ionic Bonding

For questions 1 and 2, assume a metallic Element M with two valence electrons chemically reacts with a nonmetallic Element X with seven valence electrons.

1. What kind of bond is most likely to form between M and X?

_____

2. Using Lewis diagrams, show the electron rearrangement that occurs to form a chemical bond between M and X. (Consider FIGURE C5.)

3. Write the Lewis diagrams for    a. LiF        b. $CaBr_2$.

4. Using the table below, describe the essential difference between a polar covalent bond and an ionic bond. (Consider such things as what type of atom is involved and what happens to the valence electrons and electronegativity differences.)

|  | Electrons | Type of Atoms | Amount of Charge Separation | Electromagnetic Difference |
|---|---|---|---|---|
| Polar |  |  |  |  |
| Ionic |  |  |  |  |

5. Discuss what actually happens when an ionic compound is formed from its elements.

_____

_____

_____

_____

# C.11 Covalent Bonds

When two hydrogen atoms combine, they will likely form a hydrogen molecule held together by a covalent bond. The sharing of a pair of electrons by the two hydrogen atoms is accompanied by the ***electrostatic interactions*** of the electrons and protons within and between the atoms. Since the ***attractive forces*** are sufficiently strong, the combining hydrogen atoms will form a stable hydrogen molecule.

When the bonding atoms are just the right distance apart, the attractions hold the molecule together. Moving the atoms any closer would cause excessive repulsion between nuclei; if the atoms are moved apart, the attractions pull the atoms back to the optimum bond distance. When explaining how a bond functions, generally only the *attractive forces* are considered, even though it is understood that the *repulsive forces* do exist.

The diagram in FIGURE C6 illustrates the attractive forces only. The result of such a consideration of attractive forces is the definition of a **covalent bond** as *the simultaneous attraction of a pair of shared electrons by two nuclei within a molecule.*

FIGURE C6
Electrostatic
Interactions in a
Hydrogen Molecule

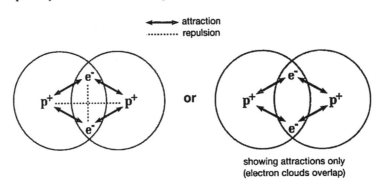

showing attractions only
(electron clouds overlap)

## Summary of the Theory of Covalent Bonds

When summarizing the theory of covalent bonding, the following are the most important considerations.

1. Covalent bonding occurs between nonmetallic atoms forming molecular substances.
2. Atoms tend to fill their valence orbitals: that is, two electrons in each of the four valence orbitals (with the exception of hydrogen) — **octet rule**.
3. Unpaired electrons in the valence orbitals are available for bonding (sharing).
4. When two atoms containing unpaired electrons combine, a covalent bond may form by sharing the previously unpaired electrons.
5. Covalent bonds are explained in terms of the simultaneous attraction of the pair of shared electrons by two nuclei.
6. The numbers of atoms that form molecules are in a definite and fixed ratio. *The number of covalent bonds that each atom forms* (**bonding capacity**) is limited. Bonding capacity is determined by the tendency of the atom to share electrons until it has the same electron structure as that of the nearest noble gas. This especially stable structure *usually* consists of eight electrons in the valence energy level and is *often* called the octet structure (octet rule).

Using the Lewis diagrams is a simple and effective way of illustrating the bonding capacity of the atoms and achieving octets within molecules. The Lewis diagrams of atoms can be extended to make predictions of the structural and molecular formulas of molecules.

# C.12 Lewis Diagrams and Structural Formulas

Consistent with the octet rule, atoms share an appropriate number of electrons to attain eight valence electrons—the stable electron configuration characteristic of noble gases. (Hydrogen, an important exception to the octet rule, tends to attain two valence electrons—the structure characteristic of the noble gas, helium.) *Omitting the lone electron pairs and substituting a dash for each bonding pair of electrons* is one method often used to simplify bonding representation. The resulting representation is called a **structural formula**. (The structural formula does not generally represent the shape of the molecule, it merely represents the bonding arrangement that occurs.)

Consider, for example, the electron-dot diagram for water, $H_2O$. The two bonding electrons in oxygen combine with two hydrogen atoms, each containing one bonding electron, so that each atom obtains the necessary number of electrons equal to its nearest noble gas:

FIGURE C7
**The Water Molecule**
A space-filling model is used to show how the atoms overlap and shows the size and shape of molecules better than structural formulas.

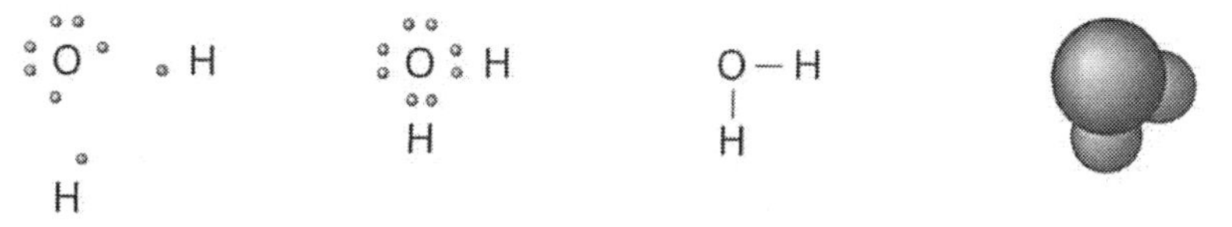

| Lewis Diagram of Individual Atoms | Lewis Diagram of Molecule | Structural Formula of Molecule | Space-Filling Model |

Notice that this method satisfactorily explains why only two atoms of hydrogen combine with one atom of oxygen to form water: a) each atom has reached its bonding capacity, b) there are no more bonding electrons left to share with other atoms, and c) each atom now has the electron structure of the nearest noble gas.

FIGURE C8
**Lewis Diagrams and Structural Formulas for Several Molecules**

| Molecular Substance | Molecular Formula | Lewis Diagram of Atoms Involved | Lewis Diagram of Molecule | Structural Formula |
|---|---|---|---|---|
| chloroform | $CHCl_{3(l)}$ |  | 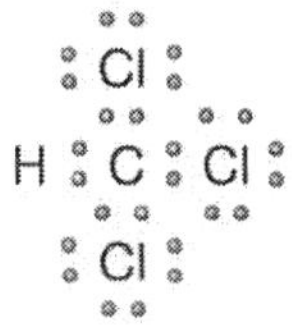 | 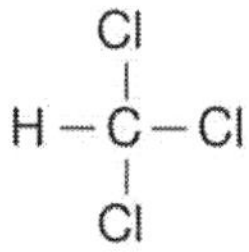 |
| ammonia | $NH_{3(g)}$ |  | 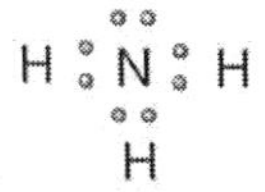 | 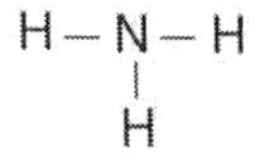 |
| bromine | $Br_{2(l)}$ |  | 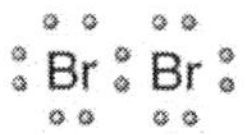 | Br — Br |
| methanol | $CH_3OH_{(l)}$ | 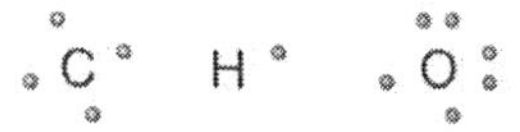 | 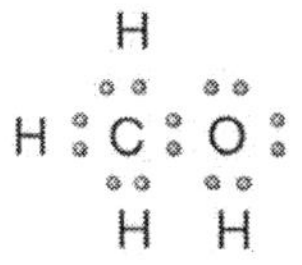 | 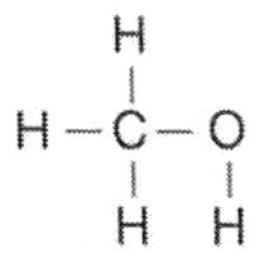 |

# C.13 Exercises  Lewis Molecular Theory

Use Lewis Molecular Theory to confirm the molecular formulas of the following substances:

| Molecular Substance | Lewis Diagram of Atoms Involved | Lewis Diagram of Molecule | Structural Formula |
|---|---|---|---|
| 1. HCl | | | |
| 2. $Cl_2$ | | | |
| 3. $C_2H_6$ | | | |

Use Lewis Molecular Theory to predict the molecular formula of the following substances. Use as many of each type of atom as necessary in order to reach the bonding capacity of that atom.

| Atoms Combined to Form a Molecule | Lewis Diagram of Atoms | Predicted Lewis Diagram of Molecule | Predicted Structural Formula of Molecule | Predicted Molecular Formula |
|---|---|---|---|---|
| 4. I atoms | | | | |
| 5. N & Cl atoms | | | | |
| 6. O & F atoms | | | | |

| Procedure | $NH_3$ | $CCl_4$ | $O_2$ | $C_2H_2$ |
|---|---|---|---|---|
| **Step 1:** *Count valence electrons.* | 1 N = 1 x 5 = 5<br>3 H = 3 x 1 = 3<br>———<br>8 | 1 C = 1 x 4 = 4<br>4 Cl = 4 x 7 = 28<br>———<br>32 | 2 O = 2 x 6 = 12 | 2 C = 2 x 4 = 8<br>2 H = 2 x 1 = 2<br>———<br>10 |
| **Step 2:** *Draw a skeleton structure.* | H  N  H<br>H | Cl<br>Cl  C  Cl<br>Cl | O  O | H  C  C  H |
| **Step 3:** *Put a pair of electrons between the atoms.* | H ⦂ N ⦂ H<br>H<br><br>(8 – 6 = 2 v.e. remaining) | Cl<br>Cl ⦂ C ⦂ Cl<br>Cl<br><br>(32 – 8 = 24 v.e. remaining) | O ⦂ O<br><br>(12 – 2 = 10 v.e. remaining) | H ⦂ C ⦂ C ⦂ H<br><br>(10 – 6 = 4 v.e. remaining) |
| **Step 4:** *Distribute the remaining electrons as lone pairs.* | H ⦂ N ⦂ H<br>H<br><br>(8 – 8 = 0 v.e. remaining) | ⦂ Cl ⦂<br>⦂ Cl ⦂ C ⦂ Cl ⦂<br>⦂ Cl ⦂<br><br>(32 – 32 = 0 v.e. remaining) | ⦂ O ⦂ O ⦂<br><br>(12 – 12 = 0 v.e. remaining) | H ⦂ C ⦂ C ⦂ H<br><br>(10 – 10 = 0 v.e. remaining) |
| **Step 5:** *If there are too few electrons, move lone pairs on outside atoms to inside positions.* | (Not applicable since all atoms are filled.) | (Not applicable since all atoms are filled.) | double bond<br>⦂ O ⦂⦂ O ⦂<br><br>(12 – 12 = 0 v.e. remaining. All atoms filled.) | triple bond<br>H ⦂ C ⦂⦂⦂ C ⦂ H<br><br>(10 – 10 = 0 v.e. remaining. All atoms filled.) |
| **Structural Formula** *(lone pairs are not shown)* | H – N – H<br>H | Cl<br>\|<br>Cl – C – Cl<br>\|<br>Cl | O = O | H – C ≡ C – H |

# C.14 Lewis Diagrams for Molecules

Lewis Molecular Theory is not generally used to *predict* the formulas of compounds. Instead it is used to explain the bonding of existing molecules. Covalent bonds within molecules exist as three types:

1. **Single bond:** one pair of electrons ($2 \text{ e}^-$) between bonded atoms, X:X or X – X
2. **Double bond:** two pairs of electrons ($4 \text{ e}^-$) between bonded atoms, X::X or X = X
3. **Triple bond:** three pairs of electrons ($6 \text{ e}^-$) between bonded atoms X:::X or X = X

Follow the rules given below to get a simple method of drawing Lewis diagrams for molecules, regardless of the type of covalent bond involved.

Step 1. *Count valence electrons* in the molecule.

Step 2. *Draw a skeleton structure* for the molecule. Try to keep the molecule as symmetrical as possible. The central atom is usually the atom that occurs least frequently in the formula. (Generally the central atom is the atom with the most bonding electrons.)

Step 3. *Put a pair of electrons between the atoms* to show a covalent bond. If all valence electrons are used and all atoms have 8 electrons, except H (hydrogen), which needs only 2 electrons, then the diagram is finished.

Step 4. Beginning with all the outside atoms and ending with the central atom, *distribute the remaining electrons as lone pairs* so that each atom has the required number of electrons. If all valence electrons are used and the octet rule is followed for each atom (except H), then the diagram is finished.

Step 5. *If there are too few electrons* to give each atom 8 electrons, *move lone pairs on outside atoms to inside positions* (between bonded atoms), thus forming double bonds (4 electrons) or triple bonds (6 electrons). **Keep in mind**, multiple bonds are limited almost exclusively to C, N and O. If all valence electrons are used and the octet rule is followed for each atom (except H), then the diagram is finished.

# C.15 Exercises    Lewis Diagrams for Molecules

Show a Lewis Diagram and Structural Formula for each of the following formulas:

| Formula (Name) | Lewis Diagram | Structural Formula |
|---|---|---|
| 1. $F_2(g)$ (*fluorine*) | | |
| 2. $S_2Cl_2(l)$ (*disulfur dichloride*) | | |
| 3. $CH_3OH(l)$ (*methanol*) | | |

| | | |
|---|---|---|
| 4. $N_2(g)$<br>(nitrogen) | | |
| 5. $CO_2(g)$<br>(carbon dioxide) | | |
| 6. $C_2F_4(g)$<br>(tetrafluoroethene) | | |
| 7. $C_2Cl_2(g)$<br>(dichloroethyne) | | |
| 8. HCHO(l)<br>(methanal) | | |

Sometimes *groups of atoms can bond covalently and gain or lose electrons* to form what is known as **polyatomic ions**. (The charge indicates the number of valence electrons gained or lost.) Write the diagrams for the following polyatomic ions.

| | | |
|---|---|---|
| 9. $OH^-$<br>(*hydroxide ion*)<br>(gains one<br>electron) | | |
| 10. $NO_3^-$<br>(*nitrate ion*)<br>(gains one<br>electron | | |

# C.16 Stereochemistry—VSEPR Theory

All molecules have a definite three-dimensional shape. *The study of the shape of molecules and ions* is called **stereochemistry**. The <u>V</u>alence <u>S</u>hell <u>E</u>lectron <u>P</u>air <u>R</u>epulsion Theory (VSEPR Theory) provides a relatively *simple and reliable basis for understanding and predicting **molecular geometry***. Molecular geometry can be determined from Lewis electron-dot diagrams.

The VSEPR theory was developed by Ronald James Gillespie and Dr. Ronald Nyholm around 1956–57.

The VSEPR Theory proposes a set of rules for predicting molecular geometry based on the idea that the arrangement *in space* of the covalent bonds formed by an atom depends on the arrangement of electron groups in the outermost or valence shell of the central atom. It says, in essence, that these electron groups try to push each other as far away as possible while still bonding to the central atom.

The VSEPR Theory presented in this textbook will be purposely restricted to molecules containing hydrogen and/or atoms which obey the octet rule and which share unpaired (bonding) electrons but not paired (lone pair) electrons. The restricted VSEPR theory presented will make accurate predictions for all molecules encountered in these materials.

## Stereochemistry (Shapes Around Central Atoms)

All molecules have a definite three-dimensional shape. The number of electron pairs surrounding a central atom can be used to predict the stereochemistry of a molecule. The electron pairs repel each other and take up positions as far from one another as possible. When determining the shape of molecules, the electron pairs of a multiple bond count as only one pair of electrons for stereochemistry purposes. Examples of commonly encountered molecular shapes are given in FIGURE C10.

Sometimes it is convenient to represent molecules generically using a general formula. It is a shorthand way of showing that many different molecules have a similar pattern. The General Formula uses:

- the letter A to represent the central atom,
- the letter X to represent the atoms bonded to the central atom, and
- the letter E to represent the lone pairs on the central atom.

Atoms with four electron density groups on the central atom ($AX_4$, $AX_3E$, $AX_2E_2$) have variations on the tetrahedral configuration; atoms with three electron density groups on the central atom ($AX_3$, $AX_2E$) have variations on the trigonal planar configuration; atoms with two electron density groups, both groups being atoms ($AX_2$), will be linear.

The preceding general descriptions established the terminology and the basis for predicting the stereochemistry of molecules according to VSEPR Theory. FIGURE C10 summarizes the fundamental aspects of VSEPR theory as used for predicting shapes around central atoms in molecules.

For our purposes, the most important rules are:
1. Valence electron pairs, both shared (bonding) and lone pairs, arrange themselves around the central atom in a molecule in such a way as to minimize repulsion. Thus, the bonding and lone pairs of electrons take up positions around the central atom as far away from each other as possible.
2. For purposes of predicting molecular geometry, treat multiple bonds (double and triple bonds) as single bonds. (Only the directional character of the bond needs to be considered.)
3. Lone pairs of electrons occupy more space than bonding pairs of electrons.

The systematic application of VSEPR Theory can be shown as a sequence of steps. The sequence of steps is illustrated in the following examples. (See FIGURE C10.)

## The Stereochemistry of the Carbon Dioxide Molecule (Linear)

1. Draw the Lewis diagram.

$$\ddot{\text{O}} :: \text{C} :: \ddot{\text{O}}$$

2. Count the number of bonding and lone pairs surrounding the C atom. (For purposes of determining shape, the electrons of multiple bonds are counted as a single bond pair. Thus around the carbon atom, there are two bonding pairs and zero lone pairs.)

3. To minimize repulsion, the bond orientation is **linear** around each carbon.

(bond angle is 180°)    O = C = O

*Generalization*: The shape around other atoms with two bonding pairs and zero lone pairs is linear. ($AX_2$)

Other Examples: $CS_2$, any carbon atom with a triple bond in a hydrocarbon.

FIGURE C10
Stereochemistry of Some Common Molecules

| Example | Lewis Diagram | Number of Bonding Groups (X) | Number of Lone Pairs (E) | General Formula and Shape | Shape Diagram |
|---|---|---|---|---|---|
| $CO_2$ |  O :: C :: O | 2 | 0 | $AX_2$ linear (180°) | O = C = O |
| HCHO |  H C :: O / H | 3 | 0 | $AX_3$ trigonal planar (120°) | 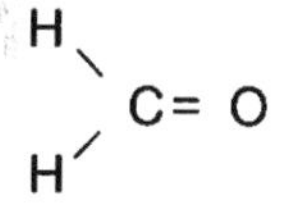 H \ C = O / H |
| $SO_2$ |  S :: O / O | 2 | 1 | $AX_2E$ angular (120°) | 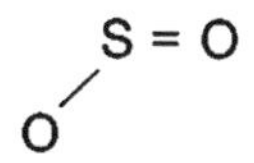 S = O / O |
| $CH_4$ | 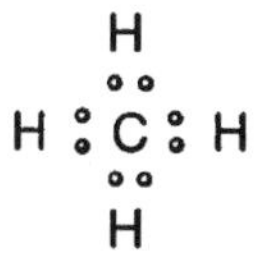 H : C : H / H / H | 4 | 0 | $AX_4$ tetrahedral (109.5°) | 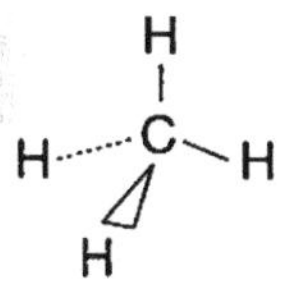 H—C—H (H, H) |
| $NH_3$ | 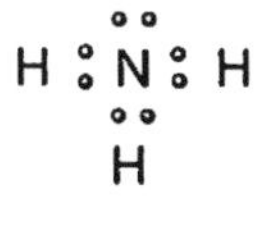 H : N : H / H | 3 | 1 | $AX_3E$ pyramidal (107°) | 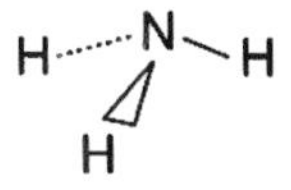 H—N—H / H |
| $H_2O$ | 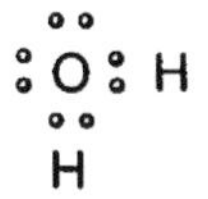 O : H / H | 2 | 2 | $AX_2E_2$ angular (105°) | 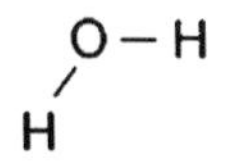 O—H / H |
| HCl | 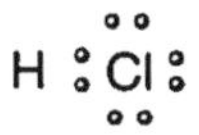 H : Cl | xxx | xxx | No central atom linear (180°) diatomic molecules | H—Cl |

The dotted line indicates that the bonds are directed *into* the plane of the paper (away from you), and the wedge indicates that the bonds are directed *out of* the plane of the paper (toward you). The solid lines represent bonds that are *in* the plane of the paper.

## The Stereochemistry of the Methanal (Formaldehyde) Molecule (Trigonal Planar)

1. Draw the Lewis Diagram.

$$H \atop H \quad {}_{\circ}^{\circ}C :: O_{\circ}^{\circ}$$

2. Count the number of bonding and lone electron pairs surrounding the C (carbon) atom. (For purposes of determining shape, multiple bonds have the same directional character as single bonds. The two electron pairs of the double bond are counted as one bonding pair for the purposes of determining the shape around a central atom.)

3. To minimize repulsion, the three electron pairs from the carbon are directed to the corners of an equilateral triangle and the shape around each carbon is described as being **trigonal planar** as illustrated below.

$$H \diagdown \quad 120° \atop H \diagup \quad C = O$$

*Generalization*: **The shape around atoms with three bonding pairs and zero lone pairs is trigonal planar. ($AX_3$)**

Other Examples: Any carbon atom with a double bond in a hydrocarbon, $SO_3$, $NO_3^-$, $CO_3^{2-}$.

## The Stereochemistry of the Sulfur Dioxide Molecule (Angular)

1. Draw the Lewis Diagram.

$$S :: O \atop O$$

2. Count the number of bonding and lone electron pairs surrounding the central atom, S. (For $SO_2$, the number of bonding pairs is two and there is one lone pair.)

3. Once again the minimization of repulsion would dictate that the electron pairs be directed to the vertices of a trigonal planar molecule. However, there are only three atoms in the molecule and the resulting molecular structure is **angular**. The shape of $SO_2$ can be represented as follows:

$$S = O \atop O \diagup 120°$$

*Generalization*: **Molecules with two bonding pairs and one lone pair around a central atom assume an angular shape around that central atom. ($AX_2E$)**

Other Examples: $O_3$, $NO_2^-$

## The Stereochemistry of the Methane Molecule (Tetrahedral):

1. Draw the Lewis Diagram.

$$H \atop H : C : H \atop H$$

2. Count the total number of bonding and lone electron pairs surrounding the central atom. (For $CH_4$, the number of bonding pairs around the carbon atom is four and there are zero lone pairs. The total number of electron pairs is four.)

3. The minimization of repulsion dictates that the four bond pairs be directed to the vertices of a regular tetrahedron (a 3-D pyramid with an equilateral triangle on each side and base), hence the shape of the methane molecule is **tetrahedral**. The geometry of $CH_4$ can be represented as follows:

(the bond angle is 109.5°)

The dotted line indicates that the bond is directed into the plane of the paper (away from you) and the wedge indicates that the bond is directed out of the paper (toward you). The solid lines represent bonds that are in the plane of the paper.

*Generalization*: **Molecules with four bonding pairs and zero lone pairs around a central atom assume a tetrahedral shape around that central atom. If there is only one central atom, the shape around the central atom becomes the shape of the molecule. ($AX_4$)**

Other Examples: $SiH_4$, $CCl_4$, $SiF_4$, $NH_4^+$.


## The Stereochemistry of the Ammonia Molecule (Pyramidal)

1. Draw the Lewis Diagram.

2. Count the number of bonding and lone electron pairs surrounding the central atom, N (nitrogen). (For $NH_3$, the number of bonding pairs around the nitrogen atom is three and there is one lone pair, for a total of four electron pairs.)

3. The minimization of repulsion would indicate that the electron pairs be directed to the vertices of a tetrahedron as in the case of $CH_4$ and indeed this is approximately so. Because the lone electron pair cannot be seen, it is customary to classify the molecular shape in terms of the atomic arrangement only. Thus ammonia has the shape of a triangular pyramid and it is called **pyramidal**. The geometry of $NH_3$ can be represented as follows:

(the bond angle is 107°)

*Generalization*: **Molecules with three bonding pairs and one lone pair around a central atom assume a pyramidal shape around that central atom. ($AX_3E$)**

Other examples: $PH_3$, $PCl_3$, $NBr_3$, $H_3O^+$.


## The Stereochemistry of the Water Molecule (Angular)

1. Draw the Lewis Diagram.

2. Count the number of bonding and lone electron pairs surrounding the central atom, O. (For $H_2O$, the number of bonding pairs is two and there are two lone pairs.)

3. Once again, to minimize repulsion, the electron pairs would be directed to the vertices of a tetrahedron. However, there are only three atoms in the molecule and the resulting molecular structure is **angular** or **bent**. The shape of $H_2O$ can be represented as follows:

*Generalization*: Molecules with two bonding pairs and two lone pairs around a central atom assume an angular shape around that central atom. ($AX_2E_2$)

Other Examples: $H_2S$, $OCl_2$, $SF_2$, $NH_2^-$.

### The Stereochemistry of Diatomic Molecules

The systematic application of VSEPR Theory has been successfully discussed in situations involving multiple bonding, particularly the double and triple bonding between carbon atoms.

The next compound that could be logically considered in this sequence would be Group 7A atoms, such as HF or any hydrogen halide. However, it is unnecessary to apply any analysis for predicting shapes of diatomic molecules, since by necessity *diatomic molecules can only be linear.*

LAB ...

## C.17 Stereochemistry

**Purpose:**
✔ To use VSEPR Theory to predict shapes around central atoms.
✔ To construct molecular models from a kit to test the predictions.

**Prelab Exercise:**
Before going to the lab, complete the "Prelab Excercises" in the following table.

**Materials:**
• Molecular Models Kit

**Procedure:**
1. Construct models of each of the following molecules using the correct colored ball for each atom. Use one stick/spring for a single bond, two springs for a double bond, and three springs for a triple bond.

2. Draw a diagram of the model under "Diagram of Actual Shape."

3. Write in the "Name to Represent Actual Shape."

4. If the actual shape corresponds with the predicted shape, check it off—if not, consult the teacher.

| Prelab Exercises | | | | | Observations | |
|---|---|---|---|---|---|---|
| Molecular Substance | Lewis Diagram | For Each Central Atom | | Name to Represent Predicted Shape | Diagram of Actual Shape | Name to Represent Actual Shape |
| | | Number of Bonding Pairs | Number of Lone Pairs | | | |
| 1. $NI_3$ | | | | | | |
| 2. $C_2Cl_4$ (2 central atoms) | | | | | | |
| 3. $CF_4$ | | | | | | |
| 4. $OCl_2$ | | | | | | |
| 5. $C_2F_2$ (2 central atoms) | | | | | | |
| 6. HOF | | | | | | |
| 7. $NHF_2$ | | | | | | |
| 8. $C_2IB_r$ (2 central atoms) | | | | | | |
| 9. $C_2HF_3$ (2 central atoms) | | | | | | |

| | | | | | | |
|---|---|---|---|---|---|---|
| 10. $CHClBr_2$ | | | | | | |
| 11. $H_2O_2$ <br> (2 central atoms) | | | | | | |
| 12. $CS_2$ | | | | | | |
| 13. $N_2H_3F$ <br> (2 central atoms) | | | | | | |
| 14. $CH_3OH$ <br> (2 central atoms) | | | | | | |
| 15. $C_3H_6$ <br> *noncyclic* <br> (3 central atoms) | | | | | | |

# C.18  Polarity of Covalent Bonds

**Nonpolar Covalent Bonds**—Covalent bonds where *the bonding electron pair is shared equally and is uniformly distributed between the nuclei of two bonded atoms* are called **nonpolar covalent bonds**. Such bonds can only result when two nuclei with the same number of protons and/or atoms of equal electronegativities (2nd line of FIGURE C11) simultaneously attract a shared pair of electrons.

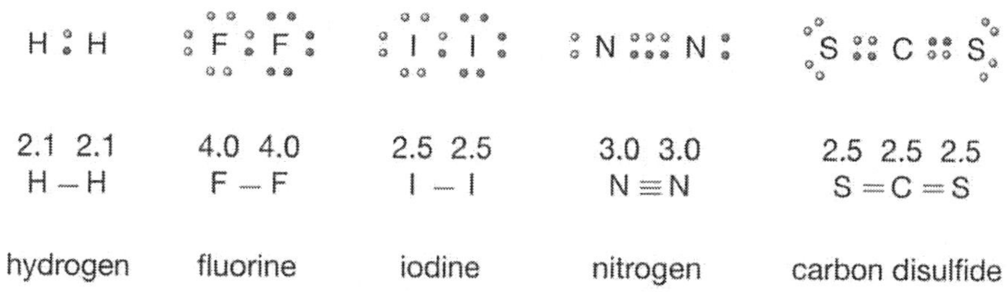

| | | | | |
|---|---|---|---|---|
| H ᐧᐧ H | ᐧᐧF ᐧᐧ Fᐧᐧ | ᐧᐧ I ᐧᐧ Iᐧᐧ | ᐧᐧN ⦂⦂⦂ Nᐧᐧ | ᐧᐧS ⦂⦂ C ⦂⦂ Sᐧᐧ |
| 2.1  2.1 | 4.0  4.0 | 2.5  2.5 | 3.0  3.0 | 2.5  2.5  2.5 |
| H — H | F — F | I — I | N ≡ N | S = C = S |
| hydrogen | fluorine | iodine | nitrogen | carbon disulfide |

FIGURE C11
**Examples of Nonpolar Covalent Bonding.**
In each case, the bonding electrons are equally shared between the bonded atoms.

**Polar Covalent Bonds**—Covalent bonds in which *the bonding electrons are unequally shared and thus asymmetrically distributed between the nuclei of two bonded atoms*, are called **polar covalent bonds**. Such bonds occur between atoms of different electronegativities.

Comparison between two molecules, chlorine ($Cl_2$) and hydrogen chloride (HCl), illustrates the difference between nonpolar and polar covalent bonding:

FIGURE C12    **Differences in Covalent Bonds**

| 3.0  3.0 | 2.1 → 3.0 |
|---|---|
| ᐧᐧCl ᐧᐧ Clᐧᐧ | H ᐧᐧ Clᐧᐧ |
| nonpolar covalent bonding | polar covalent bonding |

Both molecules are formed by sharing one pair of electrons. In the chlorine molecule, the electrons shared in the covalent bond are evenly distributed between the two chlorine atoms. However, in the hydrogen chloride molecule, the shared electrons are not evenly distributed between the hydrogen and the chlorine atoms. Chlorine has an electronegativity of 3.0 and hydrogen has 2.1. This indicates that the chlorine atom attracts the shared electrons more strongly than the hydrogen atom. The shared electrons are pulled closer to the more electronegative chlorine atom. The chlorine becomes partially[*] negative and the hydrogen partially[*] positive, because the shared electrons are displaced towards the chlorine and away from the hydrogen. (*The Greek letter delta, $\delta$, is commonly used to mean "partially." Thus $\delta^-$ means partially negative.)

FIGURE C13
**Polar Covalent Bonding in the HCl Molecule**

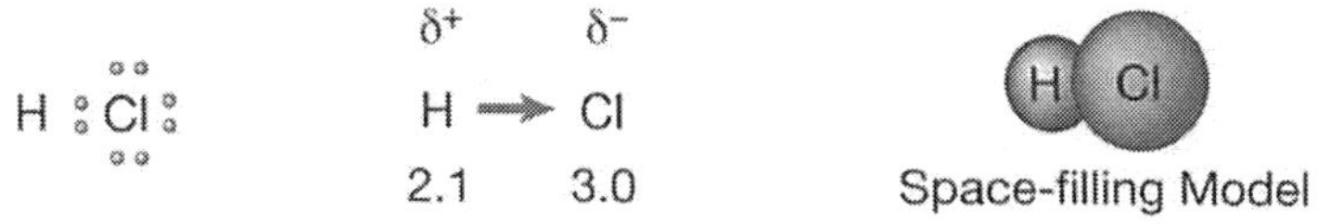

| | $\delta^+$ $\quad$ $\delta^-$ | |
|---|---|---|
| H ᐧᐧ Clᐧᐧ | H → Cl | Space-filling Model |
| | 2.1 $\quad$ 3.0 | |

The arrow pointing toward the partially negative side of the more electronegative atom represents a **bond dipole**. This bond dipole represents a charge separation between the atoms—that is, it shows that a greater percentage of the bonding electrons is on one atom than the other. Remember that in polar covalent bonds, as in the hydrogen chloride molecule just described, there is neither a loss nor gain of electrons. Thus, molecules that have polar covalent bonds are overall *electrically neutral*.

# C.19    Polarity of Molecules

A **polar molecule** *has an asymmetrical (uneven) distribution of the electron charge.* A **molecular dipole** *is another name for a polar molecule.* It is the result of the addition of all the bond dipoles within the molecule. Depending on the direction of the bond dipoles in a molecule, they do or do not cancel to produce nonpolar or polar molecules, respectively. Knowing the shape of a molecule allows you to be confident in determining whether its bond dipoles cancel or not.

In order to determine the polarity of a molecule, the stereochemistry of the molecule must be known along with the bond dipoles. The steps to be followed in determining the polarity of a molecule are:

1. Draw a Lewis diagram of the molecule.
2. Apply the VSEPR rules to draw a shape (stereochemistry) diagram of the molecule,
3. Use electronegativities to determine bond dipoles.
4. Use the shape diagram complete with bond dipoles to determine the molecular dipole—that is, determine whether the molecule is polar or nonpolar:
   - If the bond dipoles cancel, the molecule is **nonpolar**.
   - If bond dipoles do not cancel, the molecule is **polar**
     (See examples in FIGURE C14).

**Nonpolar molecules** have...
   a. all atoms with the same electronegativity

*or*

   b. their molecular shape permits the cancellations of the bond dipoles. That is, there is no net molecular dipole.

   Symmetrical shapes that allow cancellation of bond dipoles if identical atoms are bonded to the central atom are as follows:
   - tetrahedral ($AX_4$)
   - trigonal planar ($AX_3$)
   - linear ($AX_2$)

**Polar molecules** have...
   a. at least one pair of bonded atoms with different electronegativity.

*and*

   b. their asymmetric molecular shape does not cancel the bond dipoles. That is, there is a net molecular dipole.
   - pyramidal ($AX_3E$)
   - angular ($AX_2E_2$ or $AX_2E$)

FIGURE C14 summarizes the situations that give rise to molecular polarity or non polarity when the atoms bonded to the central atom are identical. If non-identical atoms are bonded to the central atom, the bond dipoles may not cancel. For example, $CH_4$ is nonpolar, but $CH_3Cl$ is polar because the C–Cl bond dipole is not canceled by the C–H bond dipoles. Similar reasoning can be applied to other cases involving non-identical atoms bonded to the central atom.

| Formula and Lewis Diagram | Bond Dipoles and Polarity | Explanation | Other Examples |
|---|---|---|---|
| $H_2$ <br><br> H : H | H — H <br><br> nonpolar | Diatomic molecule with no bond dipole, therefore molecule is nonpolar. | $O_2$, $N_2$ and diatomic halogens |
| HCl <br><br> H : Cl: | H — Cl <br> ☐▬▶ <br> polar | Diatomic molecule with bond dipole, therefore molecule is polar. | hydrogen halides |
| $CO_2$ <br><br> :O :: C :: O: | O = C = O <br> ◀— —▶ <br> nonpolar | Equal bond dipoles oppositely directed to give vector sum of zero, hence molecule is nonpolar. | $CS_2$ |
| $H_2O$ <br><br> :O: H <br> H | <br> polar | Vector sum of bond dipoles gives resultant molecular dipole, hence molecule is polar. | $H_2S$, $H_2Se$ and halides of oxygen |
| $NH_3$ <br><br> H : N : H <br> H | <br> polar | Vector sum of bond dipoles gives resultant molecular dipole, hence molecule is polar. | $PH_3$, $AsH_3$ and halides of N, P, and As |
| $CH_4$ <br> H <br> H : C : H <br> H | <br> nonpolar | Equal bond dipoles give vector sum of zero, hence molecule is nonpolar. | hydrides and halides of C and Si |
| $C_2H_4$ <br> H<sub> </sub> C :: C <sub> </sub>H <br> H ° ° H | <br> nonpolar | Equal bond dipoles give vector sum of zero, hence molecule is nonpolar. | around C double-bonded to another C |
| $C_2H_2$ <br> H : C ::: C : H | H — C ≡ C — H <br> ◀— —▶ <br> nonpolar | Equal bond dipoles oppositely directed to give vector sum of zero, hence molecule is nonpolar. | around C triple-bonded to another C |

# C.20 Exercises  Polarity of Molecules

For each of the following molecules, draw the Lewis and shape diagrams to represent the actual shape, and use arrows to indicate bond dipoles. Give the name to represent the actual shape and indicate whether the molecule is polar or nonpolar. Refer to the $NH_3$ molecule in FIGURE C14 as an example.

| Molecular Formula | Lewis Diagram | Shape Around Central Atom(s) | Shape Diagram and Bond Dipoles | Polarity of Molecule |
|---|---|---|---|---|
| $NH_3$ | H : N : H H | pyramidal | | polar |
| 1.  $N_2$ | | | | |
| 2.  HBr | | | | |
| 3.  $OCl_2$ | | | | |
| 4.  $SiCl_4$ | | | | |
| 5.  $CHI_3$ | | | | |
| 6.  $C_2H_3Cl$ | | | | |
| 7.  $C_2H_4$ | | | | |
| 8.  $CH_3OH$ | | | | |

# Unit D
# Elements, Compounds and Nomenclature

## D.1 Elements, Compounds and Nomenclature

You have observed the properties of elements and learned their chemical symbols. You have investigated the structure of atoms and learned how atoms bond together. This unit focuses on observing the properties of chemical compounds and learning to write the names and formulas of these substances. **Chemical nomenclature** is *the organized system a chemist uses to name substances and write their chemical formulas.*

A **chemical formula** represents the *number of each kind of atom bonded together* in a substance. Chemical formulas use element symbols and subscripts. A **subscript** *indicates the number of atoms or ions present in the formula.* For example, the chemical formula for water is

symbol for hydrogen $\longrightarrow H_2O \longleftarrow$ symbol for oxygen

subscript

(the 2 indicates two hydrogen atoms)

## D.2 History of Chemical Nomenclature
### Antoine Laurent Lavoisier (1743–1794)

The modern system of *naming* compounds according to their elements dates back to 1789 when Lavoisier published a chemistry book using a new nomenclature. Lavoisier was the first chemist to clearly understand the oxidations of elements. For example, in the reaction nitrogen plus two oxygen, the new compound formed is nitrogen dioxide:

nitrogen dioxide

nitrogen + (2) oxygen $\longrightarrow$

$NO_2$

**Lewis Dot Diagram**

**Space Filling Model**

*Note: Nitrogen dioxide does not obey the octet rule.*

Lavoisier in 1789 introduced the following ideas:

1. All elements have single word names.
2. All compounds have names made up of their elements.
3. A system of prefixes and suffixes should be used.

## John Dalton (1766–1844)

In 1804, John Dalton, an English schoolteacher, proposed a theory that explained chemical reactions. He proposed that:

- All substances are made of atoms.
- Atoms within one substance are alike and have the same mass.
- Chemical reactions consist of a rearrangement of atoms.
- Elements are made of "simple atoms" while compounds contain "compound atoms" (now called molecules).

To help in the writing of chemical equations, Dalton, over the period from 1806 to 1835, devised a symbol for each known element. Note that some things thought to be elements (below) are not in fact elements (e.g., barytes, lime, magnesia, potash and soda).

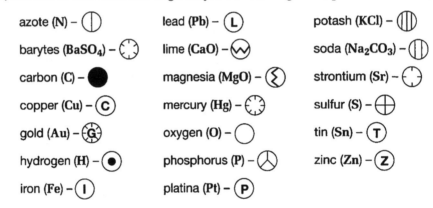

1. 1 carbon atom + 2 oxygen atoms ⟶ 1 carbon dioxide "compound atom"

2. 1 hydrogen atom + 1 oxygen atom ⟶ 1 water "compound atom"

3. 1 mercuric oxide "compound atom" ⟶ 1 mercury atom + 1 oxygen atom

(Can you find the errors in all three of Dalton's equations above?)

## Jöns Jakob Berzelius (1779–1848):

As more and more elements were discovered, the symbols devised by Dalton became awkward. In 1814, Berzelius devised a system whereby the first letter of the name of an element becomes its symbol. Where necessary a second letter of the element is used. The first letter is always written in upper case and the second letter, if used, is in lower case.

| | | |
|---|---|---|
| C - carbon | Cl - chlorine | Co - cobalt |
| Cu - copper | O - oxygen | Cd - cadmium |

Newly discovered elements have international names and their symbols are obvious to everyone. Common elements that were known to the ancients (such as gold and iron) have a different name in every language. For the latter, Berzelius suggested using the Latin names as the basis for the chemical symbol. So we have:

| | |
|---|---|
| Cu (cuprum) – copper | K (kalium) – potassium |
| Fe (ferrum) – iron | Pb (plumbum) – lead |
| Sb (stibnum) – antimony | Sn (stannum) – tin |

Placing two or more symbols side by side, one could write formulas for compounds. To make the formulas more compact, Berzelius introduced the use of the subscript. Thus carbon dioxide, which Dalton wrote as ●○○ became $CO_2$.

The system of naming compounds devised by Lavoisier is used to the present day and is sometimes called the Classical System of nomenclature. Many elements form several compounds with another given element, and a system using the suffixes *-ic* and *-ous* was devised in the nineteenth century to name these compounds. (See D.6, "Nomenclature of Multiple Ion Charges," for greater detail.) For example,

ferric oxide for $Fe_2O_3$     and     ferrous oxide for $FeO$

## Alfred Stock (1876–1949)

In 1920, Alfred Stock suggested a simpler way of giving names to compounds such as $FeCl_3$ and $FeCl_2$. Rather than use suffixes, Stock suggested writing the *charge* on the **cation** in Roman numerals after the name of the metal. The Roman numerals are written in parentheses. For example,

| | |
|---|---|
| $FeCl_2$ — iron(II) chloride, | $FeO$ — iron(II) oxide |
| $FeCl_3$ — iron(III) chloride, | $Fe_2O_3$ — iron(III) oxide |

The Stock System of nomenclature is so clear and simple that in 1940 the International Union of Pure and Applied Chemistry (IUPAC) recommended this system for use with all metallic compounds. Although the Classical System (*-ic*, *-ous*) is still found in older books, the Stock System for naming these compounds is now in general use.

# D.3 Classification of Compounds

Since elements were named in Unit A, this unit will be primarily concerned with the naming of compounds. As you learned in Unit C, **compounds** are *pure substances that contain more than one kind of atom and/or ion* and may be classified as **ionic** or **molecular**. This classification of compounds is emphasized by the different:

- types of elements that combine to form ionic and molecular compounds.
- types of chemical bonds within ionic and molecular compounds.
- ways of naming and writing chemical formulas for ionic and molecular compounds.
- physical and chemical properties of ionic and molecular compounds.

## Ionic Compounds

**Ionic compounds** *are formed when oppositely charged ions are attracted to each other* by means of an ionic bond. Recall from C.9, "A Theory of Ionic Bonding," that an ionic bond is a very strong force of electrostatic attraction between a metallic ion and a nonmetallic ion, or in more general terms, between a positive metallic ion (cation) and a negative nonmetallic ion (anion). This strong force of electrostatic attraction results in ionic compounds being high-melting-point and -boiling-point solids capable of dissolving in water.

## FIGURE D1 The Formation of Ionic Bonds

Ionic bonds are formed by combinations between metallic ions and nonmetallic ions; and between metallic and covalent polyatomic ions.

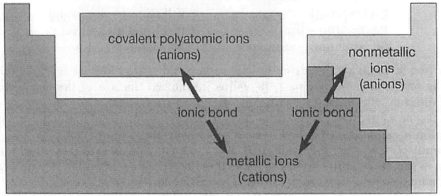

## Ions

**Cations** – positively charged ions: $Na^+$, $K^+$, $Ca^{2+}$, $Al^{3+}$, $Fe^{3+}$.

**Anions** – negatively charged ions: $Cl^-$, $F^-$, $S^{2-}$, $Se^{2-}$, $P^{3-}$.

Remember: *The charge of the ion indicates whether electrons have been lost or gained and how many!*

$Al^{3+}$ means the aluminum atom <u>lost</u> 3 electrons.

$S^{2-}$ means the sulfur atom <u>gained</u> 2 electrons.

## Molecular (Covalent) Compounds

Molecules are formed when two or more nonmetal atoms are joined together with covalent bonds. Recall that a covalent bond (See FIGURE D2) is a force of attraction that occurs when atoms share electrons to achieve their noble-gas-electron arrangement. Based on what you learned in Unit C, the two nonmetallic atoms both require a gain of electrons to attain a noble-gas-electron arrangement. Since neither atom loses electrons easily, they instead achieve their noble-gas-electron configuration by sharing electrons. The simultaneous attraction of electrons between two nuclei results in a very strong force of attraction. Although the bonds between atoms are very strong, the attractions between molecules are quite weak. As a result, **molecular compounds**, *pure substances composed of atom groupings called molecules*, are often low-melting-point and -boiling-point gases, liquids and solids. More on the properties of compounds will come later in this unit.

## FIGURE D2 The Formation of Covelent Bonds

Covalent bonds are formed by combinations between nonmetallic atoms.

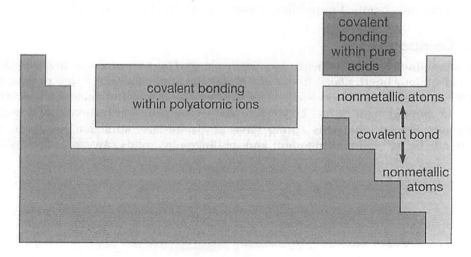

# D.4 Binary Ionic Compounds

A binary ionic compound is composed of metallic and nonmetallic ions. To qualify as binary, only two kinds of simple ions must be involved. The metallic ions are positively charged. The nonmetallic ions are negatively charged. The attraction between the positive metallic ions and the negative nonmetallic ions is called an ionic bond.

## Structure of Binary Ionic Compounds

In the pure state, molecular compounds exist as molecules, and ionic substances exist as ions. For example, molecules of sodium chloride do not exist. Sodium chloride exists as an ionic crystal lattice. Each sodium ion is surrounded by six chloride ions and each chloride ion is surrounded by six sodium ions. The ratio of sodium ions to chloride ions is 1:1. There are an equal number of sodium ions and chloride ions, but no one sodium ion is associated with one particular chloride ion.

FIGURE D3    NaCl Ionic Crystal Lattice (sodium chloride or table salt)

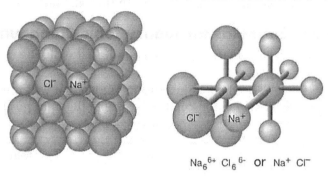

$Na_6^{6+} Cl_6^{6-}$ or $Na^+ Cl^-$

Ionic bonds are best described as the simultaneous attraction of a positive ion by the surrounding negative ions and of a negative ion by the surrounding positive ions.

## Molecules and Formula Units

Chemical formulas for molecular substances are called **molecular formulas**. A molecular formula *indicates the actual number of each kind of atom present in the molecule.* An **empirical formula** *indicates the simplest whole number ratio of atoms or ions in the compound.* The term *chemical formula* may be used either for molecular or empirical formulas. Consider, for example, the different chemical formulas for hydrogen peroxide.

$H_2O_2$
molecular formula

HO
empirical formula

Molecular substances contain molecules. **Molecules** *are separate, discrete and neutral atom groupings.* A molecule of water may be identified as a group of two hydrogen atoms and one oxygen atom sharing covalent bonds together. Regardless of whether water is a solid, liquid or gas, this group of atoms stays as an identifiable group. That is why empirical formulas are not usually used for molecular compounds.

Ionic substances do not contain molecules. There is no such thing as a molecule of sodium chloride. Instead, chemists use a term called the **formula unit** to indicate *the smallest grouping of ions in the formula for an ionic compound.* Chemical formulas for ionic substances are empirical formulas. A formula unit of sodium chloride would contain one sodium ion and one chloride ion. As explained above, no one $Na^+$ ion is attached to only one $Cl^-$ ion. Therefore, a formula unit is only an imaginary unit, to express the simplest whole number ratio of cations to anions.

## Naming Binary Ionic Compounds

When naming any ionic compounds, the rule is to simply write the name of the positive ion followed by the name of the negative ion.

In Unit B, the rules for naming *simple* ions were given:
1. Name the cation by writing the full name of the metallic element; e.g., $Na^+$ is a *sodium* ion, $Zn^{2+}$ is a *zinc* ion and $Al^{3+}$ is an *aluminum* ion.
2. Name the anion by abbreviating the full name of the nonmetallic element and adding *-ide*; e.g., $Cl^-$ is a chloride ion, $S^{2-}$ is a sulfide ion and $H^-$ is a hydride ion.

*Examples*:
NaCl (from $Na^+Cl^-$) is *sodium chloride* (table salt).
$CaCl_2$ (from $Ca^{2+}(Cl^-)_2$) is *calcium chloride* (a drying agent).

There are no *chlorine molecules, $Cl_2$*, in calcium chloride. The chlorine molecules were first changed to chloride ions before combining with the calcium ions.

## Writing Chemical Formulas for Binary Ionic Compounds

1. When given the name of a binary ionic compound, *first* write the symbols for the ions involved.
2. Next, determine the lowest whole number ratio of ions that will provide an overall net charge of zero, that is, a neutral compound where the **total positive charge = total negative charge**.

| Name of compound | silver chloride | | potassium oxide | | aluminum sulfide | |
|---|---|---|---|---|---|---|
| Ion symbol for each ion | $Ag^+$ | $Cl^-$ | $K^+$ | $O^{2-}$ | $Al^{3+}$ | $S^{2-}$ |
| Least common multiple of charges | $1 \times 1 = 1$ | | $1 \times 2 = 2$ | | $3 \times 2 = 6$ | |
| Number of ions needed to reach this multiple | 1 ion ($1 \times 1^+ = 1^+$) | 1 ion ($1 \times 1^- = 1^-$) | 2 ions ($2 \times 1^+ = 2^+$) | 1 ion ($1 \times 2^- = 2^-$) | 2 ions ($2 \times 3^+ = 6^+$) | 3 ions ($3 \times 2^- = 6^-$) |
| Final formula | $Ag_1Cl_1$ or just AgCl | | $K_2O_1$ or just $K_2O$ | | $Al_2S_3$ | |

# D.5 <u>Exercises</u>  Binary Ionic Compounds

1. How many molecules are present in the ionic compound potassium sulfide, $K_2S$? How many ions are present? Explain your answer.

_____

_____

_____

2. Keeping in mind that ionic compounds contain charged particles called ions, what is the net charge on an ionic compound? Explain.

_____

_____

_____

3. Why do chemists use empirical formulas for ionic compounds instead of true formulas?

_____

_____

_____

_____

_____

_____

4. Should the empirical formulas of silver chloride, potassium oxide and aluminum sulfide be $AgCl_2$, $KO_2$ and $AlS_8$, respectively (since chlorine is $Cl_2$, oxygen is $O_2$, sulfur is $S_8$ and all metals are monatomic)? Explain. (*Hint: What happens to chlorine molecules, oxygen molecules and sulfur molecules before combining with the metal?*) Monatomic means the substance can exist as single atoms.

_____

_____

_____

_____

5. Students sometimes write $Ba_2O_2$ for barium oxide. What is wrong with this empirical formula?

_____

_____

Complete the following table:

| Chemical Formula | Name of Compound | Description or Use [for interest only] |
|---|---|---|
| e.g. $CaCl_2$ | calcium chloride | white solid; wetting agent; dessicant |
| 6. $MgO$ | | white powder; magnesium ore |
| 7. $Al_2O_3$ | | whiting; aluminum ore |
| 8. $ZnO$ | | protective oxide on zinc metal |
| 9. $CaF_2$ | | fluorite (pretty mauve crystals) |
| 10. $NaBr$ | | in Epsom salts |
| 11. $CaO$ | | white powder; quicklime |
| 12. $Ag_2S$ | | argentite; silver ore |
| 13. $CaH_2$ | | preparation of hydrogen |

| Chemical Formula | Name of Compound | Description or Use [for interest only] |
|---|---|---|
| 14. | potassium iodide | dietary supplement for iodine |
| 15. | aluminum chloride | antiperspirant |
| 16. | lithium nitride | black solid; forms when lithium reacts with air |
| 17. | barium chloride | white solid similar to $CaCl_2$ |
| 18. | sodium chloride | white solid; table salt |
| 19. | silver bromide | photographic emulsion |
| 20. | magnesium hydride | magnesium reacted with hydrogen |
| 21. | magnesium chloride | 11% of minerals in sea water |
| 22. | zinc chloride | in soldering paste |
| 23. | potassium chloride | potash (fertilizer) |
| 24. | sodium sulfide | for toning pictures brown |
| 25. | zinc sulfide | zinc blende (zinc ore) |

# D.6 Nomenclature of Multiple Ion Charges

Because of their electron arrangement, some metals form two or more different ions. For example, an iron atom may lose either two or three electrons to form either an iron(III) ion, $Fe^{3+}$, or an iron(II) ion, $Fe^{2+}$.

As mentioned previously, two different naming systems may be used for compounds formed by metals that form ions of different charges. The preferred system is covered first—the Stock System.

## The Stock and Classical Systems

The Stock System is named after Alfred Stock and is the preferred system of the International Union of Pure and Applied Chemistry (IUPAC). The name of the ion includes the charge on the ion as Roman numerals in parentheses. (See iron on the *Periodic Table of Ions* in the Appendix.)

The mineral magnetite contains both types of iron oxides.

FIGURE D4   Stock Names for Ions and Compounds

| Formula of Ions | Name of Ions | Formula of Compound | Name of Compound |
|---|---|---|---|
| $Fe^{3+}$ $O^{2-}$ | iron(III) oxide | $(Fe^{3+})_2 (O^{2-})_3$ or $Fe_2O_3$ | iron(III) oxide |
| $Fe^{2+}$ $O^{2-}$ | iron(II) oxide | $Fe^{2+} O^{2-}$ or $FeO$ | iron(II) oxide |
| Always use the most common ion if neither is specified; i.e., "iron oxide" should be interpreted as iron(III) oxide. | | | |

FIGURE D5    Classical Names for Ions and Compounds

| Formula of Ions | Name of Ions | Formula of Compound | Name of Compound |
|---|---|---|---|
| $Fe^{3+}$ $O^{2-}$ | ferric oxide | $(Fe^{3+})_2 (O^{2-})_3$ or $Fe_2O_3$ | ferric oxide |
| $Fe^{2+}$ $O^{2-}$ | ferrous oxide | $Fe^{2+}O^{2-}$ or $FeO$ | ferrous oxide |
| One way to help remember the suffixes "-ic" and "-ous" is to use the mnemonic "H-ic up." That is, "-ic" is the upper (larger) ionic charge. | | | |

There are two disadvantages to the Classical System:
- The value for the larger and smaller charges is not the same from one element to another.
- There are frequently more than two "charges" possible for an element.

*The Stock and Classical Systems are only used when more than one ionic charge is possible.* You must look up each of the metal ions on the *Periodic Table of Ions* to decide whether or not a Roman numeral is required to name a particular ion. In general, only elements from Groups 1A and 2A, $Ag^+$, $Cd^{2+}$, $Zn^{2+}$, and $Al^{3+}$ do not need Roman numerals.

*Example*:
In the compound ZnO, the ions present are zinc, $Zn^{2+}$, and oxide, $O^{2-}$. Zinc only forms $2^+$ ions; therefore, no Roman numeral is required as part of the ion name. ZnO is named zinc oxide, not zinc(II) oxide.

FIGURE D6    Naming Formulas

| Formula | $PbO_2$ | |
|---|---|---|
| Ions Present | $Pb^{??}$ | $(O^{2-})_2$ |
| Total Charge | ?? | $(2 \times 2^-) = 4^-$ |
| Charge on lead ion | $Pb + (4^-) = 0$ $Pb = 4^+$ | |
| Name of Compound | lead(IV) oxide | |

## Determining the Name for the Formula

When given the formula for a substance in which two or more ion charges are possible for the metal, work backwards from the charge on the negative ion to determine the charge on the positive ion.

# D.7 Exercises Nomenclature of Multiple Ion Charges

1. According to the *Periodic Table of Ions*, which iron ion is the most common? How do you know?

_____

_____

_____

_____

2. Give the proper name for each of the following ions: $Mg^{2+}$, $Ni^{3+}$, $Cu^+$, $Al^{3+}$. Use Roman numerals where appropriate.

_____

_____

3. Write the correct name or formula as required for the following compounds:

a. $PbI_2$ _____

b. mercury(II) bromide _____

For each of the following chemical formulas, rewrite the formulas to indicate the ionic charges (see examples in FIGURE D4); then name the compound, with the appropriate Roman number (if applicable) to signify the ionic charge:

*Note*: Students are expected to know how to interpret those names of given compounds using the Classical System, but, in accordance with IUPAC recommendations, should not use the Classical System when naming compounds.

| Chemical Formula | Name of Compound | Description or Use [for interest only] |
|---|---|---|
| e.g. $Cu_2S$ | copper (I) sulfide | copper ore (chalcocite) |
| 4. $SnO_2$ | | tin ore (cassiterite) |
| 5. $Sb_2S_3$ | | antimony ore (cinnabar) |
| 6. $HgS$ | | mercury ore (molybdenite) |
| 7. $MoS_2$ | | molybdenum ore (molybdenite) |
| 8. $FeS$ | | also in chalcopyrite |
| 9. $HgO$ | | used in the first laboratory preparation of oxygen |
| 10. $V_2O_2$ | | a common catalyst |
| 11. $TiO_2$ | | a white paint pigment |
| 12. $AuCl_3$ | | gold tinting of pictures |
| 13. $NiBr_2$ | | forms a green solution |
| 14. | uranium (IV) oxide | uranium ore (uranite) |
| 15. | lead (IV) sulfide | lead ore (galena) |

| Chemical Formula | Name of Compound | Description or Use [for interest only] |
|---|---|---|
| 16. | manganese (IV) oxide | manganese ore (pyrolusite) |
| 17. | ferric oxide | iron ore (hematite) |
| 18. | copper (II) sulfide | copper ore (chalcopyrite) |
| 19. | lead (IV) oxide | electrode in car battery |
| 20. | stannous flouride | toothpaste additive |
| 21. | chromic oxide | a green paint pigment |
| 22. | uranium (VI) flouride | separating types of U atoms |
| 23. | cobaltous chloride | forms a pink solution |

# D.8 Polyatomic Ions

## Formation of Compounds by Polyatomic Ions

A polyatomic ion is a very stable group of atoms. Unlike neutral molecules, polyatomic ions carry an electric charge and do not exist by themselves. The nitrate ions, $NO_3^-$, in a compound such as silver nitrate, $AgNO_3$, exist as a group of one nitrogen atom and three oxygen atoms sharing electrons. The group has gained one electron to become more stable. Polyatomic ions act like simple ions when forming ionic bonds. An ionic bond is formed by the attraction of a positive simple ion to a negative polyatomic ion or of a positive polyatomic ion ($NH_4^+$) to a negative polyatomic ion. The compound formed is called an ionic compound (e.g., the compound ammonium sulfide is $(NH_4)_2S_{(s)}$. As for all ionic compounds, the total positive charge in the formula must be equal to the total negative charge. The names and charges of many common polyatomic ions are given on the *Table of Polyatomic Ions* (located with the *Periodic Table of Ions* in the Appendix).

Note that some polyatomic ions have two names listed, such as $HCO_3^-$ (hydrogen carbonate or bicarbonate). In such cases, this course will assume recognition of the ion by either name. The first name is preferred by IUPAC and should be used when writing the names of compounds.

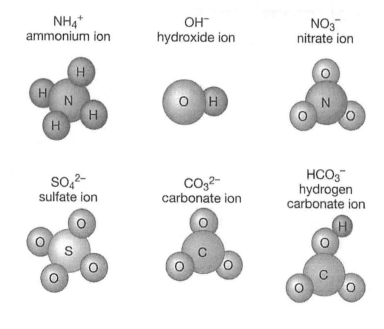

$NH_4^+$
ammonium ion

$OH^-$
hydroxide ion

$NO_3^-$
nitrate ion

$SO_4^{2-}$
sulfate ion

$CO_3^{2-}$
carbonate ion

$HCO_3^-$
hydrogen carbonate ion

Ionic compounds form when any kind of positive ions combine with any type of negative ions.

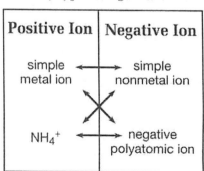

| Positive Ion | Negative Ion |
|---|---|
| simple metal ion | simple nonmetal ion |
| $NH_4^+$ | negative polyatomic ion |

| Examples | Positive Ion | Negative Ion | Compound Formed | Name | Description |
|---|---|---|---|---|---|
| Sodium ions and carbonate combine to form an ionic compound. | $Na^+$ | $CO_3^{2-}$ | $(Na^+)_2 (CO_3^{2-})_1$ $Na_2CO_3$ | sodium carbonate | washing soda |
| Ammonium ions and hydrogen phosphate ions combine to form an ionic compound. | $NH_4^+$ | $HPO_4^{2-}$ | $(NH_4^+)_2 (HPO_4^{2-})_1$ $(NH_4)_2 HPO_4$ | ammonium hydrogen phosphate | a fertilizer |
| Magnesium ions and hydroxide ions combine to form an ionic compound. | $Mg^{2+}$ | $OH^-$ | $(Mg^{2+})_1 (OH^-)_2$ $Mg(OH)_2$ | magnesium hydroxide | milk of magnesia |

The hypochlorite ion is commonly found with its formula given as $ClO^-$ or $OCl^-$. Again, this course will recognize either form, but the $ClO^-$ form should be used whenever writing the formula of a compound containing hypochlorite.

Note that whenever more than one polyatomic ion is required for the final formula of a compound that contains a polyatomic ion, the polyatomic ion **must be left in parentheses** and the subscript placed outside the parentheses.

### Naming Polyatomic Ions

Polyatomic ions usually remain as stable groups in chemical reactions, although they may become part of different compounds. Polyatomic ions are assigned special names. The most common forms of polyatomic ions are given the suffix -*ate*. The naming of the variations from the most common ion employs a system of prefixes and suffixes, and is given in the *Table of Polyatomic Ions*.

## D.9 <u>Exercises</u> Polyatomic Ions

1. What kind of bond holds together the atoms within a polyatomic ion?

_____

2. According to the *Periodic Table of Ions*, which of the following ions is the most common: $ClO_4^-$, $ClO_3^-$, $ClO_2^-$ or $ClO^-$?

_____

_____

_____

3. If $IO_3^-$ is called iodate, then what is the name of $IO_4^-$?

_____

_____

_____

For each of the following ion names (4–8), add the ionic formula; then, for 9–13, write the ionic names. Use the *Periodic Table of Ions* to complete this assignment. (Remember that polyatomic ions are not molecules. They cannot exist by themselves as they are in this exercise.)

| Ion Name | Formula | Formula | Ion Name |
|---|---|---|---|
| 4. bisulfate | _____ | 9. $NH_4^+$ | _____ |
| 5. dichromate | _____ | 10. $OH^-$ | _____ |
| 6. sulfite | _____ | 11. $NO_3^-$ | _____ |
| 7. hydrogen sulfide | _____ | 12. $HPO_4^{2-}$ | _____ |
| 8. perchlorate | _____ | 13. $CH_3COO^-$ | _____ |

The following chemical formulas involve nomenclature of ionic compounds containing polyatomic ions. Use the *Periodic Table of Ions* to answer the following questions.

| Chemical Formula | Name of Compound |
|---|---|
| 14. $K_2CO_3$ | |
| 15. $(NH_4)_2S$ | |
| 16. $Cr(NO_3)_3$ | |
| 17. $NaNO_2$ | |
| 18. $K_3PO_4$ | |
| 19. $KMnO_4$ | |
| 20. $NH_4H_2PO_4$ | |
| 21. $Na_2SO_4$ | |
| 22. | calcium hydroxide |
| 23. | magnesium silicate |
| 24. | iron(II) chlorite |
| 25. | potassium dichromate |
| 26. | ammonium sulfate |
| 27. | sodium bicarbonate |
| 28. | calcium stearate |
| 29. | sodium nitrate |
| 30. | sodium thiosulfate |
| 31. | barium perchlorate |
| 32. | sodium hydrogen sulfide |
| 33. | potassium cyanide |
| 34. | sodium glutamate (MSG) |
| 35. | potassium thiocyanate |

# D.10 Hydrated Compounds

A number of ionic compounds called **hydrates** *release water when heated.* When the formula of a hydrated compound is written, the number of water molecules is also included. For example, consider that the formula for copper(II) sulfate pentahydrate is written as $CuSO_4 \cdot 5\,H_2O$.

FIGURE D7    Naming $CuSO_4 \cdot 5\,H_2O$

| Named Using the Previous Methods | Dot (loosely bonded) | Prefix (# of Molecules) | Water Molecule |
|---|---|---|---|
| $Cu^{2+}$    $SO_4^{2-}$<br>copper (II)    sulfate | ○<br>(the following molecules are part of the compound) | 5<br>penta | $H_2O$<br>hydrate |
| mono = 1    di = 2    tri = 3    tetra = 4    penta = 5<br>hexa = 6    hepta = 7    octa = 8    nona = 9    deca = 10 | | | |

# D.11 Exercises—Hydrated Compounds

Complete the following table.

| Chemical Formula | Name of Compound | Description or Use [for interest only] |
|---|---|---|
| copper (II) sulfate pentahydrate | $CuSO_4 \cdot 5\,H_2O$ | blue vitriol, bluestone, copper plating |
| 1. | $MgSO_4 \cdot 7\,H_2O$ | Epsom salts, white solid explosives, matches |
| 2. | $MgCl_2 \cdot 6\,H_2O$ | white solid, fireproofing wood, disinfectants, parchment paper |
| 3. | $Cd(NO_3)_2 \cdot 4\,H_2O$ | white solid, photographic emulsions |
| 4. | $ZnCl_2 \cdot 6\,H_2O$ | white solid, embalming material |
| 5. | $Na_2S_2O_3 \cdot 5\,H_2O$ | photographic hypo, antichlor |
| 6. | $AlCl_3 \cdot 6\,H_2O$ | white solid, antiperspirant |
| 7. | $CaCl_2 \cdot 2\,H_2O$ | de-icer used on icy highways, added to cement mixtures (to prevent freezing during winter, white solid |
| 8. | $Na_2SO_4 \cdot 10\,H_2O$ | Glauber's salt [medicine], white solid, drying agent |
| 9. sodium carbonate decahydrate | | washing soda, soda ash, water softener, white solid |
| 10. barium chloride dihydrate | | white solid, pigments, dyeing fabrics, tanning leather |
| 11. zinc sulfate heptahydrate | | white solid, clarifying glue, preserving wood and skins |

| Chemical Formula | Name of Compound | Description or Use [for interest only] |
|---|---|---|
| 12. lithium chloride tetrahydrate | | white solid, soldering aluminum, in fireworks |
| 13. cobalt(II) chloride hexahydrate | | pink solid, humidity and water indicator, foam stabilizer in beer |
| 14. barium hydroxide octahydrate | | white solid, manufacture of glass, water softener |
| 15. nickel(II) chloride hexahydrate | | green solid, absorbent for ammonia in gas masks |

**LAB ...**

# D.12  Determining the Percentage of Water in a Hydrated Crystal

**Purpose:**
✔ To decompose a hydrated crystalline substance by using heat to drive off the water of hydration.

✔ To calculate the percentage of water in a hydrated crystal.

**Materials:**
- balance
- hot plate
- scoopula
- chemical-splash goggles
- evaporating dish
- 5 g of a hydrated compound

**Safety:**
Wear your chemical-splash goggles.

**Procedure:**
1. Wash, carefully dry, and determine the mass of an evaporating dish to the nearest 0.01 g.
2. Add about 5 grams of a hydrate to the evaporating dish and determine the mass of the evaporating dish and hydrate to the nearest 0.01 g.
3. Put the evaporating dish on a hot plate set at medium setting and leave overnight. The student should record the color changes that occur during the heating process. When the solid remains a gray color, the heating process is finished.
4. Allow the evaporating dish to cool to near room temperature. Record the mass of the dish plus the gray crystal.
5. After the calculations have been completed, add 1-2 mL of water to the final contents. Carefully feel the dish. Record your observations.
6. Wash your hands before leaving the lab.

**Data and Calculations:**
Write the following masses in grams:
1. Mass of the evaporating dish and hydrated crystal _____ g
2. Mass of empty evaporating dish _____ g
3. Mass of the hydrate _____ g
4. Mass of evaporating dish and contents after heating _____ g
5. Mass of final contents _____ g
6. Mass of water driven off _____ g

The percentage of water in the hydrate is calculated in the following way:

$$\frac{\text{mass of water driven off}}{\text{mass of the hydrate}} \times 100 = \underline{\qquad} \%$$

**Questions:**
1. If a hydrate contains water of hydration, why can't you see it?

_____

_____

_____

2. What happened to the water of hydration when you heated the hydrate?

_____

_____

3. What do the results of adding the water to the final compound tell about energy and the formation of bonds?

_____

_____

_____

_____

_____

_____

_____

_____

_____

4. Since everyone obtained nearly the same percent water of hydration, what does this tell us about the water in the hydrate?

_____

_____

_____

_____

_____

## D.13 Molecular Elements

Most nonmetallic atoms form molecules through covalent bonds with other nonmetallic atoms. While not all nonmetallic elements are molecular, all molecular elements are nonmetallic elements. Even though the molecular formulas of most of these elements could probably be predicted using Lewis Molecular Theory (Unit C), it is much faster to simply memorize the molecular formulas of these elements. FIGURE D8 gives a listing of the formulas of molecular elements.

| Nonmolecular Nonmetallic Elements | Monatomic Elements | Molecular Diatomic Elements | Other Molecular Elements |
|---|---|---|---|
| C or $C_n$ Si or $Si_n$ (a continuous 3D array of atoms) | Noble gases: He, Ne, Ar, Kr, Xe, Rn | Group 7A elements: $F_2$, $Cl_2$, $Br_2$, $I_2$, $At_2$ Also: $H_2$, $O_2$, and $N_2$ | $P_4$ (white) (pyramidal shape) $S_8$ (solid) (cyclic shape) |

Notes:
1. In this course, white phosphorus ($P_4$) is always assumed. Red phosphorus (which is the less dangerous type) would have the formula P or $P_n$.
2. The formulas for the other nonmetallic elements (boron, arsenic, selenium and tellurium) are complex and not required for the course.

Diamond Space Model

Graphite Space Model

weak forces between layers

Sulfur Space Model

Phosphorus Space Model

# D.14  Binary Molecular Compounds

A **binary molecular compound** *consists of only two kinds of nonmetallic atoms.* The majority of molecular compounds considered in the next few units are binary molecular compounds. The few nonbinary molecular compounds used in this course should be learned since they are used so often.

## The Prefix System of Nomenclature

IUPAC recommends that molecular compounds be named using the prefix system only. In the prefix system, Greek or Roman prefixes are used to indicate the number of each kind of atom having a covalent bond to another atom. These prefixes are the same as the ones used to name hydrates (See FIGURE D7).

## The Stock System of Nomenclature

The Stock System was used to name ionic compounds containing metal ions with multiple charge possibilities. It can also be used to name molecular compounds. In this case, the compound would be named as if it were ionic and a "charge" would be assigned to it. The Roman numeral would be placed after the first-named element, and the second-named element would be treated as if it was a simple negative ion.

## FIGURE D9 — Naming Binary Molecular Compounds

| Formula | Classical System | Stock System |
|---------|------------------|--------------|
| CO | carbon monoxide | carbon(II) oxide |
| $N_2O$ | dinitrogen monoxide | nitrogen(I) oxide |
| $NO_2$ | nitrogen dioxide | nitrogen(IV) oxide |
| $SO_3$ | sulfur trioxide | sulfur(VI) oxide |
| $SF_6$ | sulfur hexafluoride | sulfur(VI) fluoride |
| $PCl_5$ | phosphorus pentachloride | phosphorus(V) chloride |
| $P_2O_5$ | diphosphorus pentoxide | phosphorus(V) oxide |

*Notes*:
1. The first element in the formula should be named in full. The second element in the formula should be shortened and given an *-ide* suffix.
2. The prefix *mono* may generally be omitted. However, extreme caution is advised in the omission of prefixes, including *mono*.
3. Hydrogen compounds are molecular. However, most common hydrogen compounds have special names. Some preferred special names are *water* for $H_2O$ (vs. dihydrogen monoxide), *ammonia* for $NH_3$ (vs. nitrogen trihydride) and *hydrogen sulfide* for $H_2S$ (vs. dihydrogen sulfide).

## FIGURE D10 — Molecular Compounds

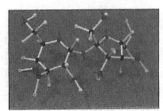

Sucrose

| Formula and State of Matter | Name | Space Models |
|-----------------------------|------|--------------|
| $O_3(g)$ | ozone | |
| HOH or $H_2O(l)$ | water | |
| $NH_3(g)$ | ammonia | (top view) |
| $CH_4(g)$ | methane (*natural gas*) | (top view) |
| $C_{12}H_{22}O_{11}(s)$ | sucrose | (see picture) |
| $CH_3OH(l)$ | methanol | |
| $C_2H_5OH(l)$ | ethanol | |
| $H_2O_2(l)$ | hydrogen peroxide | |
| $H_2S(g)$ | hydrogen sulfide | |

# D.15 Exercises Molecular Substances

Complete the following table.

| Molecular Formula | Name | Description or Use | | |
|---|---|---|---|---|
| e.g. $CCl_4$ | carbon tetrachloride | toxic cleaning fluid and solvent | | |
| 1. | nitrogen | | atmosphere | 78.03% |
| 2. | oxygen | | | 20.99% |
| 3. | argon (a noble gas) | | | 0.94% |
| 4. $CO_2$ | | | | 0.035% |
| 5. | other noble gases (5 answers) | | | 0.0016% |
| 6. NO | | | air pollutants | in automobile exhaust |
| 7. $NO_2$ | | | | Los Angeles-type smog |
| 8. | sulfur dioxide [sulfur(IV) oxide] | | | London-type smog |
| 9. $SO_3$ | | | | becomes sulfuric acid |
| 10. | carbon monoxide | | | colorless and odorless poison |
| 11. | ozone | | | protection from UV |
| 12. | ethanol | grain alcohol, ethyl alcohol | | |
| 13. | sucrose | table sugar | | |
| 14. | sulfur | yellow solid in Group 6A | | |
| 15. $P_4O_{10}$ | | oxides formed by burning white phosphorus in air | | |
| 16. $P_4O_6$ | | | | |
| 17. | chlorine dioxide [chlorine(IV) oxide] | chlorination of water | | |
| 18. | methanol | methyl alcohol, wood alcohol | | |
| 19. | phosphorus | a white solid | | |
| 20. | ammonia | a cleaner when dissolved in water | | |
| 21. $CH_4$ | | 85 – 95% of natural gas | | |
| 22. HCl | | a gas; in water is called hydrochloric acid | | |
| 23. | dinitrogen oxide [nitrogen(I) oxide] | laughing gas, anesthetic | | |
| 24. | iodine | tincture of iodine in alcohol | | |
| 25. $H_2O$ | | the most common solvent | | |

# D.16 Properties of Ionic and Molecular Substances

**Purpose:**

✔ To determine the properties of ionic and molecular substances.

✔ To make generalizations for distinguishing between ionic and molecular substances on the basis of their properties.

**Prelab Exercise:**

1. What are the three phases of matter?

2. Why should the electrical conductivity of the distilled water be tested before testing the conductivity of a solution formed using the water?

_Questions continue on next page._

| Prelab Exercise | | | Phase at Room Temp. | Soluble in Water (Yes/No) | Answer these two columns only if substance is soluble in water. | |
|---|---|---|---|---|---|---|
| Name of Substance (Use) | Formula | Ionic or Molecular | | | Color of Solution | Conductivity of Solution (Yes/No) |
| 1. iron(III) nitrate | | | | | | |
| 2.          (gypsum, plaster) | $CaSO_4$ | | | | | |
| 3. 2-propanol (rubbing alcohol) | $C_3H_7OH$ | | | | | |
| 4. cobalt(II) nitrate | | | | | | |
| 5. | $CuCl_2$ | | | | | |
| 6.          (solvent) | $C_2H_5OH$ | | | | | |
| 7. sucrose (table sugar) | | | | | | |
| 8.          (table salt) | $NaCl$ | | | | | |
| 9. ammonium sulfate (fertilizer) | | | | | | |
| 10. sulfur (fungicide) | | | | | | |
| 11.*          (fungicide) | $KMnO_4$ | | | | | |
| 12.          (fungicide) | $CuSO_4 \cdot 5H_2O$ | | | | | |
| 13. hexane ** (solvent) | $C_6H_{14}$ | | | | | |
| 14. methane (natural gas) | | | | | | |
| 15.          (limestone, chalk) | $CaCO_3$ | | | | | |
| 16. paraffin (candle wax) | $C_{25}H_{52}$ | | | | | |
| 17. unknown name | unknown formula | (student answer based on properties of the substance) | | | | |

* Powerful oxidizing agent; can explode on sudden heating; common cause of eye accidents; wear face protection. Strong skin irritant.
** This is a flammable liquid. Dispose of it as directed by your teacher.

**Conclusions:** Complete generalizations below with your instructor:

| Classification of Substance | Phase at Room Temperature | Solubility in Water | Color of Solution | Conductivity of Solution |
|---|---|---|---|---|
| Ionic | | | | |
| Molecular | | | | |

3. Using a substance's chemical formula, how do we classify it as either ionic or molecular?

_____

_____

_____

_____

_____

_____

_____

4. Fill in either the name or formula of the substance as required. Use the *Periodic Table of Ions* to classify the substances as ionic or molecular.

**Procedure:**
Complete the four Prelab Exercises and fill in the first three columns in your data table before going into the laboratory.

1. Follow any special instructions or cautions given at the laboratory station.

2. Record in the data table the phase of the pure substance as a solid, liquid or gas.

3. Rinse the small beaker provided with *distilled* water and then add about 25 mL of distilled water to the beaker.

4. Use the conductivity tester (as directed by the teacher) to test the conductivity of the distilled water. (This step is a *control* for step 9.)

5. Add a few grains of the pure substance to the distilled water.

6. Use a stirring rod to stir the mixture.

7. Record in the data table whether or not the substance dissolved in the water.

8. If the substance dissolves in water, record in the data table the color of the solution. (Use the word *colorless* to describe solutions that have no color. Do not use the word *clear* because all solutions are clear.)

9. If the substance dissolves in water, use the conductivity tester to determine whether or not the solution conducts electricity better than the distilled water in step 4.

10. Before going on to the next station:
    a. Pour off the water from any substance that did not dissolve and add the undissolved substance to the waste beaker provided (or as directed by the teacher).
    b. Follow your teacher's instructions for correct disposal.

*Note*: All ionic compounds dissolve in water to some extent. Substances such as $CaSO_4$ and $CaCO_3$ may appear to not dissolve, but in fact should be classified as *low solubility* compounds, not as *insoluble* compounds. An accurate check of the conductivity of the solutions with a sensitive conductivity tester will prove this.

**Questions:**
With questions 1 – 4, be as specific as possible. For example, in some circumstances the answer may be true, while in others it may not.

1. Can a substance be classified as ionic or molecular on the basis of its phase at room temperature? Explain fully.

_____

_____

_____

_____

2. Can a substance be classified as ionic or molecular on the basis of whether or not it dissolves in water? Explain fully.

_____

_____

_____

_____

_____

3. Can a substance be classified as ionic or molecular on the basis of the color of its solution (assuming that the substance dissolves)? Explain fully.

_____

_____

_____

4. Can a substance be classified as ionic or molecular on the basis of the electrical conductivity of its solution (assuming that the substance dissolves)? Explain fully.

_____

_____

For questions 5 – 11, use the generalizations from above to classify the following substances as ionic or molecular on the basis of their properties. If the classification is *not* possible on the basis of the stated properties, circle E for Either.:

| Properties of the Pure Substance | Ionic, Molecular, Either | | |
|---|---|---|---|
| 5. A solid that dissolves in water to form a colorless, nonconducting solution. | I | M | E |
| 6. A liquid that dissolves in water to form a colorless solution. | I | M | E |
| 7. A solid that dissolves in water to form a colorless solution. | I | M | E |
| 8. A solid that dissolves in water to form a colored solution. | I | M | E |
| 9. A solid that does not dissolve in water. | I | M | E |
| 10. A gas at room temperature. | I | M | E |
| 11. A substance that forms a conducting solution. | I | M | E |

12. Was the unknown substance (Station 17) ionic or molecular? How do you know?

_____

_____

_____

13. A gas at room temperature dissolves in water to form a colorless, conducting solution. Is the classification system developed above refined enough to classify this substance? Explain.

_____

_____

_____

_____

Some ionic compounds dissolve readily while others do not. A solubility table has been provided with the *Periodic Table of Ions* to help determine whether an ionic compound is soluble in water or has a low solubility. This solubility table is a result of experimental evidence. There is no need to memorize the whole table, but the following generalizations are very useful to learn.

**Generalizations:**

All alkali metal ($K^+$, $Na^+$, etc.), hydrogen ($H^+$), ammonium ($NH_4^+$), acetate ($CH_3COO^-$), and nitrate ($NO_3^-$) ions are soluble. For the solubility of all other ionic compounds, identify the ions present in the compound and match them with the solubility chart to determine whether the compound will be soluble or low solubility. (Generalizations regarding molecular compounds will be presented in later units.)

Do the generalizations given above and in the solubility table agree with the results obtained in the lab? Whenever the mixture had a visible solid or was cloudy, write (*s*) for solid next to the formula of those ionic compounds that were low solubility. When the mixture was clear, write (*aq*) for aqueous solution next to the formula of those ionic compounds that were soluble. List the ionic compounds with the appropriate states of matter for questions 14–21 below. For example, the first ionic compound in the lab, iron(III) nitrate, would be written as $Fe(NO_3)_3$(*aq*) since it is dissolved in water to form a clear yellow/orange solution. (Exclude the unknown compound from this list.)

| e.g.  Fe $(NO_3)_3$(*aq*) |
|---|
| 14. |
| 15. |
| 16. |
| 17. |
| 18. |
| 19. |
| 20. |
| 21. |

Use the generalizations above and the solubility table to determine if the following ionic compounds are soluble. For questions 22–31, write (*s*) or (*aq*) next to the chemical formula to indicate low solubility or soluble compounds, respectively:

| Common Name or Use | Formula | | Common Name or Use | Formula |
|---|---|---|---|---|
| 22. drain cleaner | KOH ( ) | | 27. milk of magnesia | $Mg(OH)_2$ ( ) |
| 23. Sani-Flush | $NaHSO_4$ ( ) | | 28. bleach | NaClO ( ) |
| 24. slaked lime | $Ca(OH)_2$ ( ) | | 29. in dry cells (battery) | $NH_4Cl$ ( ) |
| 25. Epsom salts | $MgSO_4$ ( ) | | 30. water clarifier | $Al_2(SO_4)_3$ ( ) |
| 26. glass container | $Na_2SiO_3$ ( ) | | 31. rock phosphorus | $Ca_3(PO_4)_2$ ( ) |

# D.17 Hydrogen Compounds and Acids

Hydrogen forms covalent bonds with other nonmetals to create molecular compounds (i.e., they may be a solid, liquid, or a gas at room temperature). However, hydrogen compounds are different from other molecular compounds in that they often form conducting solutions. These solutions are call acids. For this reason, and because of their different nomenclature, hydrogen compounds are usually studied separately from ionic and molecular compounds.

## Nomenclature of Hydrogen Compounds

Most hydrogen compounds are named as acids. The only common exceptions to this rule are the pure compounds:

$HCl(g)$ hydrogen chloride,
$H_2S(g)$ hydrogen sulfide,
and $HCN(g)$ hydrogen cyanide.

## The Properties of Acids/Acid-Forming Compounds

The properties of substances (i.e., hydrogen compounds) that form acids vary in degree, but in general they:

- are solids, liquids, and gases as pure substances at room temperature (like molecular substances).
- are soluble in water (like all ionic and some molecular substances).
- form colored and colorless solutions (like ionic compounds).
- form conducting solutions (like ionic compounds).
- form solutions that turn blue litmus red (a characteristic property of acids).

## Nomenclature of Acids

Since acids are usually in solution whenever used in reactions, this course assumes an acid formula should always be followed with the label (*aq*), meaning *aqueous* (i.e., dissolved in water).

| NAMING ACIDS |
|---|
| • hydrogen ____ide becomes hydro____ic acid |
| • hydrogen ____ate becomes ____ic acid |
| • hydrogen ____ite becomes ____ous acid |

Acids are named according to the rules in the *naming acids* section of the *Periodic Table of Ions*. These *naming acids* rules basically involve naming the hydrogen compound as though it were ionic, and then converting it to the acid name.

If these hydrogen compounds were named like ionic compounds, the name would always end in *-ide*, *-ate* or *-ite*. Each hydrogen compound name is converted to an acid name in a particular way. The three acid-naming rules from the periodic table are shown below.

# D.18 Acid Classification

Acids may be classified as:

- *binary:* if it is a hydrogen compound that contains hydrogen and one other kind of atom.
- *oxo:* if it is a hydrogen compound that contains hydrogen, oxygen and one other kind of atom.

A few acids such as carbonic acid, $H_2CO_3(aq)$, do not even contain a pure substance which can be isolated. When the water is removed from the acid solution, these hydrogen compounds such as $H_2CO_3$ decompose: $H_2CO_3(aq) \longrightarrow H_2O(l) + CO_2(g)$.

When the formula for an acid contains a COO group, the hydrogen atom is placed at the end of this group (i.e., COOH) rather than at the beginning of the formula. The most common example is the acid in vinegar, acetic acid, which is written as $CH_3COOH(aq)$ and not as $HCH_3COO(aq)$.

# D.19 Bases—Ionic Compounds with Special Properties

Bases are compounds with many properties similar to acids. They:

- are solids at room temperature (like ionic substances).
- are soluble in water (like all ionic substances).
- form conducting solutions (like ionic compounds).

However, they also

- form solutions that turn red litmus paper blue (a characteristic property of bases).

*Basic solutions neutralize the properties of acid solutions* (and vice versa). The metal hydroxides such as sodium hydroxide (NaOH), barium hydroxide ($Ba(OH)_2$), etc. all form basic solutions as does ammonium hydroxide ($NH_4OH$). For this unit, bases will just be considered a category of ionic compounds. A thorough study of bases and basic solutions will be conducted in a later unit.

# D.20 Properties of Acids and Bases

**Purpose:**
✔ To observe some of the properties of acids and bases.

**Materials:**
- 1 24-well microplate
- dropper bottle of 0.1 mol/L HCl
- several small pieces Mg
- conductivity tester
- dropper bottle of 0.1 mol/L $H_2SO_4$
- vial of baking soda
- pH paper
- dropper bottle of 0.1 mol/L $CH_3COOH$
- vial of blue litmus
- scoopula
- dropper bottle of 0.1 mol/L NaOH
- vial of red litmus
- stirring rod
- dropper bottle of 0.1 mol/L KOH
- dropper bottle of 0.1 mol/L $NH_4OH$
- safety goggles

**Lab Safety:**
Review the hazards of handling chemicals. Wear goggles and an apron. Be sure to wash hands before leaving the lab area.

**Procedure:**
1. Test each acid and each base with red litmus paper. Record your observations.
2. Test each acid and each base with blue litmus paper. Record your observations.
3. Test each acid and each base with pH paper. Record both the color and the pH of the solution.
4. Add 10 drops of each acid and each base to a <u>different well on the microplate</u>. Test the conductivity of each solution. Record your observations.
5. Add 10 drops of each acid to a different well on the microplate and put a small piece of magnesium into each. Record your observations.
6. Add 10 drops of each acid to a different well on the microplate and put in a small amount (match-head size) of baking soda into each. Record your observations.

7. Your teacher will place one drop of 0.1 mol/L NaOH solution between your fingers. Rub momentarily. *Rinse immediately!* Record your observations.
8. Repeat step 7 for KOH and $NH_4OH$. Record your observations.
9. Wash your hands before leaving lab.

**Observations:**

| Acid | Red Litmus Paper | Blue Litmus Paper | Electrical Conductivity | Reaction with Mg | Reaction with $NaHCO_3$ |
|---|---|---|---|---|---|
| HCl | | | | | |
| $H_2SO_4$ | | | | | |
| $CH_3COOH$ | | | | | |

| Base | Red Litmus Paper | Blue Litmus Paper | Electrical Conductivity | Feel *(rinse fingers immediately!)* |
|---|---|---|---|---|
| NaOH | | | | |
| KOH | | | | |
| $NH_4OH$ | | | | |

**Questions:**
1. What is true about the color of litmus paper in acid solution? In base solution?

    _____

2. What did you observe about the conductivity of acids and bases?

    _____

3. What did you observe about acids and reaction with Mg and $NaHCO_3$?

    _____

4. What do base solutions feel like?

    _____

# Unit E
# Chemical Reactions

## E.1 Chemical Reactions

Chemists tend to be very systematic in their study of matter. So far in this course, you have studied the properties of elements and compounds; you have identified the patterns of the properties as the elements are organized on the Periodic Table; you have even investigated the structure of atoms and have learned a little about how the electron structure of the atom changes when compounds are formed. But what exactly happens to the atoms in a substance when a chemical reaction takes place? How does a chemist interpret the many changes that take place as a chemical reaction occurs? Is there any way to predict the outcome of a chemical reaction *before* it takes place? These questions will be answered as you investigate the changes that occur when chemicals are combined and write equations to summarize these changes.

Making good observations and interpretations are important when making connections between what you see and how you write the appropriate chemical formula. In addition, you will practice the skill of writing **balanced equations**—*equations where the **reactants** (chemical formulas on the left side) and the **products** (chemical formulas on the right side) both have the same kind and number of each type of atom* in accordance with the Law of Conservation of Matter. For example,

$$2H_2(g) + O_2(g) \longrightarrow 2H_2O(l)$$

$$H-H \quad + \quad H-H \quad + \quad O=O \quad \longrightarrow \quad \overset{O}{\underset{H \quad H}{\diagup \diagdown}} \quad + \quad \overset{O}{\underset{H \quad H}{\diagup \diagdown}}$$

$$H_2 \quad + \quad H_2 \quad + \quad O_2 \quad \longrightarrow \quad H_2O \quad + \quad H_2O$$

Also, there will be an emphasis on some of the important chemical reactions that occur in everyday life—reactions that are responsible for making useful products and powering our vehicles, reactions that occur around the home and in the workplace, and even reactions that are responsible for much of the pollution that is on our planet.

Understanding chemical reactions is vital to a thorough understanding of chemistry.

---

**DEMO ...**

## E.2 Reaction of Copper with Nitric Acid

### Purpose:
✔ To practice observation skills and other laboratory-related skills.
✔ To give an example of how chemical observations relate to a chemical reaction.

### Background Information:
*Chemical equation:*

$$Cu(s) + 4\ HNO_3(aq) \longrightarrow Cu(NO_3)_2(aq) + 2\ NO_2(g) + 2\ H_2O(l)$$

*Other information:* Universal Indicator is a solution containing a mixture of acid-base indicators that undergo a range of colors depending on the pH of the solution.

### Materials:
• 2 500-mL Erlenmeyer flasks
• 10 mL concentrated nitric acid
• 1 1000-mL beaker
• 2 g copper turnings
• dropper bottle containing Universal Indicator
• stopper assembly
    1-hole stopper to fit first flask
    2-hole stopper to fit second flask
    glass tubing bent to specifications
    40 cm rubber tubing

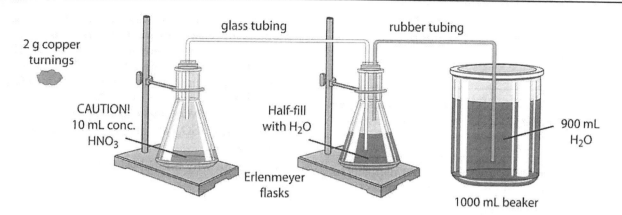

2 g copper turnings

glass tubing

rubber tubing

CAUTION!
10 mL conc.
HNO₃

Half-fill
with H₂O

900 mL
H₂O

Erlenmeyer
flasks

1000 mL beaker

**Procedure:**

1. Draw a diagram of the experimental setup.

2. Your teacher will put 10 mL of nitric acid into the first flask. Then, 2 g of copper turnings will be put into the first flask and the whole assembly securely stoppered.

3. Record your observations. The first part of the demonstration takes place immediately. The second part takes 2 to 3 minutes. Be patient!

_____

_____

_____

_____

_____

_____

_____

_____

4. After the reaction is complete, add several drops of Universal Indicator to the beaker and also to the second flask. Record your observations.

_____

_____

_____

_____

_____

_____

**Questions:**

1. Identify the color of each substance given in the balanced equation.

Reactants

Cu(s) _____

HNO₃(aq) _____

Products

Cu(NO₃)₂(aq) _____

NO₂(g) _____

H₂O(l) _____

2. a. Finish the statement: "During the reaction, the copper atoms were changed into …."

_____

   b. Write an equation to show how the copper atoms change in the way described in 2a. Show only those atoms, ions or molecules that actually change.

_____

3. a. What elements were in the colored gas?

_____

   b. From what reactant did these atoms come?

_____

4. Water is one of the products of the reaction. What reactant supplied the atoms for this molecule?

_____

5. a. How could you tell that the $NO_{2(g)}$ dissolves in the water?

_____

  b. Since the $NO_{2(g)}$ dissolves, what happens to the pressure of the gas inside the flask? Explain.

_____

_____

  c. Explain what caused the water to move from one flask to another at the end of the demonstration.

_____

_____

6. a. When the $NO_{2(g)}$ dissolved in the water, the Universal Indicator changed color. Was the solution acidic, basic, or neutral?

_____

  b. Write the equation for the reaction between nitrogen dioxide and water:

$$2\ NO_{2(g)}\ +\ H_2O_{(l)} \longrightarrow \underline{\qquad}\ +\ \underline{\qquad}$$
$$\text{(nitric acid)} \qquad \text{(nitrous acid)}$$

7. Nonmetal oxides like $CO_2$, $SO_2$, $SO_3$, $NO_2$, and others all react with water to form acid solutions like that shown in question 6b. $CO_2$ occurs naturally in the atmosphere, but has been increasing in amount due to the burning (combustion) of fossil fuels. Nitrogen oxides (*abbreviated NO_x*) and sulfur oxides (*abbreviated SO_x*) are also produced during combustion.

  a. Explain why normal rainfall is slightly acidic.
      (pH $\approx$ 5.5)

_____

_____

_____

  b. Explain why air polluted with $NO_x$ and $SO_x$ produces rainfall with a pH below 5.5. (Acid rain has a pH in the range of 1.0 to 5.0.)

_____

_____

_____

_____

_____

As the unit progresses you will have many opportunities to see how observations can be interpreted in terms of chemical reactions.

## E.3  Balancing Chemical Equations

Balancing chemical equations involves the use of experimental evidence from chemical reactions. The experimental evidence indicates (below) that:

- atoms are conserved.
- mass is conserved.
- energy is conserved.

Chemical equations represent what happens in a chemical reaction. A chemical equation must:

*Step 1:* Represent the correct formula and phase for each reactant and product (the phase for elements is given on the Periodic Table and all ionic compounds are solid at room temperature and normal pressure). (See the D.16 Lab.)

*Step 2:* Show that atoms or ions are conserved.

## Example 1:

*Given:* Magnesium reacts in the air to produce magnesium oxide.

    **or**    *magnesium + oxygen ⟶ magnesium oxide*

*Step 1:* Write the correct chemical formulas.

    ___ $Mg_{(s)}$ + ___ $O_{2(g)}$ ⟶ ___ $MgO_{(s)}$

    *Note:* In this first step do not worry about the fact that the oxygen "atoms" are not balanced. Look at each chemical formula separately to be sure it is correct.

*Step 2:* Count the number of each type of atom present.

    ___ $Mg_{(s)}$ + ___ $O_{2(g)}$ ⟶ ___ $MgO_{(s)}$

                1 – Mg – 1
                2 – O – 1

*Step 3:* Balance atoms (*do not change chemical formulas*).

Balance atoms by using coefficients to indicate the number of formula units or molecules of each reactant and product required.

Balance the greatest number of same-kind atoms first. Find the lowest common multiple of the number of reactant and product atoms.

    ___ $Mg_{(s)}$ + ___ $O_{2(g)}$ ⟶ _2_ $MgO_{(s)}$

         (oxygen atoms balanced)

                1 – Mg – 2
                2 – O – 2

Then continue progressively to balance the rest of the atoms:

    _2_ $Mg_{(s)}$ + ___ $O_{2(g)}$ ⟶ _2_ $MgO_{(s)}$

         (magnesium atoms balanced)

                2 – Mg – 2
                2 – O – 2

## Example 2:

Copper metal *reacts with* silver nitrate solution *to produce* silver *and* aqueous copper(II) nitrate.

*Step 1:* ___ $Cu_{(s)}$ + ___ $AgNO_{3(aq)}$ ⟶ ___ $Ag_{(s)}$ + ___ $Cu(NO_3)_{2(aq)}$

                          1 – Cu – 1
                          1 – Ag – 1
                          1 – N – 2
                          3 – O – 6

*Step 2:* ___ $Cu_{(s)}$ + _2_ $AgNO_{3(aq)}$ ⟶ _2_ $Ag_{(s)}$ + ___ $Cu(NO_3)_{2(aq)}$

                          1 – Cu – 1
                          2 – Ag – 2
                          2 – N – 2
                          6 – O – 6

Example 3:

lead(II) nitrate + potassium iodide $\longrightarrow$ lead(II) iodide + potassium nitrate

Step 1: __ $Pb(NO_3)_2$(aq) + __ $KI$(aq) $\longrightarrow$ __ $PbI_2$(s) + __ $KNO_3$(aq)

$$1 - Pb - 1$$
$$2 - N - 1$$
$$6 - O - 3$$
$$1 - I - 2$$
$$1 - K - 1$$

Step 2: __ $Pb(NO_3)_2$(aq) + _2_ $KI$(aq) $\longrightarrow$ __ $PbI_2$(s) + _2_ $KNO_3$(aq)

$$1 - Pb - 1$$
$$2 - N - 2$$
$$6 - O - 6$$
$$2 - I - 2$$
$$2 - K - 2$$

## LAB ...

# E.4 Balancing Chemical Equations

**Purpose:**

✔ To illustrate the conservation of atoms in balancing the following equations.

✔ To illustrate the meaning of the coefficients vs. the subscripts in a balanced equation.

**Materials:**

• Molecular Models Kit

**Prelab Exercise:**

Count the total number of each kind of reactant and product atom and record the number below.

**Procedure:**

1. Construct the required number of molecules of each reactant. (If using ball and spring models, always twist clockwise.)

2. Draw structural diagrams for each of the reactant molecules.

3. Disassemble the reactant molecules. (If using ball and spring models, always twist clockwise to avoid unraveling the springs.)

4. Assemble the product molecules (or ions). No atoms should be added or left over. (That is, the atoms are conserved.)

5. Draw structural and Lewis diagrams for each of the product molecules (or ions).

6. Disassemble the product molecules (or ions) unless they are required for a subsequent equation. (Twist clockwise.)

7. Do as many as possible in the time provided.

**Observations:**

1. Rocket fuel may be produced from the decomposition of water.

$$2\,H_2O(l) \longrightarrow 2\,H_2(g) + O_2(g)$$

| Number of Reactant Atoms | Structural Formulas (To be done in lab with molecular model kit.) | Number of Product Atoms |
|---|---|---|
| #H = 4 | | #H = 4 |
| #O = 2 | | #O = 2 |

2. Rocket fuel is burned in a Saturn rocket.

$$2\,H_2(g) + O_2(g) \longrightarrow 2\,H_2O(l)$$

3. Natural gas (mostly methane) is burned as a heating fuel.

$$CH_4(g) + 2\,O_2(g) \longrightarrow CO_2(g) + 2\,H_2O(g)$$

4. Hydrogen chloride gas is produced for the production of hydrochloric acid.

$$H_2(g) + Cl_2(g) \longrightarrow 2\,HCl(g)$$

5. Ammonia for fertilizers is produced from nitrogen and hydrogen.

$$N_2(g) + 3\,H_2(g) \longrightarrow 2\,NH_3(g)$$

6. Ammonia dissolves in water to form some ammonium hydroxide.

$$NH_3(g) + H_2O(l) \longrightarrow NH_4^+(aq) + OH^-(aq)$$

7. In the A.5 Lab, hydrogen peroxide was decomposed.

$$2 H_2O_2(aq) \longrightarrow 2 H_2O(l) + O_2(g)$$

8. Sulfur dioxide from a sulfur extraction gas plant or coal burning plant may cause acid rain.

$$SO_2(g) + H_2O(l) \longrightarrow H_2SO_3(aq)$$

9. Carbon tetrachloride (a toxic solvent) may be produced from carbon disulfide and chlorine.

$$CS_2(l) + 3 Cl_2(g) \longrightarrow CCl_4(l) + S_2Cl_2(g)$$

10. Carbon monoxide from automobile exhaust may react with oxygen to produce carbon dioxide.

$$2 CO(g) + O_2(g) \longrightarrow 2 CO_2(g)$$

| 7. | | |
|---|---|---|
| #H = | | #H = |
| #O = | | #O = |
| 8. | | |
| #S = | | #S = |
| #H = | | #H = |
| #O = | | #O = |
| 9. | | |
| #C = | | #C = |
| #S = | | #S = |
| #Cl = | | #Cl = |
| 10. | | |
| #C = | | #C = |
| #O = | | #O = |

| Number of Reactant Atoms | Structural Formulas (To be done in lab with molecular model kit.) | Number of Product Atoms |
|---|---|---|
| 1. #H = 4  #O = 2 | | #H = 4  #O = 2 |
| 2. #H =  #O = | | #H =  #O = |
| 3. #C =  #H =  #O = | | #C =  #H =  #O = |
| 4. #H =  #Cl = | | #H =  #Cl = |
| 5. #N =  #H = | | #N =  #H = |
| 6. #N =  #H =  #O = | | #N = 4  #H = 4  #O = 2 |

**Questions:**

1. Write out in words what the following equation represents:

$$N_2(g) + 3 H_2(g) \longrightarrow 2 NH_3(g)$$

*One molecule of gaseous nitrogen (each molecule composed of two nitrogen atoms)...*

_____

_____

_____

_____

Determine what is wrong with these structural formulas and correct the formulas themselves.

2. $H_2SO_3(aq)$    3. $2 NH_3(g)$    4. $2 O_2(aq)$

# E.5 Types of Chemical Reactions

In this unit, six types of chemical reactions are introduced. Students will be required to identify and balance the six types and predict products for five types of reactions.

The six basic types of chemical reactions are:

1. simple composition (sc)      (element + element → compound)
2. simple decomposition (sd)      (compound → element + element)
3. single replacement (sr)      (element + compound → element + compound)
4. double replacement (dr)      (compound + compound → compound + compound)
5. hydrocarbon combustion (hc)      (hydrocarbon + oxygen → carbon dioxide + water vapor)
6. other (o)

## States of Matter

In order to better describe a chemical reaction, the state of matter of each substance should be indicated in the chemical equation. The **state of matter** is *an indication of whether a substance is solid (s), liquid (l), gas (g), or dissolved in solution (aq).* There is a general pattern for states of matter as they relate to reaction types:

1. simple composition (sc) — generally all pure substances (elements)
2. simple decomposition (sd) — generally all pure substances
3. single replacement (sr) — generally a solid metal or aqueous nonmetal plus an aqueous solution
4. double replacement (dr) — generally two aqueous solutions as reactants
5. hydrocarbon combustion (hc) — generally $C_xH_y + O_{2(g)} \rightarrow CO_{2(g)} + H_2O_{(g)}$
6. other (o)

# E.6 <u>Exercises</u>   Classifying Reactions and Balancing Chemical Equations

Classify each of the following reactions by writing *sc, sd, sr, dr, hc* or *o* to the left of the equation. Balance the equations using the simplest whole numbers possible:

___ 1.    ___ $Cu_{(s)}$ + ___ $O_{2(g)}$ ⟶ ___ $CuO_{(s)}$

___ 2.    ___ $H_2O_{(l)}$ ⟶ ___ $H_{2(g)}$ + ___ $O_{2(g)}$

___ 3.    ___ $Fe_{(s)}$ + ___ $H_2O_{(g)}$ ⟶ ___ $H_{2(g)}$ + ___ $Fe_3O_{4(s)}$

___ 4.    ___ $AsCl_{3(aq)}$ + ___ $H_2S_{(aq)}$ ⟶ ___ $As_2S_{3(s)}$ + ___ $HCl_{(aq)}$

___ 5.    ___ $CuSO_4 \cdot 5\,H_2O_{(s)}$ ⟶ ___ $CuSO_{4(s)}$ + ___ $H_2O_{(g)}$

___ 6.    ___ $Fe_2O_{3(s)}$ + ___ $H_{2(g)}$ ⟶ ___ $Fe_{(s)}$ + ___ $H_2O_{(l)}$

___ 7.    ___ $CaCO_{3(s)}$ ⟶ ___ $CaO_{(s)}$ + ___ $CO_{2(g)}$

___ 8.    ___ $Fe_{(s)}$ + ___ $S_{8(s)}$ ⟶ ___ $FeS_{(s)}$

___ 9.    ___ $H_2S_{(aq)}$ + ___ $KOH_{(aq)}$ ⟶ ___ $HOH_{(l)}$ + ___ $K_2S_{(aq)}$

___ 10.    ___ $NaCl_{(l)}$ ⟶ ___ $Na_{(l)}$ + ___ $Cl_{2(g)}$

___ 11.    ___ $Al_{(s)}$ + ___ $H_2SO_{4(aq)}$ ⟶ ___ $H_{2(g)}$ + ___ $Al_2(SO_4)_{3(aq)}$

___ 12.    ___ $H_3PO_{4(aq)}$ + ___ $NH_4OH_{(aq)}$ ⟶ ___ $HOH_{(l)}$ + ___ $(NH_4)_3PO_{4(aq)}$

___ 13.    ___ $C_3H_{8(g)}$ + ___ $O_{2(g)}$ ⟶ ___ $CO_{2(g)}$ + ___ $H_2O_{(g)}$

___ 14.    ___ $Al_{(s)}$ + ___ $O_{2(g)}$ ⟶ ___ $Al_2O_{3(s)}$

___ 15.    ___ $CH_{4(g)}$ + ___ $O_{2(g)}$ ⟶ ___ $CO_{2(g)}$ + ___ $H_2O_{(g)}$

For the following problems:

A. Classify the reaction, then complete the balanced equation and the word equation.

B. Remember that the first step is to get correct chemical formulas before trying to balance the equation.

C. Provide the state of matter beside each chemical formula. The state of pure substances is determined by the generalizations from the D.16 Lab. The state of ionic compounds in water is determined by using the solubility table on the Periodic Table of Ions.

16. Reaction type: _____

   Balanced equation: _____ + _____ ⟶ _____

   Word equation:        sodium   +   chlorine   ⟶ sodium chloride


17. Reaction type: _____

   Balanced equation: __ $K_2S_{(aq)}$   +   __ $CuBr_{2(aq)}$   ⟶   __ $CuS_{(s)}$   +   __ $KBr_{(aq)}$

   Word equation: _____ + _____ ⟶ _____ + _____

   Why is CuS shown as a solid in the above equation when all the other ionic compounds are shown as $(aq)$?


18. Reaction type: _____

   Balanced equation: _____ + _____ ⟶ _____ $CO_{2(g)}$ + _____ $H_2O_{(g)}$

   Word equation:        methane +   oxygen   ⟶ _____ + _____


19. Reaction type: _____

   Balanced equation: ___ $Zn_{(s)}$ + ___ $Pb(CH_3COO)_{2(aq)}$ ⟶ _____ + _____

   Word equation: _____ + _____ ⟶ lead   + zinc acetate


20. Reaction type: _____

   Balanced equation: _____ ⟶ _____ + _____ $H_{2(g)}$

   Word equation:        ammonia gas   ⟶   nitrogen   + _____


21. Reaction type: _____

   Balanced equation: _____ + _____ ⟶ _____ $H_2SO_{4(aq)}$

   Word equation:        sulfur trioxide +   water   ⟶ _____


22. Reaction type: _____

   Balanced equation: __ $Ca(NO_3)_{2(aq)}$ + __ $Na_3PO_{4(aq)}$ ⟶ _____ + _____

   Word equation: _____ + _____ ⟶ calcium   +   sodium
                                                 phosphate       nitrate

# E.7 Classifying Reactions and Balancing Chemical Equations

**Purpose:**

✔ To identify six types of chemical reactions.

✔ To provide examples of the six types of chemical reactions.

✔ To introduce balancing of chemical equations.

✔ To introduce predicting of products for five of the six types of chemical reactions.

✔ To illustrate the use of phase subscripts with chemical formulas in a chemical equation.

**Predemo Exercise:**

1. Predict the state of matter of each substance in the unbalanced equations below.

2. Balance the equations below.

**Observations:**

1. Simple Composition

element + element $\longrightarrow$ compound

zinc + sulfur $\longrightarrow$ zinc sulfide

___ Zn( ) + ___ S$_8$( ) $\longrightarrow$ ___ ZnS( )

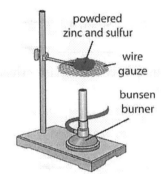

powdered
zinc and sulfur

wire
gauze

bunsen
burner

2. Simple Decomposition

compound $\longrightarrow$ element + element

mercury(II) oxide $\longrightarrow$ mercury + oxygen

___ HgO( ) $\longrightarrow$ ___ Hg( ) + ___ O$_2$( )

However, this involves the use of mercury and mercury compounds, which are considered to be quite toxic. As a safer alternative, hydrogen peroxide will be used. While technically not *simple* decomposition, it is still a decomposition reaction and also produces oxygen gas. The hydrogen peroxide reacts so slowly that $MnO_2$ is added as a catalyst. (A **catalyst** is a *compound used to speed up a reaction, but is not consumed by the reaction.*)

___ H$_2$O$_2$( ) $\longrightarrow$ ___ H$_2$O( ) + ___ O$_2$( )

What test is used to prove that a gas is oxygen?

_____

_____

_____

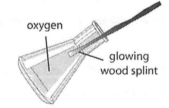

oxygen

glowing
wood splint

What test could be used to prove that a gas is carbon dioxide?

_____

_____

_____

_____

3. Single Replacement

a.   metal   +   compound   ⟶   metal   +   compound

copper   +   silver nitrate   ⟶   silver   +   copper(II) nitrate

___ Cu( ) + ___ AgNO$_3$( ) ⟶ ___ Ag( ) + ___ Cu(NO$_3$)$_2$( )

**Note:** *The metal replaces the metal ion in the compound as indicated by the double arrow above.*

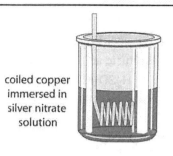

coiled copper immersed in silver nitrate solution

What color is the silver nitrate solution? _____

What color is the copper(II) nitrate solution? _____

Why write down Cu(NO$_3$)$_2$ rather than CuNO$_3$? _____

_____

b.   nonmetal +   compound   ⟶   nonmetal +   compound

chlorine + sodium iodide   ⟶   iodine   + sodium chloride

___ Cl$_2$( ) + ___ NaI( )   ⟶   ___ I$_2$( ) + ___ NaCl( )

**Note:** *The nonmetal replaces the nonmetal ion in the compound as indicated by the double arrow.*

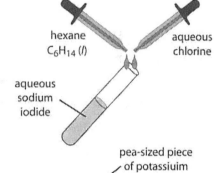

hexane C$_6$H$_{14}$ (*l*)

aqueous chlorine

aqueous sodium iodide

c.   active metal +   water   ⟶ hydrogen +   compound

potassium   +   water   ⟶ hydrogen + potassium hydroxide

___ K( )   + ___ HOH( ) ⟶ ___ H$_2$( ) + ___ KOH( )

**Note:** *For single replacement reactions, water is written as HOH (l).*

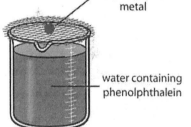

pea-sized piece of potassiuim metal

water containing phenolphthalein

How is the flame color produced?

_____

What was the color of the Universal Indicator in the potassium hydroxide solution?

_____

What type of compound is indicated by this color?

_____

4. Double Replacement

a.   compound   +   compound   ⟶   compound +   compound

lead(II) nitrate + potassium iodide   ⟶ lead(II) iodide + potassium nitrate

___ Pb(NO$_3$)$_2$( ) + ___ KI( )   ⟶   ___ PbI$_2$( ) + ___ KNO$_3$( )

**Note:** *The metal ions in each compound replace each other.*

potassium iodide solution

lead (II) nitrate solution

How do you know the lead(II) iodide would form a precipitate?

_____

b. A special type of double replacement is **neutralization**.

$$\text{acid} \quad + \quad \text{base} \quad \longrightarrow \quad \text{water} \quad + \quad \text{a salt}$$

$$\text{sulfuric acid} + \text{sodium hydroxide} \longrightarrow \text{water} \quad + \text{sodium sulfate}$$

___ $H_2SO_4(\ )$ + ___ $NaOH(\ )$ $\longrightarrow$ ___ $HOH(\ )$ + ___ $Na_2SO_4(\ )$

*Note: For double replacement reactions, water is written as HOH(l).*

Since many acids, bases, and salts form colorless solutions, an indicator solution is used to observe the changes that occur as an acid is added to a base and vice versa. For this demo, *Universal Indicator* is being used—the color indicates the pH of the solution.

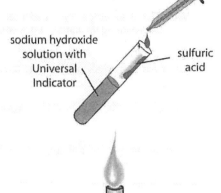

sodium hydroxide solution with Universal Indicator

sulfuric acid

| Color: | R | O | Y | G | B | I | V |
|--------|-----|---|---|---|---|---|-----|
| pH: | ≤4 | 5 | 6 | 7 | 8 | 9 | ≥10 |

methane

air

5. Hydrocarbon Combustion
a. hydrocarbon + oxygen $\longrightarrow$ carbon dioxide + water + heat

methane + oxygen $\longrightarrow$ carbon dioxide + water + heat

___ $CH_4(\ )$ + ___ $O_2(\ )$ $\longrightarrow$ ___ $CO_2(\ )$ + ___ $H_2O(\ )$

*Note: 1. Water is written as H₂O(g) for hydrocarbon combustion reactions.*

*2. Carbon and hydrogen atoms are balanced first and oxygen atoms are balanced last.*

1000 mL beaker inverted over burning candle until flame extinguished

b. candlewax + oxygen $\longrightarrow$ carbon dioxide + water + heat

___ $C_{25}H_{52}(\ )$ + ___ $O_2(\ )$ $\longrightarrow$ ___ $CO_2(\ )$ + ___ $H_2O(\ )$

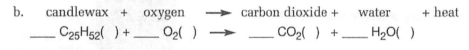

Procedure
1. Invert 1000-mL beaker over burning candle until the flame is extinguished.
2. Test thin liquid film with a strip of blue cobalt(II) chloride paper.
3. Moisten a second piece of blue cobalt(II) chloride test paper with drop of tap water.

What color did the cobalt(II) chloride paper turn when the beaker film was tested?

_____

What color did the cobalt(II) chloride paper turn when a drop of water was tested?

_____

What conclusion can be drawn from the observations above?

_____

Where did the liquid film on the beaker come from?

_____

c.   candlewax  +   oxygen   ⟶   carbon dioxide +   water   + heat

___ $C_{25}H_{52}($  $) +$ ___ $O_2($  $) \longrightarrow$   ___ $CO_2($  $) +$ ___ $H_2O($  $)$

250 mL Erlenmeyer flask inverted over burning candle until flame extinguished

Procedure
- Invert 250-mL Erlenmeyer flask over burning candle until the flame is extinguished.
- After the candle flame is extinguished, quickly place flask upright on table.
- Obtain second clean 250-mL Erleneyer flask to be used as a control.
- Add about 25 mL of limewater solution to each flask and swirl the flasks simultaneously until a change occurs in one of the flasks.

   What causes the candle flame to be extinguished when the Erlenmeyer flask is inverted over the flame?

   _____

   _____

   What gas is essential for combustion of hydrocarbons?

   _____

6. Other:

   Procedure

   1. Exhale into limewater solution through a straw or glass tubing.

straw or glass tubing

limewater solution

The word equation or chemical reaction must be given for reactions other than the above five types.  You are not expected to predict products for this type of reaction.

   carbon dioxide +    limewater   ⟶  calcium carbonate +   water

   ___ $CO_2($  $)$   +___ $Ca(OH)_2($  $) \longrightarrow$   ___ $CaCO_3($  $)$   +___ $H_2O($  $)$

What gas caused the limewater solution to turn milky?

_____

What gases are produced when combustion of hydrocarbons occurs?

_____

_____

_____

# E.8  <u>Exercises</u>   Simple Composition and Simple Decomposition Reactions

A. Identify the reaction type by writing **sc** or **sd** in front of each equation.

B. Provide the correct chemical formulas for reactants and/or products where necessary.

C. Where needed, place subscripts to indicate the phase (at room temperature unless otherwise stated).

D. Use the simplest whole number coefficients to balance the chemical equations.

**Examples:**

Simple Composition Reactions:
  element + element ⟶ compound
  e.g., $2\,Mg(s) + O_2(g) \longrightarrow 2\,MgO(s)$

Simple Decomposition Reactions:
  compound ⟶ element + element
  e.g., $8\,HgS(s) \longrightarrow 8\,Hg(l) + S_8(s)$

*Notes:*
1. Simple composition and decomposition reactions generally involve only pure substances. Use the generalizations from the D.16 Lab to predict the states of these pure substances.
2. Remember when predicting products to write the correct chemical formulas first (see Unit D) and then balance the equation.

___ 1. The first step in the production of sulfuric acid is to burn sulfur.
  ___ $S_8(s)$ + ___ $O_2(g) \longrightarrow$ ___ $SO_2(g)$

___ 2. In 1774, Joseph Priestley discovered oxygen by decomposing the **calx** (historical name for oxide) of mercury.
  ___ $HgO(s) \longrightarrow$ ___ $Hg(l)$ + ___ $O_2(g)$

___ 3. Molten (melted) table salt is industrially decomposed to produce molten sodium.
  ___ $NaCl(l) \longrightarrow$ ___ $Na(l)$ + ___ $Cl_2(g)$

___ 4. Nitrogen from the air reacts with hydrogen to produce ammonia for fertilizers.
  ___ $N_2(g)$ + ___ $H_2(g) \longrightarrow$ ___ $NH_3(g)$

___ 5. Rocket fuel burns to propel a satellite into space.
  ___ $H_2(g)$ + ___ $O_2(g) \longrightarrow$ ___ $H_2O(g)$

___ 6. Copper ore is decomposed to remove the copper metal.
  $CuO(s) \longrightarrow$ _____

___ 7. Barbecue charcoal undergoes incomplete combustion to produce deadly carbon monoxide.
  ___ $C(s)$ + ___ $O_2(g) \longrightarrow$ _____

___ 8. Freshly cut lithium reacts with nitrogen from the air. _____

___ 9. A silver spoon or coin tarnishes when exposed to sulfur. _____

___ 10. Molten lye is decomposed industrially into its elements.
  $NaOH(l) \longrightarrow$ _____

# E.9 <u>Exercises</u>  Single and Double Replacement Reactions

A. Follow the previous instructions concerning identification of reaction type, writing correct chemical formulas, indicating the state of matter, and balancing the chemical equation.

B. Polyatomic ions are assumed to remain intact and are balanced as complete units.

C. It is easier when balancing equations to write water as HOH for single and double replacement reactions.

**Examples:**

Single Replacement Reactions:
  element + compound ⟶ element + compound
  e.g., $Cl_2(aq) + 2\,NaI(aq) \longrightarrow I_2(aq) + 2\,NaCl(aq)$

Double Replacement Reactions:

$$\text{compound} + \text{compound} \longrightarrow \text{compound} + \text{compound}$$

e.g., $Pb(NO_3)_{2(aq)} + 2 KI_{(aq)} \longrightarrow PbI_{2(s)} + 2 KNO_{3(aq)}$

*Note:* Use the solubility table on the bottom of the *Periodic Table of Ions* to predict the solubility of the products of single and double replacement reactions in water.

___ 1. Sodium metal reacts vigorously with water.

    ____ $Na_{(s)}$ + ___ $HOH_{(l)} \longrightarrow$ ____ $H_{2(g)}$ + ____ $NaOH_{(aq)}$

___ 2. Hydrogen chloride gas is produced in the laboratory from table salt.

    __ $NaCl_{(s)}$ + __ $H_2SO_{4(aq)} \longrightarrow$ __ $HCl_{(g)}$ + __ $Na_2SO_{4(aq)}$

___ 3. Molten iron is produced in the highly exothermic Thermit reaction.

    ____ $Al_{(s)}$ + ____ $Fe_2O_{3(s)} \longrightarrow$ ____ $Fe_{(l)}$ + ____ $Al_2O_{3(s)}$

___ 4. Slaked lime precipitates magnesium ions from hard water.

    __$Ca(OH)_{2(aq)}$ + __$Mg(HCO_3)_{2(aq)} \longrightarrow$ __$Mg(OH)_{2(s)}$ + __$Ca(HCO_3)_{2(aq)}$

___ 5. Aluminum was first produced in 1825 by Hans Oersted using the following reaction:

    ____ $K_{(s)}$ + ____ $AlCl_{3(s)} \longrightarrow$ ____ $Al_{(s)}$ + ____ $KCl_{(s)}$

___ 6. Silver is recovered from silver ore by converting the ore into silver sulfate, which is then reacted with copper.

    ____ $Cu_{(s)}$ + ____ $Ag_2SO_{4(aq)} \longrightarrow$ _____

___ 7. Phosphoric acid is produced at a fertilizer plant.

    ____ $H_2SO_{4(aq)}$ + ____ $Ca_3(PO_4)_{2(s)} \longrightarrow$ _____

___ 8. Bromine is commercially produced from $MgBr_2$ found in seawater.

    ____ $Cl_{2(g)}$ + ____ $MgBr_{2(aq)} \longrightarrow$ _____

___ 9. Hydrogen sulfide (sour) gas from a wild natural gas well reacts with the lead(II) chromate pigment in paint on homes. (The house changes color!)

    ____ $H_2S_{(g)}$ + ____ $PbCrO_{4(s)} \longrightarrow$ _____

___ 10. Hydrogen sulfide gas from a wild sour (due to acidic compounds) natural gas well reacts with the silver in cutlery and ornaments at home.

    ____ $H_2S_{(g)}$ + ____ $Ag_{(s)} \longrightarrow$ _____

# E.10 Exercises  Hydrocarbon Combustion and Other Reactions

A. Follow previous instructions concerning identification of reaction type, writing correct formulas, indicating the state of matter, and balancing the chemical reaction.

B. Except for methane, the formula and phase of the hydrocarbons will be provided in all questions.

C. For other types of reactions, the total equation will be given; products cannot always be predicted easily.

Hydrocarbon Combustion Reactions:

    hydrocarbon + oxygen $\longrightarrow$ carbon dioxide + water vapor

**Example:** Ethane, $C_2H_6(g)$, is burned in air.

*Step 1:* List all reactants and products:

$$C_2H_6(g) + O_2(g) \longrightarrow CO_2(g) + H_2O(g)$$

*Step 2:* Balance carbon, hydrogen, and oxygen (in that order):

$$C_2H_6(g) + \tfrac{7}{2} O_2(g) \longrightarrow 2 CO_2(g) + 3 H_2O(g)$$

*Step 3:* Multiply by 2 to get the simplest whole number ratio:

$$2 C_2H_6(g) + 7 O_2(g) \longrightarrow 4 CO_2(g) + 6 H_2O(g)$$

*Notes:*

1. Write water as $H_2O(g)$ in equations for hydrocarbon combustion reactions. When written as $H_2O(g)$, balancing is easier. Water is produced as a gas, $H_2O(g)$, because so much heat is produced in hydrocarbon combustion reactions.
2. Balance C and H atoms first, O atoms last.

___ 1. A Bunsen burner, gas furnace and gas hot-water tank all burn natural gas.

___ $CH_4(g)$ + ___ $O_2(g) \longrightarrow$ ___ $CO_2(g)$ + ___ $H_2O(g)$

___ 2. Propane is used as a fuel for trailers and where natural gas is not available.

___ $C_3H_8(g)$ + ___ $O_2(g) \longrightarrow$

___ 3. Oxygen gas may be produced in the laboratory by heating potassium chlorate.

___ $KClO_3(s) \longrightarrow$ ___ $KCl(s)$ + ___ $O_2(g)$

___ 4. Limestone, mined in Kansas, is decomposed by heating to produce lime.

___ $CaCO_3(s) \longrightarrow$ ___ $CaO(s)$ + ___ $CO_2(g)$

___ 5. Gasoline is mixed with air in the carburetor and then exploded by a spark in the cylinder of a car motor.

___ $C_8H_{18}(l)$ + ___ $O_2(g) \longrightarrow$ _____

___ 6. A rock may be tested for limestone content ($CaCO_3(s)$) by adding muriatic acid ($HCl(aq)$).

__ $CaCO_3(s)$ + __ $HCl(aq) \longrightarrow$ __ $CaCl_2(aq)$ + __ $H_2O(l)$ + __ $CO_2(g)$

___ 7. A candle (assume $C_{25}H_{52}$) is burned for emergency or dining light.

_____

Glass is prepared by heating sand with limestone and washing soda:

__ 8. ___ $SiO_2(s)$ + ___ $CaCO_3(s) \longrightarrow$ ___ $CaSiO_3(s)$ + ___ $CO_2(g)$

__ 9. ___ $SiO_2(s)$ + ___ $Na_2CO_3(s) \longrightarrow$ ___ $Na_2SiO_3(s)$ + ___ $CO_2(g)$

__ 10. Kerosene (assume $C_{14}H_{30}$) is a mixture of hydrocarbons and is burned as a fuel for stoves and lanterns. _____

# E.11 Classifying Chemical Reactions

**Purpose:**

✔ To review nomenclature, balancing equations, reaction types, predicting products and evidence for chemical reactions.

✔ To improve observation skills and confirm phases of reactants and products.

**Prelab Exercise:**

1. Identify and write down the reaction type.

   *sc* simple composition

   *sd* simple decomposition

   *sr* single replacement

   *dr* double replacement

   *hc* hydrocarbon combustion

   *o* other

2. Complete the balanced chemical equation next, including the state of matter.

3. Complete the word equation last.

**Procedure:**

1. Describe the reactants before observing the reaction; i.e., color and state (gas, liquid, solid, or aqueous solution).

2. Follow the instructions to obtain the required chemical reaction.

3. Describe the products after observing the reaction.

4. Indicate the evidence that a chemical reaction has occurred:
   a. a precipitate forms
   b. a color change occurs
   c. an energy change occurs
   d. a gas is produced

5. Follow disposal procedure as indicated. Clean up the laboratory station and then move on to the next station.

| **Example:** As a prelab assignment, complete the *reaction type*, *word equation* and *balanced equation* from the given partial word equation. | | | | *Reaction Type:* **SR** |
|---|---|---|---|---|
| *Word Equation:* | magnesium + hydrochloric acid ⟶ hydrogen + magnesium chloride | | | |
| *Balanced Equation:* | $Mg_{(s)}$ + 2 $HCl_{(aq)}$ ⟶ $H_2{(g)}$ + $MgCl_2{(aq)}$ | | | |
| Descriptions: | silvery solid covered with gray oxide | colorless aqueous solution | colorless gas | colorless aqueous solution |
| Reaction Evidence: | Gas produced, perhaps some heat also; magnesium disappears. | | | |

| 1. Adjust the Bunsen burner to obtain a blue flame. Using the tongs, hold a small piece of magnesium ribbon in the Bunsen burner flame. When the magnesium ribbon ignites, do not stare at the flame. Hold the burning magnesium over a beaker or ceramic pad. When finished, you may leave the burner on, but adjust it to a visible yellow flame. | | | *Reaction Type:* |
|---|---|---|---|
| *Word Equation:* | magnesium + oxygen ⟶ | | |
| *Balanced Equation:* | + ⟶ | | |
| Descriptions: | | | |
| Reaction Evidence: | | | |

2. Observe the burning candle. What is the state of matter of each of the reactants and products? Hold a beaker full of cold water over the flame. Record the observations. Leave the candle lit when leaving the station. Clean the beaker.

*Reaction Type:*

| Word Equation: | candle wax | + | oxygen | $\longrightarrow$ | | + | |
|---|---|---|---|---|---|---|---|
| Balanced Equation: | $C_{25}H_{52}$ ( ) | + | | $\longrightarrow$ | | + | |
| Descriptions: | | | | | | | |
| Reaction Evidence: | | | | | | | |

3. Observe the electrolytic decomposition of water into two gases. Note the relative volumes of the two gases produced.

*Reaction Type:*

| Word Equation: | water | $\longrightarrow$ | + | |
|---|---|---|---|---|
| Balanced Equation: | | $\longrightarrow$ | + | |
| Descriptions: | | | | |
| Reaction Evidence: | | | | |

4. Put some water in a beaker and test with red litmus paper. Add a piece of calcium to the water. Observe. Use tweezers to remove the calcium. Now test the solution with red litmus paper. Dispose of calcium and paper properly.

*Reaction Type:*

| Word Equation: | calcium | + | water | $\longrightarrow$ | | + | |
|---|---|---|---|---|---|---|---|
| Balanced Equation: | | + | | $\longrightarrow$ | | + | |
| Descriptions: | | | | | | | |
| Reaction Evidence: | | | | | | | |

5. Add an eyedropper-full of chlorine water, $Cl_2(aq)$, to a small test tube. Add an eyedropper-full of sodium iodide solution to the same test tube. Stopper the test tube and invert several times. Record the observations and rinse out the test tube.

*Reaction Type:*

| Word Equation: | chlorine | + | sodium iodide | $\longrightarrow$ | | + | |
|---|---|---|---|---|---|---|---|
| Balanced Equation: | | + | | $\longrightarrow$ | | + | |
| Descriptions: | | | | | | | |
| Reaction Evidence: | | | | | | | |

6. Use tweezers to add a piece of mossy zinc to the beaker containing hydrochloric acid. Record the observations. Use the tweezers to remove the piece of zinc. Return the zinc to the container. Leave the hydrochloric acid in the beaker. (Caution: Do not get any acid on hands or clothes.)

*Reaction Type:*

| Word Equation: | zinc | + | hydrochloric acid ⟶ | | + | |
|---|---|---|---|---|---|---|
| Balanced Equation: | | + | ⟶ | | + | |
| Descriptions: | | | | | | |
| Reaction Evidence: | | | | | | |

7. Obtain a blue flame with the Bunsen burner. Obtain two or three strands of steel wool. Use crucible tongs to hold the strands of steel wool in the hottest part of the flame. Record the observations. Leave the Bunsen burner lit (with a visible, yellow flame).

*Reaction Type:*

| Word Equation: | iron | + | oxygen ⟶ | |
|---|---|---|---|---|
| Balanced Equation: | | + | ⟶ | |
| Descriptions: | | | | |
| Reaction Evidence: | | | | |

8. Add an eyedropper-full of each solution below to a small test tube. Record the observations. Rinse out the test tube.

*Reaction Type:*

| Word Equation: | cobalt (II) chloride | + | sodium hydoxide ⟶ | | + | |
|---|---|---|---|---|---|---|
| Balanced Equation: | | + | ⟶ | | + | |
| Descriptions: | | | | | | |
| Reaction Evidence: | | | | | | |

9. Add an eyedropper-full of each solution below to a small test tube. Record the observations. Rinse out the test tube.

*Reaction Type:*

| Word Equation: | nickel (II) nitrate | + | sodium carbonate ⟶ | | + | |
|---|---|---|---|---|---|---|
| Balanced Equation: | | + | ⟶ | | + | |
| Descriptions: | | | | | | |
| Reaction Evidence: | | | | | | |

10. Add an eyedropper-full of each solution below to a small test tube. Note the odor of the ammonium hydroxide solution by wafting the gas to your nose with your hand. Record the observations. Rinse out the test tube.

*Reaction Type:*

| Word Equation: | iron (III) chloride | + | ammonium hydroxide | ⟶ | | + | |
|---|---|---|---|---|---|---|---|
| Balanced Equation: | | + | | ⟶ | | + | |
| Descriptions: | | | | | | | |
| Reaction Evidence: | | | | | | | |

11. Add an eyedropper-full of each solution below to a small test tube. Record the observations. Rinse out the test tube.

*Reaction Type:*

| Word Equation: | sodium nitrate | + | potassium chloride | ⟶ | | + | |
|---|---|---|---|---|---|---|---|
| Balanced Equation: | | + | | ⟶ | | + | |
| Descriptions: | | | | | | | |
| Reaction Evidence: | | | | | | | |

12. Add an eyedropper-full of each solution below to a small test tube. Record the observations. Rinse out the test tube. Carefully feel the outside of the test tube. (**Caution**: corrosive solutions!)

*Reaction Type:*

| Word Equation: | sulfuric acid | + | sodium hydroxide | ⟶ | | + | |
|---|---|---|---|---|---|---|---|
| Balanced Equation: | | + | | ⟶ | | + | |
| Descriptions: | | | | | | | |
| Reaction Evidence: | | | | | | | |

13. Bring an eyedropper-full of each solution below next to each other. Do not touch! Record the observations.

*Reaction Type:*

| Word Equation: | | + | | ⟶ | |
|---|---|---|---|---|---|
| Balanced Equation: | HCl (g) | + | NH₃ (g) | ⟶ | |
| Descriptions: | | | | | |
| Reaction Evidence: | | | | | |

| | | |
|---|---|---|
| 14. Add an eyedropper-full of each solution below to a small test tube. Record the observations. Rinse out the test tube. | | *Reaction Type:* |

| | | | |
|---|---|---|---|
| *Word Equation:* | copper (II) sulfate + aqueous ammonia ⟶ | | copper (II) tetraammonia sulfate solution |
| *Balanced Equation:* | + | ⟶ | $Cu(NH_3)_4SO_4(aq)$ |
| Descriptions: | | | |
| Reaction Evidence: | | | |

**Questions:**

*(Some of these questions will need to be discussed with your instructor.)*

1. Identify at least five (5) stations in this lab that showed an energy change.

2. Why was the candle flame at Station 2 yellow rather than blue? (Look on the underside of the beaker at Station 2. Where did the soot come from and how does it cause the yellow flame?)

3. What are the steps for lighting a Bunsen burner?

4. What chemical test could be used to prove that a gas is carbon dioxide? (See #5 of the E.7 Demo.) Describe a positive test.

5. What is the balanced chemical equation for the carbon dioxide test?

6. What test is used to prove that a gas is hydrogen? (Teacher demo at Station 3, above.) Describe a positive test.

7. What is the balanced chemical equation for the hydrogen test? (What does the hydrogen react with in the previous demo?)

8. What test is used to prove that a gas is oxygen? (Teacher demo at Station 3, above.) Describe a positive test.

9. What test is used to prove that a colorless liquid contains water? (See the A.5 Lab.)

10. What tests are used to prove that a solution is acidic or basic or neither? (See the A.5 Lab and the E.7 Demo.) Describe a positive test.

11. Match the following aqueous ions to their color in solution. The colors (not in proper order) are purple, green, orange-brown, orange, blue, pink, and yellow. Some of these aqueous ions were not in this lab, but were in the D.16 Lab.

| | |
|---|---|
| a. | $Fe^{3+}(aq)$ |
| b. | $MnO_4^-(aq)$ |
| c. | $Co^{2+}(aq)$ |
| d. | $CrO_4^{2-}(aq)$ |
| e. | $Ni^{2+}(aq)$ |
| f. | $Cr_2O_7^{2-}(aq)$ |
| g. | $Cu^{2+}(aq)$ |

} See your teacher to view solutions of these two ions.

h. Note the position of the atoms composing these colored aqueous ions on the *Table of Polyatomic Ions.* What classification of elements produce a colored solution?

_____

12. Identify at least four (4) precipitates that were formed in this lab. (Give name, formula, and station number.)

| Name | Formula | Station |
|---|---|---|
| | | |
| | | |
| | | |
| | | |

13. At station 11, there was no visible evidence for a reaction and, in fact, there was no reaction — even if you did predict *sodium chloride* and *potassium nitrate* as new products. Check the solubilities of all the compounds and explain why it is that there was no reaction.

_____

# Unit F
## Measurement and The Mole

### F.1 Measurements

Discovering patterns is an important part of science. In previous units, you learned about patterns of physical and chemical properties found in the Periodic Table, patterns of naming ionic and molecular compounds, and patterns of different classes of chemical reactions. Nearly all of these patterns were observed as a result of very careful measurements taken during experiments. Making accurate measurements and using them to perform necessary calculations are an essential part of chemistry. In this unit, you will learn rules for dealing with those measurements as well as simple methods to handle the mathematics of chemistry.

Scientists often make observations in their attempts to explain the behavior of various substances under their investigation. While **qualitative** observations such as hot, cold, color, odor and presence of bubbles are valuable to the chemist, it is much more useful to obtain a **quantitative** observation—an indication of "*how much*": what is the specific temperature, volume, mass or some other information needed by the experimenter. To find "how much," a chemist must make a measurement using an appropriate measuring device. A **measurement** always includes three things:

1. a *number* that tells the amount measured,
2. a *unit* that tells the kind of measurement made, and
3. the possibility of *error* in a measurement.

You have undoubtedly used different measuring devices such as rulers, graduated cylinders and balances before and understand how numbers and units are obtained. You may not have thought much about the errors that arise when taking measurements. Experimental errors are generally classified as three types:

Good Precision
but Poor Accuracy

- **Personal errors**—primarily due to personal bias, carelessness in reading an instrument, or recording errors.
  - **Parallax** — not reading graduated cylinder at eye level or at bottom of **meniscus**.
  - **Sampling Errors** — Always taking a measurement of a sample at the beginning of an experiment.

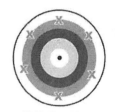

Poor Precision
but Good Accuracy
(take average value)

- **Systematic errors**—include improperly calibrated instruments (e.g., barometer — set to read *29.80 in* when the actual pressure is *29.95 in*), improperly "zeroed" instruments (e.g., scale showing 0.2 mg when empty), and human reaction time (e.g., hand-eye coordination time).

- **Random errors**—due to unknown and unpredictable variations in experimental situations (e.g., dirt in the mechanism).
  - Air current passes by balance, just as reading is taken.
  - Fluctuations in line voltage.

Both Good Precison
and Good Accuracy

FIGURE F4 — X's
on a Bull's Eye

### Accuracy and Precision

The **accuracy** of a measurement signifies *how close it comes to the true or accepted value*—how "correct" the measurement is. *The difference between an observed value* (or the average of observed values) *and the true value* is called the inaccuracy or **error**. The magnitude of this difference is an indication of the "accuracy." As the difference between the *true value* and the *observed value* decreases, the accuracy increases and the inaccuracy decreases.

## Example:

Suppose the true time is 15:28:36, that is, a little before three-thirty in the afternoon. If *I* say the time is 15:30 and *you* say it is 15:29, you would be more accurate than I am. My version of the time has a greater error than yours.

The **precision** of a measurement refers to *the repeatability of the measurement*. It signifies "the spread" or scatter in a series of "identical" measurements. In FIGURE F1, each "x" signifies the arrow on a target (bull's eye).

For our purposes, the precision will be indicated by the number of digits to the right of the decimal point.

## Example:

John states that the time a lightning flash occurred was 15:30, Ed states that it was at 15:29:50, and Mary states that the time was 15:29:50.0. Ed's time was more precise than John's (more significant digits), and Mary's was the most precise (most decimal places). Actually it would in one case be possible for John to be more "accurate" than the others. Suppose, for example, they found out later that they had set their timepieces by a clock that was three minutes slow. (That is, the "true time" of the lightning flash was 15:32:50.0000 exactly.) Then John's original observation would have a smaller error and be more accurate than the other original observations, but their observations would still be more precise.

| Individual | Originally Measured Time | Error | Corrected Time | Error |
|------------|--------------------------|-------|----------------|-------|
| John | 15:30 | – 2:50 | 15:33 | Off by ten seconds |
| Ed | 15:29:50 | – 3:00 | 15:32:50 | Correct to nearest second |
| Mary | 15:29:50.0 | – 3:00.0 | 15:32:50.0 | Correct to nearest tenth of a second |

FIGURE F2 — Comparison of Measured Times

# F.2 Uncertainty in Measurement and Significant Digits

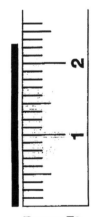

**FIGURE F3**
**Significant Digits in a Measurement**

Since every measurement has the potential for errors, there is some degree of uncertainty in every measurement. When scientists record and communicate data, it is important that others understand the degree of uncertainty. One method of indicating uncertainty is by the number of significant digits recorded.

**Significant digits** are those digits obtained from a properly taken measurement. Significant digits, as obtained from a measurement, consist *of all the certain digits from a measurement plus one estimated (uncertain) digit.* Whether values are taken from a measurement or determined by calculation, significant digits are those digits that are known with certainty plus one uncertain digit. Said another way, significant digits give the "degree of confidence" in the measurement. In some ways it shows the quality of the measuring device being used. (The better the device, the more precise can be the measurement.) Only significant digits are recorded.

For example, the object in FIGURE F3 is between 2.2 and 2.3 cm long. A ruler of this type can give another decimal place if the user estimates the last digit. In this case the length is reported as 2.2*5* cm. (*The digit in italics represents the one estimated digit.*)

## Rules for Counting Significant Digits

1. Digits to be counted (significant digits) include:

   a. all nonzero digits from 1 to 9, plus

   b. all "trapped" zeros in between nonzero digits, and

   c. most zeros following nonzero digits* ("Trailing Zeros"; see FIGURE F4 for examples)

2. Do not count zeros in front of a value ("Leading Zeros") because they only serve to set the decimal place (i.e., 21.5 g and 0.0215 kg are both the same value and both have three significant digits).

*Note: When a number ends in zeros that are to the left of the decimal point, the trailing zeros may or may not be significant. Technically, these digits are considered to be uncertain in mathematics because of the potential ambiguity, but practically speaking these zeros are generally understood from the context of the situation to be significant to the measurement. For example, if someone says the volume is 50 mL, it is understood that 2 significant digits are meant. If more significant digits are intended, they should be written. (It is the responsibility of the individual to record the correct number of significant digits.) For example, if the measurement is precise to 2 decimal places, it would be written as 50.00 mL. The uncertainty is avoided by using scientific notation (presented in Section F.4). For convenience, the textbook will include all "trailing" zeros as significant digits unless otherwise specified.

### FIGURE F4 — Counting Significant Digits
The digits in italics are considered uncertain (estimated).

| Measured Value | # of Significant Digits | Measured Value | # of Significant Digits |
|---|---|---|---|
| 156 g | 3 | 120.50 L | 5 |
| 0.2608 m | 4 | 0.05003 s | 4 |
| $6.02 \times 10^{23}$ molecules | 3 | 7.00°C | 3 |
| 500. mL | 3 | 500 mL | *1 |

If a decimal point is included, count the zeros. If there is no decimal point, the zeros do not count. Do not start counting until the first nonzero digit is reached as viewed from left to right.

\* If there is no decimal point, the zeros are considered ambiguous and are not included.

## Exact Numbers

Exact numbers are not uncertain and are said to have an infinite number of significant digits.

There are two types of exact numbers:

1. Numbers that are *defined*.

   For example: 100 cm = 1 m (This is exactly true—a metric definition. It does not need to be measured.)

2. Numbers that result from *counting objects*. (These items are either included in the count, or they are not. They do not need to be measured first.)

   For example: 32 students, 158 beakers, $4.95 (exactly 495 cents).

## Rounding Off

1. Determine the number of significant digits.
2. Examine the first digit following the last significant digit (*viewing the number from left to right*).
   a. If this digit is 4 or less, all digits remain the same.
      - For example, round off the measurement 2.249 g to 2 significant digits.
      - 2.249 g = 2.2 g (The "4" comes after the last significant digit. Therefore, no change to the significant digits.)
   b. If this digit is 5 or more, the last significant digit is increased by one.
      - For example, round off 12.654 $cm^3$ to 3 significant digits.
      - 12.654 $cm^3$ = 12.7 $cm^3$ (The "5" comes after the last significant digit. The "6" rounds up to "7.")

# F.3  <u>Exercises</u>  Measurement and Uncertainty

For each measured value, write the number of significant digits (e.g., 12.42 g: 4):

1.  0.1407 m  _____

2.  10.0 mL  _____

3.  1000°C  _____

4.  0.060 h  _____

5.  126 km  _____

6.  15.00 t  _____

7.  0.0004 kPa  _____

8.  40. s  _____

9.  0.0100 L  _____

10. 100 cm/m  _____

For each calculated value, use the number of significant digits shown in parentheses to arrive at the rounded-off values (e.g., 0.1495 $m^2$ [3]:0.150 $m^2$ ):

11. 29.95 m/s  (3) _____

12. 139.49 $cm^3$  (3) _____

13. 10.54 mol  (3) _____

14. 100.4°C  (3) _____

15. 9.998 g  (2) _____

16. 80.46 km/h  (2) _____

17. 197.042 L  (4) _____

18. 0.0462 $m^3$  (2) _____

19. 82.9 g/mol  (2) _____

20. 5.49 mm  (1) _____

# F.4  Scientific Notation

Scientific notation is a method of expressing a number in terms of powers of ten in the form of

$$D.dd \times 10^n$$

where the **D.dd** represents the *significant digits* of the measurement or the derived digits of a calculation and **n** is the required exponent for a number..

For example,

| | |
|---|---|
| $6\ 000\ 000 = 6.000 \times 10^6$ | (4 significant digits) |
| $6\ 000\ 000 = 6 \times 10^6$ | (1 significant digit) |
| $7\ 200 = 7.20 \times 10^3$ | (3 significant digits) |
| $7\ 200 = 7.2 \times 10^3$ | (2 significant digits) |
| $0.000\ 50 = 5.0 \times 10^{-4}$ | (2 significant digits) |
| $0.000\ 102\ 4 = 1.024 \times 10^{-4}$ | (4 significant digits) |

There is a tendency to overuse scientific notation. Do not use scientific notation unless it is required:

- for expressing the proper number of significant digits, or
- for making the value less cumbersome in written work or calculations.

## Examples:

$150\ 000\ 000$ km is $1.50 \times 10^8$ km (the distance to the sun)
 ♦ *proper significant digits and less cumbersome*

$0.000\ 000\ 000\ 000\ 006$ m is $6 \times 10^{-15}$ m (the diameter of a nucleus)
 ♦ *less cumbersome*

# F.5  Exercises  Scientific Notation

| Convert to scientific notation and round off to the number of significant digits in parentheses: | Convert the following to conventional notation: |
|---|---|
| 1.  72 000  (3)  = _____ | 6.  $2.59 \times 10^3$  = _____ |
| 2.  106 200  (2)  = _____ | 7.  $6.40 \times 10^{-6}$  = _____ |
| 3.  0.004 365 9  (4)  = _____ | 8.  $1.3 \times 10^8$  = _____ |
| 4.  0.000 008 12  (2)  = _____ | 9.  $7.644 \times 10^{-2}$  = _____ |
| 5.  86 402 159 321  (3)  = _____ | 10.  $18.1 \times 10^9$  = _____ |

# F.6  The Metric System

In order for measurements to be useful, it is helpful for everyone to be using the same reference standard. For example, if one person measures the length of a table to be 54 inches and another measures the same table to be 137 cm, it is difficult to know whether or not they have both measured the table accurately. It is important for both people to use the same measuring units. Historically, measuring units were based on size of body parts, barleycorns and other convenient objects. Since body parts and grains come in different sizes, these units varied from time to time and location to location. A standard system of weights and measures was needed.

Over the years the reference standard accepted by the scientific community was the metric system. It was adopted for several reasons:

1. *The units were based on the decimal system.* This easily allows a series of prefixes to be used that indicate larger and smaller versions of the original unit.

2. *The units are interrelated.* Once the *meter* was defined as the standard unit of length\*, this allowed a standard unit of volume and mass as well: one cubic decimeter (1 dm$^3$) was defined as the standard unit of volume and was named the *liter*; the mass of one cubic centimeter (1 cm$^3$ = 1 mL) of water at 4°C is defined as one *gram*.

*\*Note: A meter was originally defined as one minute (1/21 600) of the earth's circumference. Then it was changed to be the length of a pendulum that swings once per second. Later, for convenience, a platinum-iridium bar was etched with two marks one meter apart. Through the years, a more and more accurate standard was developed. Now, since time can be measured so accurately, a meter is defined to be the distance traveled by light in a vacuum during 1/299 792 458 of a second. It is approximately the distance of one large walking step.*

Since all scientists use the same system, it is easier to compare and understand results that are made by different scientists. This system begins with some essential units of measurement such as:

| | | | | |
|---|---|---|---|---|
| *mass* | = | gram | = | g |
| *volume* | = | liter | = | L |
| *length* | = | meter | = | m |

This system also uses prefixes based on powers of ten to form new units that are either larger or smaller than the essential units.

FIGURE F5     Metric System Units, Symbols and Prefixes

| | $10^6$<br>1 000 000<br>mega | $10^3$<br>1 000<br>kilo | $10^2$<br>100<br>hecto | $10^1$<br>10<br>deka | $10^0$<br>1 | $10^{-1}$<br>0.1<br>deci | $10^{-2}$<br>0.01<br>centi | $10^{-3}$<br>0.001<br>milli | $10^{-6}$<br>0.000 001<br>micro |
|---|---|---|---|---|---|---|---|---|---|
| **Symbol** | M | k | h | da | | d | c | m | μ |
| **Mass** | Mg | kg | | | g | | cg | mg | μg |
| **Volume** | ML | kL | | | L | | | mL | μL |
| **Length** | Mm | km | | | m | dm | cm | mm | μm |

Main Units

*Notes:*
1. The most *commonly used prefixes* are shown in **boldface**. Other units are not shown because there is no common use for them—they are simply placeholders. A list of all metric prefixes is given on the Data Sheet in the Appendix.
2. The equality *1 mL = 1 cm$^3$* is used often and should be learned.

If a number is too large or too small, it is expressed in different units to avoid using as many leading or trailing zeros or scientific notation. To change to a new unit, do the following:

1. Count the number of steps required to move from one unit to another.
2. Decide which direction to move the decimal.

A step to the right moves the decimal to the right:
**g → mg moves the decimal 3 places to the right**

A step to the left moves the decimal to the left.
**cm → m moves the decimal 2 places to the left**

## Example:

1690 m (3 sig. digits) = 1.69 km (From $m$ to $km$ is 3 places to the left on the chart.)
or 1.69 x $10^3$ m (Using scientific notation.)

7.48 x $10^{-6}$ g = 7.48 µg (From $g$ to µg) is 3 + 3 = 6 places to the right.)
53 000 mL (2 sig. digits) = 53 L (From $mL$ to $L$ is 3 places to the left on the chart.)
or 5.3 x $10^4$ mL (Using scientific notation.)

9.2 x $10^{-3}$ mm = 9.2 µm (What would be the best unit?)

# F.7 Exercises   The Metric System

Perform the following metric conversions (e.g., 50. m = 5.0 x $10^4$ mm):

1. 650. mL = _____ L

2. 42 m = _____ cm

3. 0.075 L = _____ mL

4. 15.4 kg = _____ g

5. 0.0035 L = _____ mL

6. 7.15 kg = _____ g

7. 15 µm = _____ mm

8 86 cm = _____ km

9. 3.46 x $10^4$ m = _____ km

10. 1.41 x $10^8$ L = _____ ML

# F.8  International System of Metric Units (SI Units)

There is now an updated version of the metric system that uses certain *base units:* the meter (m) for length, the kilogram (kg) for mass, and the second (s) for time (see FIGURE F6). These standards of measurement are based on *natural* universal constants provided for in an international agreement and are used to derive all other units of mass and measurement.

FIGURE F6   SI (Système Internationale) Base Units

| Physical Property | Name of Unit | Symbol |
|---|---|---|
| Length | meter | m |
| Mass | kilogram | kg |
| Time | second | s |
| Temperature | Kelvin | K |
| Amount of Substance | mole | mol |

The General Conference of Weights and Measures officially adopted these units in 1960 with the purpose of making communication easier among scientists and engineers in different subjects and different countries.   With SI, the base units, and some correspondingly derived units, are often too large to be conveniently used by chemists. For example, grams (g) are used instead of kilograms (kg) for mass, milliliters (mL) or cubic centimeters ($cm^3$) instead of cubic meters ($m^3$) for volume, and centimeters (cm) instead of meters (m) for length. While using only SI base units is often impractical and awkward, converting to larger or smaller units using the prefix system is an easy way to deal with these inconveniences.

| Variable | Unit | Unit Symbol | Approximation | Sample Everyday Application |
|---|---|---|---|---|
| length | meter | m | • distance from your nose to the tips of your fingers | • races, medium distances, medium lengths and dimensions |
| | millimeter | mm ($10^{-3}$ m) | • thickness of a dime | • film width, length of nails, thickness of plywood |
| | centimeter | cm ($10^{-2}$ m) | • width of small fingernail | • body sizes, lengths of skis, linens, paper |
| | kilometer | km ($10^3$ m) | • 11 football fields end to end | • highway and air distances, lengths of rivers and lakes |
| area | square hectometer (or hectare) | $hm^2$ $(10^2$ m$)^2$ or ha | • one football field length by one football field length | • land area |
| volume | liter | L | • a liter of milk | • volume of fluids and capacity of containers |
| | milliliter | mL ($10^{-3}$ L) | • a cubic fingernail | • small milk, soft drinks, toothpaste, shampoo |
| | cubic centimeter | $cm^3$ $(10^{-2}$ m$)^3$ | • 1 $cm^3$ = 1 mL | • volumes obtained by mathematical calculation |
| | cubic meter | $m^3$ | • a typical kitchen stove is a little less than 1 $m^3$ | • water and natural gas, gravel, concrete |
| mass | kilogram | kg ($10^3$ g) | • small container of salt or sugar | • meat, butter, body mass, fertilizer |
| | tonne | t ($10^6$ g) | • 1 t = 1000 kg | • truck loads, ore mined |
| | milligram | mg ($10^{-3}$ g) | • 1000 mg = 1 g | • vitamins, minerals, drugs |
| | gram | g | • small-sized raisin | • small goods–especially food |
| amount of substance | mole | mol | • varies | • oil and gas production |
| time | second, minute, hour, day, year | s, min, h, d, a | • used all the time in measurement systems | • the twenty-four-hour clock is used by the military |
| temp | Kelvin degrees Celsius | K °C | • f.p. of water 273 K, 0°C • b.p. of water 373 K, 100°C | • room temp. 293K, 20°C; • body temp. 310K, 37°C |
| pressure | kilopascal pascal | kPa Pa | • air pressure = 101 kPa | • atmospheric, water, tire, and all other pressures |

## SI Rules

Some of the rules or standards for use of SI are as follows:

1. Unit symbols are lower case letters (unless named after a person; e.g., °C [Celsius] and Pa [Pascal]). An exception is L for liters. (A lower case L is easily confused with the digit number "1.") The full names of units are always in lower case letters with the exceptions being Kelvin and degrees Celsius.

2. A period should not follow the unit symbol (i.e., kg not kg.).

3. There is no difference between the unit symbols for singular or plural (i.e., kg not kgs).

4. The symbol cc (cubic centimeter) must not replace mL or cm³.

5. The term *meter* should not be confused with the measuring instrument; determine length by context.

6. Kilometer should be pronounced in the same manner as kilogram, kiloliter and kilowatt. The prefix kilo should not be used by itself to refer to a kilogram.

7. In general, the term mass replaces the term weight.

8. A specific temperature and a temperature change both have units of degrees Celsius (°C).

9. Use the unit symbol in preference to words for units:
e.g., 10.0 g/mol not 10.0 grams/mole. (10.0 grams per mole is incorrect but ten grams per mole is correct.)

10. For values less than one, use a zero in front of the decimal point: e.g., 0.0695 mol, not .0695 mol.

11. Use a space (not a comma) to separate sets of three digits to the left and right of the decimal point. The practice is optional where there are only four digits to the left or right of the decimal point (e.g., write 3 405 638.297 05, not 3,405,638.29705).

12. Use decimal fractions (0.5) rather than common fractions (½).

# F.9  Exercises    SI Rules

Find the SI error(s) in each of the following statements and make the correction(s). (*The number of errors is indicated in parentheses at the end of the sentence.*)

1. Michael bought 2 kilos of hamburger. (*1*)
2. The recipe called for 1.0 ML of vanilla and 100 c.c. of milk. (*2*)
3. Jill bought 6.0 liters of gasoline for her 250 c.c. motorcycle. (*2*)
4. Trevor's temperature dropped by .9 c° (from 39.2°celcius to 38.3 degrees centigrade) in 12 hr. (*7*)
5. The car accelerated from rest to 100 Km. per hour in 10 sec. (*5*)
6. The weight of 1 Ml of water is exactly 1 gms. (*4*)
7. The package was marked as containing 500 Gm. of spaghetti. (*3*)
8. The height of the precipitate in the test tube was 2-1/2 c.m. (*2*)
9. Cameron calculated that, if the molar weight of calcium carbonate was 100 g/mole, then the number of mol in 0.543 gms was .00543 mols. (*7*)

# F.10  Exercises    Scientific Notation and SI Prefixes

For the following values, change the measured value to proper scientific notation. Also convert to an appropriate SI prefix. Be sure to record the final answer to a numerical value between 1 and 999 with proper significant digits:

| Scientific Notation | Value (# of Significant Digits) | Using SI Prefixes |
|---|---|---|
| | 1.  0.007 06 g      (2) | |
| | 2.  4 000 000 m     (3) | |
| | 3.  43 059 mL       (3) | |
| | 4.  0.003 49 L      (1) | |
| | 5.  38 100 mm       (4) | |
| | 6.  0.004 45 s      (2) | |

# F.11 The Conversion Factor Method

You will often find it easy enough to convert from one unit to another by simply moving the decimal point. However, you may run across more difficult problems and you may not be quite sure which way to move the decimal point.

Therefore, another method of converting from one unit to another makes use of what is called a conversion factor. This method of calculation is appropriately called the **Conversion Factor Method** of solving problems. (Other names include: factor-label method, unit analysis, or dimensional analysis.)

A **conversion factor** *is a ratio, obtained from an equality, which relates one unit to another.* For example, consider the following equality

$$1000 \text{ mm} = 1 \text{ m}$$

If you divide both sides of this equality by 1 m (multiplying or dividing both sides of a math equation by the same factor does not change the equality), you get

$$\frac{1000 \text{ mm}}{1 \text{ m}} = \frac{1 \text{ m}}{1 \text{ m}} = 1$$

The fraction $\frac{1000 \text{ mm}}{1 \text{ m}}$ equals 1 because 1000 mm and 1 m are equal.

This fraction is called a *conversion factor*. Therefore, if you multiply a measurement in meters by this conversion factor, the size of the measurement doesn't change because the fraction = 1; just the unit changes.

Units can be multiplied or divided the same way as variables or numbers in algebra. For example, in the following calculation, since the variable "a" is in both the top (numerator) and the bottom (denominator), "a" cancels. This leaves "b" as the only variable and $2 \times 12 = 24$ as the number:

$$2a \times \frac{12b}{a} = 24b$$

There is a general method of setting up a problem to be solved using the conversion factor method. You should ask yourself two questions:

a. What am I asked to find? (i.e., What are the required units of the final answer?)

b. What information am I given? (i.e., What are the given measurements and their units?)

c. What conversion factors can be used to change from what is given to what is wanted? (Start with the information you are given and multiply by the appropriate ratio so the units cancel out and the desired units remain.)

These questions will lead you to set up a problem as follows:

## Example 1:

How many mm are in 6 m?

A. Begin by writing the units that you want in the final answer.
$$6 \text{ m} = ?? \text{ mm}$$

B. Then write the given information and multiply by the appropriate conversion factor(s) to get the final answer.

$$\underline{\quad ? \quad} \text{ mm} = 6 \text{ m} \times \frac{1000 \text{ mm}}{1 \text{ m}} = 6000 \text{ mm (Actually } 6 \times 10^3 \text{ mm. Why?)}$$

$$\underbrace{6 \text{ m}}_{\substack{\text{Given} \\ \text{Info}}} \quad \underbrace{\frac{1000 \text{ mm}}{1 \text{ m}}}_{\substack{\text{Conversion} \\ \text{Factor}}} \quad \underbrace{6000 \text{ mm}}_{\substack{\text{Final} \\ \text{Answer}}}$$

C. Check that all the units that are not required are cancelled, and all units that are required are arranged properly to give the desired final answer.

The equality used earlier, 1000 mm = 1 m, also yields another conversion factor. If both sides of this equality are divided by 1000 mm, the result is:

$$\frac{1000 \text{ mm}}{1000 \text{ mm}} = \frac{1 \text{ m}}{1000 \text{ mm}} = 1$$

The fraction $\frac{1 \text{ m}}{1000 \text{ mm}}$ could also be used to convert a measurement in millimeters to meters.

## Example 2:

How many meters are there in 635 mm? Using the conversion factor method the problem would be solved as follows:

$$\underline{\phantom{?}\text{?}} \quad \text{mm} = 635 \text{ m̶m̶} \times \frac{1 \text{ m}}{1000 \text{ m̶m̶}} = 0.635 \text{ m}$$

Overall then, the *one* equality, 1000 mm = 1 m, yielded *two* conversion factors:

$$\frac{1000 \text{ mm}}{1 \text{ m}} \quad \text{and} \quad \frac{1 \text{ m}}{1000 \text{ mm}}$$

The conversion factor method of problem solving has a number of advantages:

A.  This same method can be used to solve more difficult problems that involve a number of calculation steps. In fact, it can be used to solve most chemistry problems involving measurements in general.

B.  By showing how the *units* multiply, divide and cancel, this method shows you *immediately* whether the problem has been solved properly. In other words, this method eliminates such questions as, "Do I multiply, or divide by 1000?"

Suppose in Example 1 you multiplied 6 m by the wrong conversion factor:

$$6 \text{ m} \times \frac{1 \text{ m}}{1000 \text{ mm}} = 0.0006 \frac{\text{m}^2}{\text{mm}}$$

Since we were looking for a final answer with "mm" units, the answer 0.0006 m²/mm is *definitely wrong!*

C.  This method can also be applied to problems in other fields, such as physics, which make use of measurements and units.

## Example 3:

What is the volume, in liters, of 36 mL?

*Solution A:* Using the metric table (FIGURE F5), the decimal point must be moved 3 digits to the left. 36 mL = 0.036 L

*Solution B:* From the metric definitions you know that 1 L = 1000 mL. Therefore,

$$\underline{\phantom{?}\text{?}} \quad \text{L} = 36 \text{ m̶L̶} \times \frac{1 \text{ L}}{1000 \text{ m̶L̶}} = 0.036 \text{ L}$$

## Example 4:

How many centimeters are there in 0.30 m?

*Solution A:* Using the metric table (FIGURE F5), the decimal point must be moved 2 digits to the right. 0.30 m = 30 cm

*Solution B:* From metric definitions, you know that 100 cm = 1 m. Therefore,

$$\underline{\phantom{?}\text{?}} \quad \text{cm} = 0.30 \text{ m̶} \times \frac{100 \text{ cm}}{1 \text{ m̶}} = 30 \text{ cm}$$

## Example 5:

How many g/mL are there in 8625 mg/L?

*Solution A:* This problem is a bit more complicated because it requires *two* conversions. First, convert 8625 mg to g by moving the decimal to the left 3 places. Second, convert 1 L to mL by moving the decimal to the right 3 places. Last, divide the two conversions as follows:

$$\underline{\quad ? \quad} \frac{g}{mL} = \frac{8.625\ g}{1000\ mL} = 0.008\ 625\ \frac{g}{mL}$$

*Solution B:* Problems involving multiple conversions are best solved by the conversion factor method:

(1) Convert mg/L to g/L:  $\underline{\quad ? \quad} \dfrac{g}{L} = \dfrac{8625\ \cancel{mg}}{1\ L} \times \dfrac{1\ g}{1000\ \cancel{mg}} = 8.625$

Since g/L is *not* the final unit required, there must be at least one more step.

(2) Convert g/L to g/mL:  $\dfrac{8.625\ g}{1\ \cancel{L}} \times \dfrac{1\ \cancel{L}}{1000\ mL} = 0.008\ 625\ \dfrac{g}{mL}$

Notice that the two conversion factors used were the ones necessary in order that the units that were *not* wanted would cancel, and the units that *were* wanted appeared in their proper place in the answer.

This problem could have been set up *all in one line* as follows:

$$\underline{\quad ? \quad} \frac{g}{mL} = \frac{8625\ \cancel{mg}}{\cancel{L}} \times \frac{1\ g}{1000\ \cancel{mg}} \times \frac{1\ \cancel{L}}{1000\ mL} = 0.008\ 625\ \frac{g}{mL}$$

This makes the mathematics very easy because you can now enter **all the numbers and operations into your calculator at once**. This eliminates having to get separate answers after each step and prevents additional error due to rounding each time.

# F.12 Exercises   The Conversion Factor Method

Do the following exercises using the conversion factor method:

1. How many centimeters are in 100 m?

2. How many grams are in 56 mg?

3. How many milliliters are there in 6.23 L?

4. How many m/min are there in 72 km/h?

# F.13 Addition and Subtraction Calculations

Since all measurements involve some uncertainty, the calculated answers using measured values must show the same uncertainty. There are many rules for determining the number of significant digits in an answer. The addition and subtraction rule will be used throughout the textbook.

## The Addition and Subtraction Rule:

1. *Add or subtract as usual.*
2. *Look at the number of decimal places in each measurement.*
3. *Round off the final answer to the smallest number of decimal places contained in the question.*

   *The answer cannot be more precise than the least precise measurement.*

## Examples:

|  |  |  |  |
|---|---|---|---|
| 5.6 g | 1 decimal place (least precise measurement) | 2.01 g | The digits in italics |
| 14.72 g | 2 decimal places | 32.1 g | are uncertain. |
| + 0.53 g | 2 decimal places | + 74.0 g | |
| 20.85 g | = 20.9 g (greatest precision allowed) | 108.11 g | = 108.1 g |
| | final answer has 1 decimal place | | |

A *measured value* always yields those digits that are *certain plus one uncertain digit*. A *calculated value* should also contain *only one uncertain digit*.

# F.14 Exercises  Addition and Subtraction Calculations

Add or subtract the following values as required. Express the answers to the correct number of significant digits. For all measured values, the last digit is uncertain. The different precision could result from either different measuring instruments or from being calculated from other data.

*Note: When more than one size of unit is involved, convert all of the values to the largest unit used and then add or subtract.*

1. Add

    8.42 g
    3.6 g
+ 10.04 g

2. Add

760   km
+ 42.6 km

3. Add

  6.54 mL
10.1  mL
+ 4.63 mL

4. Add

    4.00 m
  52.6 cm
+ 406.5 mm

5. Subtract

129   g
− 2.49 g

6. Subtract

14.56 mL
− 4.2  mL

7. Add

942   m
+ 1.2 km

8. Add

  9.99 mol
+ 51.9  mol

9. Add

852  mg
  1.76 g
+ 10.9 cg

## F.15 Multiplication and Division Calculations

The following rules involving multiplication and division will be used throughout the textbook.

### The Multiplication and Division Rules:

1.  a.  *Multiply or divide as usual.*
    b.  *Round off the answer to the smallest number of significant figures found in the question.*

$$
\begin{array}{ll}
13.52 \text{ g/mol} & \text{(4 significant digits; last one is uncertain)} \\
\times\ 2.1 \text{ mol} & \text{(2 significant digits; last one is uncertain)} \\
\hline
1.352 & \text{(An uncertain digit multiplied by a certain digit is} \\
27.04 & \text{uncertain and vice versa} \\
\hline
28.392 \text{ g} & \text{(1 certain + 1 uncertain digit = 1 or 2 uncertain digits)}
\end{array}
$$

The answer is 28 g. (Rounded to 2 significant digits)

2.  *When multiplying or dividing an uncertain value by an **exact number**, the answer has the same precision (number of decimal places) as the measured value with uncertainty.*

$$
5.2 \text{ mol} \ \times \ \frac{3}{1} = 15.6 \text{ mol}
$$

$$
\begin{pmatrix} \text{measured} \\ \text{value} \end{pmatrix} \qquad \begin{pmatrix} \text{exact} \\ \text{ratio} \end{pmatrix}
$$

3.  *When multiplying or dividing a measured value in order to use a different SI prefix, the original significant digits are retained identically.*

$$
0.030 \text{ g} \times \frac{1000 \text{ mg}}{1 \text{ g}} = 30 \text{ mg}
$$

$$
\begin{pmatrix} \text{measured} \\ \text{value} \end{pmatrix} \qquad \begin{pmatrix} \text{exact} \\ \text{ratio} \end{pmatrix}
$$

## F.16 Exercises Multiplication and Division Calculations

Write the number of significant digits for the following calculations:

| Calculation | # of Significant Digits |
|---|---|
| 1.  $5.2 \text{ mol} \times 72.0 \ \frac{g}{mol}$ | |
| 2.  $6 \times 40.1 \ \frac{g}{mol}$ | |
| 3.  $2 \text{ mL} \times 1.01 \ \frac{g}{mL}$ | |
| 4.  $10 \times 14.0 \ \frac{g}{mol}$ | |
| 5.  $4123 \text{ cm} \div \frac{100 \text{ cm}}{m}$ | |
| 6.  $0.240 \text{ g} \div 100.1 \ \frac{g}{mol}$ | |

Multiply or divide the following values and units as required. Write the final answer to include both the correct number of significant digits and the correct units.

7.  $4.2 \text{ mol} \times 4.00 \dfrac{g}{\text{mol}} =$ _____

8.  $\dfrac{8.0 \text{ g}}{4.0 \text{ g/mol}} =$ _____  or  $\left( 8.0 \text{ g} \times \dfrac{1 \text{ mol}}{4.0 \text{ g}} =$ _____ $\right)$

9.  $31.2 \text{ mL} \times \dfrac{1 \text{ L}}{1000 \text{ mL}} =$ _____

10. $\dfrac{19.3 \text{ g}}{\text{cm}^3} \times 4.5 \text{ cm}^3 =$ _____

11. $\dfrac{91.2 \text{ g}}{4.2 \text{ g/doz.}} =$ _____  or  $\left( 91.2 \text{ kg} \times \dfrac{1 \text{ doz.}}{4.2 \text{ g}} =$ _____ $\right)$

12. $2.046 \text{ t} \times \dfrac{1000 \text{ kg}}{1 \text{ t}} =$ _____

13. $\dfrac{46.2 \text{ kg}}{2.310 \text{ kg/gross}} =$ _____  or  $\left( 46.2 \text{ kg} \times \dfrac{1 \text{ gross}}{2.310 \text{ kg}} =$ _____ $\right)$

14. $\dfrac{2.44 \text{ g}}{1.14 \text{ g/mL}} =$ _____  or  $\left( 2.44 \text{ g} \times \dfrac{1 \text{ mL}}{1.14 \text{ g}} =$ _____ $\right)$

15. $\dfrac{457.7 \text{ g}}{2.01 \text{ mol}} =$ _____

16. Convert $100 \dfrac{\text{km}}{\text{h}}$ into $\dfrac{\text{m}}{\text{s}}$. Use the Conversion Factor Method.

# F.17 Density

Density is one of many characteristic properties that can be used to identify a substance. Density is a measure of how much matter is packed into a certain space.

$$\text{density} = \frac{\text{amount of matter}}{\text{volume it occupies}} \text{ or } d = \frac{\text{mass}}{\text{volume}} = \frac{m}{v}$$

$$\text{or } m = vd \text{ or } v = \frac{m}{d}$$

Since both mass and volume must be measured, the calculation of density involves rounding off the final answer and using significant digits and units.

The densities of the elements are found in the Periodic Table.

$$d_{H_2O(l), \, 4 \, °C} = 1.00 \frac{g}{\text{cm}^3}$$

$$1 \text{ cm}^3 = 1 \text{ mL}$$

**Water displacement** is a method of finding the volume of a solid, non-soluble object. When the object is placed in water, the water level rises an amount equal to the volume of that object. (This is also known as Archimedes' Principle.)

When doing density problems, be sure to show all work by:

  a. writing the equation you are using,
  b. "plugging" the correct numbers into the equation, and
  c. rounding off the final answer to the correct number of significant digits.

Example:

A piece of lead has a mass of 22.7 g. It occupies a volume of 2.00 cm³. What is the density of lead?

$$d = \frac{m}{v} = \frac{22.7 \text{ g}}{2.00 \text{ cm}^3} = 11.35 \frac{g}{cm^3} = 11.4 \frac{g}{cm^3} \text{ (correctly rounded)}$$

# F.18 <u>Exercises</u> Density

Perform the following density problems:

1. A small piece of titanium measures 4.53 cm³. What is the mass of this titanium?

2. A sample of zinc has a mass of 22.85 g. What volume does it occupy?

3. A sample of copper having a mass of 44.5 g occupies a volume of 5.00 cm³. What is the density of the copper?

4. A sample of iron having a mass of 393.0 g has what volume?

5. What is the mass of 53.9 mL of water?

6. A piece of metal was measured to be 14.99 g. It is placed in a graduated cylinder containing 12.3 mL of water. The water level rises to 13.6 mL. What is the density of the metal?

7. A rectangular slab of a metal measures 2.3 cm wide, 5.8 cm long, and 1.6 cm high. Its mass is 56.8 g.
   a. What is the density of the metal?

   b. If we assume the metal is a pure element, what could it possibly be?

# F.19 Determining the Density of Several Substances

**Purpose:**
- ✔ To gain practice in developing an experimental procedure.
- ✔ To use equations learned in mathematics to solve density problems.
- ✔ To identify substances based on density.
- ✔ To use the method of water displacement to find the volume of an object.

**Materials:**
- Problem #1: 1 new piece of chalk; metric ruler; balance
- Problem #2: 2 unknown liquids; 2 10-mL graduated cylinders; balance
- Problem #3: small piece of paraffin wax; 1 100-mL graduated cylinder; balance; probe to submerge wax

**Lab Challenges:**

*Problem #1:* Determine the density of a piece of chalk provided to you by your teacher. Do **not** get the chalk wet.

*Problem #2:* Determine the density of two unknown liquids and *identify them* by comparing their density with the list below.

| Substance | Density (g/mL at 20°C) |
|---|---|
| acetone | 0.792 |
| benzene | 0.899 |
| ethanol | 0.791 |
| methanol | 0.792 |
| glycerol | 1.260 |
| ethylene glycol | 1.109 |
| water | 0.998 |
| carbon tetrachloride | 1.595 |
| hexane | 0.660 |
| TTE | 1.564 |

*Problem #3:* Determine the density of a block of paraffin provided to you by your teacher.

**Prelab Exercises:**

1. Describe the basic techniques you will use to solve each of the three problems described.

_____

_____

_____

2. Devise three separate procedures, in picture format, to solve each problem.

3. Paraffin (wax) floats in water.

a. How will you have to modify your procedure to take the flotation into account?

_____

_____

_____

b. Knowing that the less dense substance floats on the more dense substance, what would be a quick check to see whether your calculated density for paraffin is reasonable?

_____

_____

4. Now get instructor approval on your procedures and complete the lab.

**Lab Safety:**
Assume the liquids that are tested in Problem #2 are toxic. Do not purposely inhale the fumes. Wear chemical splash goggles and an apron when doing this lab.

**Procedure:**
1. Carry out your approved procedures to answer each problem.

2. Record your observations for each of the problems. This includes colors, odors, texture, etc. Be sure to include the identification code of the unknown liquids as given on the bottle.

3. Include all data in chart/table form so the information is easy to locate and read. Have a separate chart for each problem section.

Remember, all measurements have to be made to the limit of the measuring instrument! The balance measures to two decimal places; the ruler to 0.01 cm; the 10-mL graduated cylinder to 0.1 mL; the 100-mL graduated cylinder to 0.5 mL. Include the correct number of significant digits when recording the measurement. For example, if you decide that something is 22 cm exactly, then be sure to write 22.00 cm in your data chart.

**Calculations:**
1. a. Calculate the density of the chalk.

   b. Calculate the density of the two unknown liquids. Be sure to include the identification code shown on the bottle.

   c. Calculate the density of the paraffin wax.

Show all equations and calculations. Round off your answers to the correct number of significant digits.

**Post-lab Questions:**
1. The diameter of a single piece of chalk is very difficult to determine. Assuming that each piece of chalk is exactly the same, why would you get a more accurate measurement by determining the average diameter of ten pieces of chalk lying side-to-side? (Assume that the number of significant digits is related to the accuracy of the measurement.)

2. Suppose the density of the liquid was 0.789 g/mL. Why is it not possible to determine which liquid it is from density alone?

3. Why is it necessary to completely submerge the paraffin before determining its density?

4. Tell how each of the following errors would affect the density.

   a. small chips in the chalk

b. graduated cylinder not dry before adding
   unknown liquid

_____

_____

_____

c. using a probe to submerge the paraffin wax

_____

_____

_____

_____

**Conclusions:**
• Discuss at least three things you learned. Include
  something on the statement given in the
  Purpose.

_____

_____

_____

_____

• Discuss four errors that actually occurred or are
  possible in the procedure and how each error
  would affect the results.

_____

_____

_____

_____

_____

• Include comments concerning any difficulties you
  encountered and what you did to solve each
  problem. What did you like/dislike about this lab?

_____

_____

_____

_____

_____

_____

## F.20 The Mole

Since atoms, molecules and ions are extremely small particles, it is not practical to talk about 1, 2 or 3 of these particles reacting or being produced in a chemical reaction. In fact it may not be possible to see evidence of 1, 2 or 3 **million** of these particles reacting or being produced in a chemical reaction! A practical number of particles to use is $6.02 \times 10^{23}$. This is because it takes $6.02 \times 10^{23}$ atoms to produce the atomic mass of an element when that mass is expressed in grams.

Just as 2 objects can be a couple, 12 items are called a dozen, and 144 objects are a gross, *$6.02 \times 10^{23}$ items* are called a **mole**. (The SI symbol for mole is **mol**.)

• One mole of Mg atoms is $6.02 \times 10^{23}$ Mg atoms.
• One mole of $O_2$ molecules is $6.02 \times 10^{23}$ $O_2$ molecules.
• One mole of MgO formula units is $6.02 \times 10^{23}$ MgO formula units.

### Reading Balanced Equations

$$2\ Mg_{(s)} + O_{2(g)} \longrightarrow 2\ MgO_{(s)} \quad \textit{may be read as:}$$

2 Mg atoms + 1 $O_2$ molecule produce 2 MgO formula units

*or* 2 dozen Mg atoms + 1 dozen $O_2$ molecules produce 2 dozen MgO formula units

*or* $12.04 \times 10^{23}$ Mg atoms + $6.02 \times 10^{23}$ $O_2$ molecules produce $12.04 \times 10^{23}$ MgO formula units

*or* 2 mol Mg atoms + 1 mol $O_2$ molecules produce 2 mol MgO formula units

*or merely:* Two moles of magnesium react with one mole of oxygen to produce two moles of magnesium oxide.

## Other Examples:

$$Cu_{(s)} + 2\ AgNO_{3(aq)} \longrightarrow 2\ Ag_{(s)} + Cu(NO_3)_{2(aq)}$$

One mole of copper reacts with two moles of silver nitrate to produce two moles of silver and one mole of copper(II) nitrate.

$$2\ Na_3PO_{4(aq)} + 3\ Ba(OH)_{2(aq)} \longrightarrow 6\ NaOH_{(aq)} + Ba_3(PO_4)_{2(s)}$$

Two moles of sodium phosphate plus three moles of barium hydroxide yields six moles of sodium hydroxide plus one mole of barium phosphate.

*Note:* There are three reasons for introducing the mole concept here:

1. It is impractical for 1, 2 or 3 atoms, molecules or formula units to react.

2. A mole of atoms, molecules or formula units can be easily measured—a single atom, molecule or formula unit cannot.

3. The term mole eliminates the need to say atoms, molecules or formula units each time a balanced equation is read.

# F.21 The Mole and Molar Mass

As discussed, the mole is a convenient number of atoms, ions or molecules to work with in the laboratory. This convenient number, $6.02 \times 10^{23}$ (called **Avogadro's Number** in honor of Amedeo Avogadro who studied the number of molecules in a specific volume of gas), also has significance in terms of the atomic mass of elements. The mole is defined as the number of atoms in exactly 12.00000 g of the carbon-12 isotope. This particular isotope is the most common isotope of carbon—with 6 protons and 6 neutrons.

### The Green Pea Analogy

If you select a hundred ($10^2$) average-sized peas, you would find that they occupy roughly a volume of 20 $cm^3$. A million ($10^6$) peas are just enough to fill an ordinary household refrigerator and a billion ($10^9$) peas will fill a three-bedroom house from cellar to attic. A trillion ($10^{12}$) peas will fill a thousand houses, the number you might find in a medium-sized town. A quadrillion ($10^{15}$) peas will fill all the buildings in a larger city such as Portland, OR, or Toronto, ON.

Obviously you will run out of buildings fairly soon. Let us try a larger measure, for instance the state of Texas. Suppose that there is a blizzard over Texas, but instead of regular snow, it snowed peas. Texas is covered with a blanket of peas about one meter deep all the way from Louisiana out to New Mexico and all the way from Mexico to Oklahoma. This blanket of peas drifts over roads and banks up against the sides of houses, and covers all the fields and forests. Think of flying across the state with the blanket of peas extending out as far as you can see. This gives you an idea of our next number. There will be a blanket of about a quintillion ($10^{18}$) peas. Imagine that this blizzard of peas falls over all the continents on the globe — Africa, North and South America, Europe, Australia and Asia. All of the continents are covered with peas one meter deep. This global blanket will contain sextillion ($10^{21}$) peas. Then imagine that the oceans are frozen over and the blanket of peas covers the entire land and sea area of Earth.

Go out among the neighboring stars and collect 250 planets the size of Earth and cover each of these with a blanket of peas one meter deep. Then you have a mole of peas.

Furthermore, go out into the farthest reaches of the Milky Way, and collect 417 000 planets, each the size of the Earth. Cover each one with a blanket of peas one meter deep. You now have a cotillion ($10^{27}$) — a number corresponding to the number of atoms in your body.

## Molar Mass

One mole is defined as the number of atoms of carbon-12 in exactly twelve grams. The mass of one mole of all other elements is determined relative to the mass of one mole of carbon-12. The average mass of one mole of atoms of an element is given to the nearest hundredth of a gram on the *Periodic Table*. For example, the **molar mass** of chlorine atoms (*mass of 6.02 x $10^{23}$ Cl atoms*) is 35.45 g/mol. This molar mass is an average value that takes into account that a sample of chlorine is composed of several naturally occurring isotopes of chlorine as was discussed in Unit B.

The molar mass of compounds may be determined by adding the molar masses of their component atomic elements. Examples of how to determine these molar masses (always in grams per mole, g/mol) will follow.

**Molar mass** is a general term, which may refer to *the mass of one mole of atoms, molecules, formula units, etc.* In order to avoid confusion, the term **atomic molar mass** should be used to refer to *the mass of one mole of atoms* (versus molecules or formula units).

Example Calculation:

Here we determine the molar mass of $Ca(HCO_3)_2$ by summing the masses of its component parts.

$$
\begin{array}{llll}
1\ Ca & = 1 \times 40.08 & = & 40.08 \\
2\ H & = 2 \times 1.01 & = & 2.02 \\
2\ C & = 2 \times 12.01 & = & 24.02 \\
+\ \ 6\ O & = 6 \times 16.00 & = & 96.00 \\
\hline
& & & 162.12\ \text{g/mol}
\end{array}
$$

# F.22 <u>Exercises</u> Molar Mass Calculations

Determine the molar mass of each of the following substances. Show all work as in the example above. (*Reminder: A number with two decimal places multiplied by an exact number has two decimal places in the answer.*)

**Notes:**

1. The rule for multiplication and division and the rule for addition and subtraction are followed in this example and throughout the textbook. These rules are used in the key for answers and on exams. If these rules are followed, everyone can expect to get the same answers.

2. For hydrates, memorizing the molar mass of water (18.02 g/mol) makes it easier to do the calculations.

| | Chemical Formula | Chemical Name | Calculation of Molar Mass | Common Name or Use |
|---|---|---|---|---|
| 1. | $FeSO_4$ | | | iron pills |
| 2. | | magnesium sulfate | | Epsom salts |
| 3. | | sodium carbonate decahydrate | (List water of hydration as $10\,H_2O = 10 \times 18.02 = 180.20$) | washing soda |
| 4. | $MgSiO_3$ | | | asbestos |
| 5. | | sodium hypochlorite | | laundry bleach |
| 6. | $Al(OH)_3$ | | | water clarifier |
| 7. | | sodium chloride | | table salt |
| 8. | | calcium carbonate | | limestone |
| 9. | | dinitrogen oxide | | anesthetic (laughing gas) |
| 10. | $Na_2S_2O_3 \cdot 5\,H_2O$ | | | photographic hypo |
| 11. | $NH_4H_2PO_4$ | | | fertilizer |

# F.23 Percent Composition

It has been known for centuries that the elements in a compound always combine in a constant proportion by mass. For example, 1 g of hydrogen combines with 8 g of oxygen to produce 9 g of water. This is called the Law of Definite Proportions or the Law of Definite Composition. John Dalton first proposed that all matter is made up of atoms partly based on the idea that only whole particles (atoms) could participate in such a way as to produce this constant mass ratio.

One common way to express this proportion is called **percent composition** and is calculated as follows:

$$\text{Percent by mass of element } X = \frac{\text{mass of element } X}{\text{total mass of sample}} \times 100$$

## Quantitative Analysis

One way to determine the percent composition of a compound is by an experimental determination of the elements in a given sample of a compound.

### Example:

0.250 g of magnesium are burned under carefully controlled conditions to produce 0.415 g of magnesium oxide. Calculate the percent composition of a) magnesium, and b) oxygen in this compound.

*Solution:*

a. Percent magnesium by mass =

$$\frac{0.250 \text{ g magnesium}}{0.415 \text{ g magnesium oxide}} \times 100 = 60.2\% \text{ Mg}$$

b. If 0.250 g magnesium react with oxygen to produce 0.415 g magnesium oxide, then the mass of oxygen must be

$$0.415 \text{ g} - 0.250 \text{ g} = 0.165 \text{ g oxygen}$$

As a check to be sure the calculations were done correctly, add the percentages to see if they add up to 100%:

$$60.2\% \text{ magnesium} + 39.8\% \text{ oxygen} = 100.0\%$$

## Using Molar Mass Calculations

Another way to determine the percent composition is to use the element masses from the calculation of the molar mass for the compound.

### Example:

What is the percent by mass of each of the elements in the compound magnesium sulfate (Epsom salts), $MgSO_4$?

*Solution:*

a. First calculate the molar mass of $MgSO_4$.

$$1 \text{ Mg} = 1 \times 24.31 = 24.31 \text{ g}$$
$$1 \text{ S} = 1 \times 32.07 = 32.07 \text{ g}$$
$$\underline{4 \text{ O} = 4 \times 16.00 = 64.00 \text{ g}}$$
$$MgSO_4 \qquad\qquad = 120.38 \text{ g/mol}$$

b. Percent magnesium by mass = $\dfrac{24.31 \text{ g Mg}}{120.38 \text{ g MgSO}_4} \times 100 = 20.19\% \text{ Mg}$

c. Percent sulfur by mass = $\dfrac{32.07 \text{ g S}}{120.38 \text{ g MgSO}_4} \times 100 = 26.64\% \text{ S}$

d. Percent oxygen by mass = $\dfrac{64.00 \text{ g O}}{120.38 \text{ g MgSO}_4} \times 100 = 53.16\% \text{ O}$

e. Check: $20.19\% + 26.64\% + 53.16\% = 99.99\%$

*(This total is nearly 100% and is close enough considering small deviations due to rounding.)*

# F.24 <u>Exercises</u>   Percent Composition

1. If 2.50 g of iron react with an excess of chlorine, 4.76 g of an iron chloride compound is formed.

   a.  What is the percent by mass of iron in the compound?

   b.  What is the percent by mass of chlorine in the compound?

2. Calculate the percent composition of carbon in sucrose, $C_{12}H_{22}O_{11}$.

3. Calculate the percent composition of N in ammonia, $NH_3$.

## Challenge Question:

4. Combustion analysis of 0.500 g of an unknown hydrocarbon yielded 1.541 g of $CO_2$ and 0.710 g $H_2O$.

   a. What is the percent by mass of carbon in the compound?

   b. What is the percent by mass of hydrogen in the compound?

# F.25 The Percent of Copper and Zinc in a Penny

**Purpose:**

✔ To determine the percent of copper and zinc in a post-1982 penny.

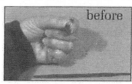

**Materials:**
- balance
- hotplate
- pair of tweezers or crucible tongs
- penny dated after 1982
- triangular file
- 20 mL acetone (optional)
- 20 mL 6.0 mol/L HCl
- 2 50-mL beakers

**Background Information:**

Recall from the B.9 Lab that pennies made after 1982 are made of solid zinc with a thin coating of copper. Hydrochloric acid reacts quite vigorously with zinc, but does not react with copper. If the penny is filed slightly in several places along its edge, thus exposing the zinc inside, the penny can be placed in the hydrochloric acid solution, removing the zinc and leaving the thin copper shell behind.

**Lab Safety:**
- Wear goggles and an apron
  **CAUTION:** 6.0 mol/L HCl is extremely corrosive. Wash your hands before leaving the lab area.

**Procedure:**

1. Obtain a penny dated after 1982.

2. Polish the penny slightly with steel wool.

3. Determine the mass of the penny.

4. Use the file to expose the zinc in four places around the edge of the penny.

5. Carefully place the penny in a beaker containing 20 mL of 6.0 mol/L HCl and let sit overnight.

6. By the next day, the "penny" should be floating. If it is not, it may be necessary to use a stirring rod to break up the "penny" a bit and expose more of the zinc inside. In that case it may be necessary to wait another day.

7. Use the tweezers to remove the "penny" from the acid and place the "penny" in distilled water to wash off the acid.

8. Remove the "penny" from the distilled water and wash it in the beaker of acetone. (The acetone will help speed the drying process.)

9. Place the "penny" on the hotplate for just a moment to allow it to dry.

10. Determine the mass of the dried "penny."

11. Record your data and observations below.

**Data and Observations:**

Data:

Mass of original penny: _____

Mass of penny "shell": _____

Observations:

**Calculations:**

1. Determine the percent copper in the original penny. Show all needed equations. Include proper significant digits.

2. Compare your results to the accepted percent copper in a penny. (See B.9 Lab – Background Information for the accepted percent copper in a penny dated after 1982)

_____

_____

_____

# F.26 What's the Count?

**Purpose:**

✔ To learn about counting a large number of objects by finding their mass.

**Materials:**
- dried peas or beans
- rice
- balance

**Procedure:**

Determine the mass of 20 dried peas. Then calculate the average mass of 1 pea. Next, calculate the mass of 100 peas. Mass out a sample you think should contain 100 peas. Don't count yet! Calculate the mass of 20 rice grains and then one rice grain. With this information, calculate the mass of 100 grains. Mass out a sample of rice you think would contain 100 grains. No counting!

mass of 20 peas = _____

mass of 1 pea = _____

mass of 100 peas = _____

mass of 20 rice grains = _____

mass of 1 rice grain = _____

mass of 100 rice grains = _____

You now have two samples—a sample of peas that you hope contains 100 peas and a sample of rice that should contain 100 rice grains. How close does the count for each sample come to 100? How does it compare with the results that other students in your class have reported?

Let's suppose you were asked to obtain 1000 peas or 1000 grains of rice. Counting all the peas and all the rice would get to be a real bore. It's clear that *massing* out the appropriate amount would be much faster (*and probably just as accurate as trying to count that many objects*).

Write clear directions for "counting" 1000 peas or 1000 grains of rice by massing appropriate amounts. Then calculate the mass of 2000 dried peas and 12 000 grains of rice.

# F.27 Calculations Involving Mass and Moles

When chemicals react, particles in the form of atoms, ions and molecules combine to produce new substances. As you know, these particles are too small to consider only a few of each. Instead, we refer to *moles* of particles involved in a chemical reaction. Since atoms are so small, they are impossible to count directly. So chemists use the molar mass of the substance to count the moles of particles *indirectly!* This section gives practice in using the molar mass as a type of conversion factor to do calculations involving moles.

## Part A: Mass to Moles Calculations

The number of identical things contained in a sample may be determined from the mass of the sample. For example, the number of dozens of beans in a sample of beans can be determined by:

$$\text{number of dozen beans} = \frac{\text{mass}}{\text{mass of one dozen beans}}$$

The number of moles of molecules or formula units in a sample can be determined by:

$$\text{number of moles} = \frac{\text{mass of sample}}{\text{mass of one mole of particles (molar mass)}}$$

or if n = number of moles, m = mass and M = molar mass then

$$n = \frac{m}{M}$$

Or these calculations may be done using the molar mass as a type of conversion factor instead:

$$\underbrace{\frac{?\ \cancel{g}}{}}_{\substack{\text{Given}\\\text{number}\\\text{of grams}}} \times \underbrace{\frac{1\ \text{mol}}{x\ \cancel{g}}}_{\substack{\text{Calculated}\\\text{molar}\\\text{mass}}} = \underbrace{\#\ \text{mol}}_{\substack{\text{Calculated}\\\text{number}\\\text{of moles}}}$$

## Example:

How many moles of sodium chloride, NaCl, are in 1000. g of pure table salt?

| Molar Mass Calculation | Solving Process |
|---|---|
| 1 Na = 1×22.99 = 22.99<br>1 Cl = 1×35.45 = 35.45<br>              = 58.44 g/mol | *Equation Method*<br>$n_{NaCl} = \dfrac{m}{M} = \dfrac{1000.\ g}{58.44\ g/mol} = 17.11\ mol\ NaCl$<br><br>*Factor-Label Method*<br>$1000.\cancel{g}\ NaCl \times \dfrac{1\ mol\ NaCl}{58.44\ \cancel{g}\ NaCl} = 17.11\ mol\ NaCl$ |

# F.28 Exercises  Mass to Moles Calculations

Determine the number of moles in 1000 g (1.000 kg) of each of the following. Show all work exactly as in the example. Use correct SI symbols and significant digits.

| | Amount of Substance (common name) | Chemical Name | Chemical Formula | Molar Mass | Calculation of Moles |
|---|---|---|---|---|---|
| 1. | 1000. g (Baking Soda) | | $NaHCO_3$ | | |
| 2. | 1000. g (Washing Soda) | sodium carbonate | | | |
| 3. | 1000. g (Epsom Salts) | | $MgSO_4 \cdot 7\ H_2O$ | | |
| 4. | 1000. g (TSP Cleaner) | sodium phosphate | | | |
| 5. | 1000. g (Contents in Fire Extinguisher) | carbon dioxide | | | |
| 6. | 1000. mL (Distilled Water) *(How will you handle the mL?)* | water | | | |

7. The container with the greatest number of moles in 1000 g of compound is _____.

## Part B: Moles-to-Mass Calculations

In order to determine the mass of a number of identical things, multiply the number of things by the mass of one thing.

|    | mass | = number of things x mass of one thing |
|----|------|----------------------------------------|
| or | mass | = number of dozens x mass of one dozen |
| or | mass | = number of moles x molar mass |
| or | if m | = mass, n = number of moles, and M = molar mass, then |
|    | m | = nM |

## Example:

How many grams of sodium chloride, NaCl, are in 0.21 mol of pure table salt?

| Molar Mass Calculation | Solving Process |
|------------------------|-----------------|
| 1 Na = 1×22.99 = 22.99<br>1 Cl = 1×35.45 = 35.45<br>$\quad\quad\quad\quad$ = 58.44 g/mol | *Equation Method*<br><br>$m_{NaCl}$ = n M = 0.21 mol × 58.44 g/mol = 12 g NaCl<br><br>*Factor-Label Method*<br><br>0.21 mol NaCl × $\dfrac{58.44 \text{ g NaCl}}{1 \text{ mol NaCl}}$ =12 g NaCl |

# F.29 Exercises  Moles to Mass Calculations

Follow the example above to show all work and calculate the mass of each sample. Use correct significant digits and SI symbols.

|    | Amount of Substance (common name) | Chemical Name | Chemical Formula | Molar Mass | Calculation of Mass |
|----|-----------------------------------|---------------|------------------|------------|---------------------|
| 1. | 0.100 mol<br>(cream of tartar) | potassium hydrogen tartrate | $KHC_4H_4O_6$ | | |
| 2. | 1.2 mol<br>(detergent filler) | | $Na_2SO_4 \cdot 10H_2O$ | | |
| 3. | 0.15 mol | white phosphorus | | | |
| 4. | 55.56 mol | water | | | |
| 5. | 0.025 mol<br>(formerly used as a tooth decay preventative) | tin (II) flouride | | | |
| 6. | 0.400 mol<br>(gypsum) | | $CaSO_4 \cdot 2H_2O$ | | |

# F.30 Moles of Chalk on a Chalkboard

**Purpose:**

✔ To use the concept of moles in a lab setting.

✔ To practice solving problems using chemical mathematics.

**Materials:**
- chalk
- chalkboard
- balance

**Lab Safety:**

No safety precautions are required in this lab.

**Lab Challenges:**

*Problem #1:* Determine the number of moles of calcium carbonate that are in a piece of chalk if we assume the chalk is pure calcium carbonate.

a. Explain, without writing out a full procedure, how you will solve this problem.

_____

_____

_____

_____

b. Obtain a piece of chalk from the instructor. Perform this "experiment." Record your Observations/Data below. Label the data.

c. Complete the necessary calculation below. Show all needed equations. Incude proper significant digits.

*Problem #2:* After writing your result to Problem #1 on the chalkboard, determine the number of moles of calcium carbonate written on the board.

a. Explain, without a full procedure, how you will solve this problem.

_____

_____

_____

b. When solving Problem #2, write the names of the people in your group as well as your answer to calculation #1. (The main idea here is to deposit a significant amount of chalk on the board. Have fun!)

Include all data in chart/table form so the information is easy to locate.

c. Complete the necessary calculations below. Show all equations and calculations. Round off your answers to the correct number of significant digits.

*Problem #3 (Optional):* Calculate the number of calcium ions left on the board.

*Hint #1:* How many moles of calcium ions are produced for each mole of calcium carbonate present? Look at the formula for calcium carbonate to help you decide.

*Hint #2:* 1 mol of anything = $6.02 \times 10^{23}$ things. 1 mol $Ca^{2+}$ = $6.02 \times 10^{23}$ $Ca^{2+}$ ions.

*Hint #3:* Calculate in this sequence: moles of $CaCO_3$ ⟶ moles of calcium ions ⟶ number of calcium ions.

**Questions:**

1. How would the following affect the calculations?

   a. The chalk was only 95% calcium carbonate.

   _____

   _____

   _____

b. Some of the chalk settled onto the tray rather than staying on the chalkboard.

_____

_____

_____

_____

_____

c. The original piece of chalk had already been used before you received it.

_____

_____

_____

_____

_____

# F.31 Mass-Mole-Volume-Density Problems

When doing problems involving mass, moles, volume and density, it is important to know all the interrelationships of all these quantities. The flowchart shows how each of these is connected and how to use either an equation or a conversion factor to change from one to another. Simply determine the given amount of substance found in the problem. Then apply the required equations or conversions to change the given amount into the desired amount of substance for the problem.

FIGURE F8 — Mass-Moles-Volume-Particles Flow Chart

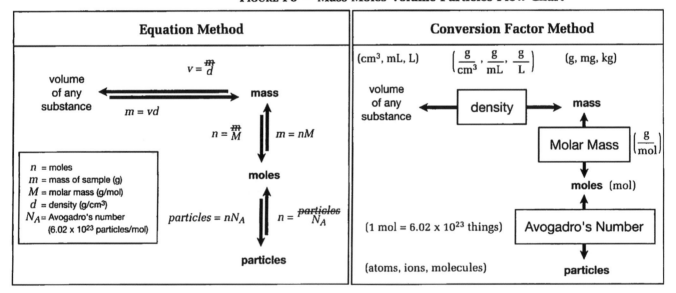

# F.32 <u>Exercises</u> Mass-Mole-Volume-Density Problems

Show all equations and setups for each problem. Be sure to round off each answer to the correct number of significant digits.

1. Which has a greater mass?

   a. A ball of lead with a diameter of 2.00 cm  ($V_{sphere} = \frac{4}{3} \pi r^3$).

   b. A cylinder of iron with a diameter of 3.00 cm and a height of 8.00 cm ($V_{cylinder} = \pi r^2 h$).

2. A student performed an experiment where a strip of copper was placed in an aqueous solution of silver nitrate. The following data were obtained:

   initial mass of copper  = 2.97 g
   final mass of copper    = 1.54 g

   How many moles of copper reacted?

3. A student obtained the following data from a reaction between a zinc strip and a solution of copper(II) sulfate:

   beginning mass of zinc metal   = 16.58 g
   ending mass of zinc metal      = 14.84 g

   How many moles of zinc reacted?

4. What is the volume of 0.071 mol of nickel metal?

# Unit G
# Mathematics of Chemical Reactions

The Law of Conservation of Matter is a statement that says the total mass of a system remains constant during a chemical reaction. You learned earlier that a reaction is a result of atoms rearranging to form new combinations—new chemical substances. You have also learned that each substance has a specific molar mass. This allows chemists to predict how much of a reactant is needed or how much of a specific product will be formed—the topic of this unit.

## Exercises  The Law of Conservation of Mass

The Law of Conservation of Mass states that mass is conserved in a chemical reaction (i.e., the sum of the masses of the reactants equals the sum of the masses of the product.

Obtain answers for the following conservation of mass problems. Use the Periodic Table and the rule for addition and subtraction of significant digits to obtain the proper number of significant digits in the answer.

1. Lavoisier dehydrated gypsum by heating it

    $CaSO_4 \cdot 2H_2O(s) \rightarrow CaSO_4(s) + 2H_2O(g)$
    172.2 g      $\rightarrow$  _____ + _____

2. Lavoisier heated mercury in air. He then further heated the mercury calx which had formed. The mercury calx decomposed back into its elements.

    mercury + oxygen  $\rightarrow$  mercuric oxide  $\rightarrow$  mercury + oxygen
    201g + 32.0g    $\rightarrow$  _____  $\rightarrow$  _____ + _____

3. Lavoisier performed his chemical experiments such as the ones above in sealed vessels. When he burned phosphorus in air, he could possibly have obtained the following results.

    $P_4(s) + 5O_2(g) \rightarrow P_4O_{10}(s)$
    mass of phosphorus          124 g
    mass of phosphorus calx     284 g

    Lavoisier then broke his sealed vessel, air rushed in and the mass of the vessel plus phosphorus calx increased. Find the increase in mass of the vessel plus contents (assume air and oxygen have the same mass).

4. When Lavoisier burned a diamond, he could have obtained the following data.
    mass of diamond 2.1 g
    mass of vessel (full of air) 43.5 g
    What would be the mass of the sealed vessel after the reaction?

# G.1 Mathematics of Chemical Reactions

The technical term for the use of mathematics in balanced chemical equations is **stoichiometry**, from the Greek word *stoicheion* (meaning "element") and the English suffix *-metry* (meaning "to measure"). This unit will look at stoichiometry—*the prediction of how much of one substance will react or be produced in a chemical reaction relative to the amount of another substance in the reaction.* In this unit, the amount of substances may be expressed as number of moles (in moles) or mass (in grams). Gravimetric stoichiometry refers to stoichiometry involving the measurement of mass (*gravi-metric* means "to measure using gravity") as opposed to measurement of solution volume or gas volume. Solution stoichiometry and gas stoichiometry will be studied in later units.

### Stoichiometry is a Review

The study of gravimetric stoichiometry assumes knowledge of Unit B (formulas of elements and ions), Unit D (nomenclature), Unit E (writing balanced chemical equations and predicting products for chemical reactions) and Unit F (converting mass to number of moles and number of moles to mass). In many ways gravimetric stoichiometry will serve as a review of the earlier units of this course — refer back when necessary.

### Practical Importance of Stoichiometry

Everyday applications of stoichiometry are numerous; some of these applications are listed below:

1. The gasoline-to-air mixture in a car or motorcycle engine is regulated by the fuel injection system. Proper proportions of gasoline and air are necessary for maximum power and good gasoline mileage.

2. Since cooking food involves chemical reactions, every recipe suggests the proper proportion of chemicals to produce a complete reaction. For example, if there are not the proper proportions of baking soda and cream of tartar, some of one or the other will be in excess. An excess of one component (reactant) may adversely affect the end product. It may not taste good or could have a bad odor.

3. Antacid tablets may be harmful if taken in excess. Each antacid tablet contains a certain amount of chemical, which neutralizes stomach acid. If too many tablets are taken, too much stomach acid is destroyed, and proper digestion cannot occur.

# G.2 Mole-to-Mole Stoichiometry

In Unit E, chemical equations were balanced, and in Unit F you learned that the equations can be read in terms of moles. Consider, for example, the following equation for the formation of ammonia:

| Balanced Equation | $N_{2(g)}$ + 3 $H_{2(g)}$ → 2 $NH_{3(g)}$ |
|---|---|
| Interpretations | 1 mol $N_{2(g)}$ + 3 mol $H_{2(g)}$ → 2 mol $NH_{3(g)}$ |
| | 3.0 mol $N_{2(g)}$ + 9.0 mol $H_{2(g)}$ → 6.0 mol $NH_{3(g)}$ |
| | 0.296 mol $N_{2(g)}$ + 0.888 mol $H_{2(g)}$ → 0.592 mol $NH_{3(g)}$ |

The first two interpretations under the first equation are simple extensions of the balanced equation. The third interpretation illustrates the need for a planned problem-solving approach.

## Generalized Solving Method

*Step 1:* Write the balanced chemical equation.

*Step 2:* List the given amount under the appropriate substance in the equation. Put a question mark (?) with the necessary units under the substance you are looking for.

*Step 3:* Multiply the given amount by the mole ratio. If done correctly, the units of the given amount will cancel and the desired units will remain (conversion factor method).

$$? \text{ mol desired} = \# \text{ mol given} \times \frac{\text{coefficient of desired substance}}{\text{coefficient of given substance}}$$

(coefficients from balanced equation)

*Step 4:* Apply necessary rounding and significant digit rules to report the final answer.

## Example 1:

Henry Cavendish proved in 1781 that water was the only product resulting from the combustion of hydrogen. How many moles of hydrogen are required to react exactly with 4.13 mol of oxygen?

*First:* Write a balanced chemical equation for the reaction and list knowns and unknowns.

$$2 H_2(g) \quad + \quad O_2(g) \quad \rightarrow \quad 2 H_2O(g)$$
$$? \text{ mol} \qquad 4.13 \text{ mol}$$

*Next:* Use the mole ratio from the balanced equation to calculate the number of moles of the required substance.

$$n_{H_2} = n_{O_2} \times \text{mole ratio}$$

The coefficients in the balanced equation indicate that 2 mol of $H_2$ are involved for every 1 mol of $O_2$ in this reaction.

Since there is more hydrogen expressed in the equation than oxygen, the number of moles of hydrogen involved must be greater than the number of moles of oxygen. Therefore, the mole ratio used when finding the number of moles of hydrogen must be $^2/_1$, not $^1/_2$.

$$n_{H_2} = 4.13 \text{ mol } O_2 \times \frac{2 \text{ mol } H_2}{1 \text{ mol } O_2} = 8.26 \text{ mol } H_2$$

(mole ratio conversion)

Note that canceling the term $O_2$, the answer is left in units of moles of $H_2$. Obtaining the correct unit serves as a check that the correct mole ratio was used.

## Example 2:

The lack of a good air supply to a Bunsen burner or natural gas furnace results in incomplete combustion, which produces a poisonous gas (carbon monoxide). For complete combustion, sufficient air must be provided.

Determine the number of moles of natural gas (methane) that must undergo combustion to produce 1.62 mol of water vapor.

$$CH_4(g) + 2 O_2(g) \rightarrow CO_2(g) + 2 H_2O(g)$$
$$? \text{ mol} \qquad\qquad\qquad\qquad 1.62 \text{ mol}$$

$n_{CH_4}$ must be found. The equation deals with 1 mol of $CH_4$ and 2 mol of $H_2O$, i.e., there is less $CH_4$ than there is $H_2O$. Therefore the mole ratio must be 1:2.

$$n_{CH_4} = 1.62 \text{ mol } H_2O \times \frac{1 \text{ mol } CH_4}{2 \text{ mol } H_2O} = 0.810 \text{ mol } CH_4$$

(mole ratio conversion)

Note the consistent use of unit symbols and significant digits. The coefficients that are used in the mole ratio are exact numbers and therefore represent an infinite number of significant digits.

# G.3 Exercises  Mole-to-Mole Stoichiometry

Balance the equations and determine the number of moles of each chemical that reacts or is produced. Try to do the calculation without writing anything down other than the answer. (Use correct significant digits.)

____ $N_2(g)$   +   ____ $Cl_2(g)$   →   ____ $NCl_3(l)$ (unbalanced)

| Number of Moles $N_2$ | Number of Moles $Cl_2$ | Number of Moles $NCl_3$ |
|---|---|---|
| e.g.  2.0 mol | 6.0 mol | 4.0 mol |
| 1.    3.0 mol | | |
| 2.    1.10 mol | | |

____ $C_3H_8(g)$ +  ____ $O_2(g)$   →   ____ $CO_2(g)$   +   ____ $H_2O(g)$

| Number of Moles $C_3H_8$ | Number of Moles $O_2$ | Number of Moles $CO_2$ | Number of Moles $H_2O$ |
|---|---|---|---|
| 3. | 0.50 mol | | |
| 4. | | 6.00 mol | |
| 5.    4.0 mol | | | |

For questions 6–8, show the work for the two steps exactly as illustrated by Examples 1 and 2 in Section G.2. (The method of showing work will become very important for more difficult problems later.)

6. Nitrogen in the cylinder of a car reacts with oxygen to produce the pollutant nitrogen monoxide. How many moles of nitrogen monoxide are produced from the combustion of 1.52 mol of nitrogen?

$N_2(g) + O_2(g) \rightarrow 2 \, NO(g)$

7. Lithium metal reacts with nitrogen gas in the air to produce a black solid. How many moles of nitrogen are required to react with 1.83 mol of lithium?

____ $Li(s)$  +  ____ $N_2(g) \rightarrow$ ____ $Li_3N(s)$

8. An orange-brown precipitate can be produced by the reaction of ammonium hydroxide with iron(III) nitrate. Determine the number of moles of ammonium hydroxide required to produce 0.13 mol of precipitate. (The reactants are aqueous solutions.)

ammonium hydroxide + iron(III) nitrate → ammonium nitrate + iron(III) hydroxide

Show the work for the two steps exactly as illustrated by the examples in Section G.2. (The initial statement in the question is provided for interest only and is not part of the solution to the problem.)

9. One of the steps in the production of sodium carbonate (washing soda) is the reaction to produce ammonium hydroxide. How many moles of ammonium chloride are required for an exact reaction with 420 mol of calcium hydroxide (slaked lime)?

$$\_\_\_\_ \ NH_4Cl_{(aq)} \ + \ \_\_\_\_ \ Ca(OH)_{2\,(s)} \ \rightarrow \ _____$$

10. The first step in the production of nitric acid (for fertilizer production) is the reaction of ammonia with oxygen from the air. How many moles of nitrogen monoxide will be produced from the reaction of 200. kmol of ammonia?

ammonia + oxygen → nitrogen monoxide + water

11. The mixture of gasoline and air coming out of the fuel injection system in a gasoline engine is very important to the performance of the engine. How many moles of oxygen are required for the complete combustion of one liter (6.14 mol) of gasoline (assume $C_8H_{18}$)?

$$\_\_ \ C_8H_{18\,(l)} \ + \ \_\_ \ O_{2\,(g)} \quad \rightarrow \quad \_\_ \ CO_{2\,(g)} \ + \ \_\_ \ H_2O_{(g)}$$

12. Ammonia for the production of fertilizers may be produced by the reaction of hydrogen with nitrogen from the air. Determine the number of moles of hydrogen gas required to react with excess nitrogen to prepare 0.602 kmol of ammonia.

$$\_\_ \ H_{2\,(g)} \ + \ \_\_ \ N_{2\,(g)} \quad \rightarrow \quad \_\_ \ NH_{3\,(g)}$$

13. Barbecues burning charcoal briquettes are unsafe for inside use because of the colorless, odorless, poisonous gas produced. Assuming the charcoal is pure carbon, determine the number of moles of oxygen gas that react with one charcoal briquette (2.04 mol) to produce carbon monoxide.

14. White (yellow) phosphorus must be stored under water because it ignites in the air. How many moles of oxygen must react with 0.56 mol of phosphorus to produce solid tetraphosphorus decaoxide?

**DEMO ...**

# G.4   The Reaction of Copper with Aqueous Silver Nitrate

**Purpose:**
✔ To illustrate data collection for stoichiometric chemistry problems.

**Pre-Demo Information:**
*Theoretical Yield:* The expected amount of product based on the calculations from a balanced chemical equation. It is the amount of product obtained when the conditions are *perfect*.

*Actual Yield:* The amount of product obtained when the experiment is actually done. It includes error due to splashes, incomplete reaction, incomplete drying, etc.

*Percent Yield:*    $\dfrac{\text{actual yield}}{\text{theoretical yield}} \times 100 = \%$ yield

*Percent Error:*

$\dfrac{(\text{actual yield} - \text{theoretical yield})}{\text{theoretical yield}} \times 100 = \%$ error

Label the following diagram. Use the following terms: *filter paper, filtrate, funnel, precipitate.*

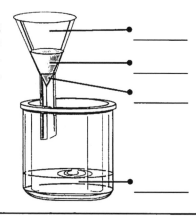

**Materials:**
• 1 vial containing 3-5 g of silver nitrate
• 1 30-cm length heavy gauge unlacquered copper wire
• 1 piece of quantitative filter paper
• 1 piece of steel wool
• 1 wash bottle containing distilled water
• 1 stirring rod with rubber policeman (scraper attached)
• 1 centigram balance
• 1 ring stand
• 1 funnel rack
• 1 filter funnel
• 1 400-mL beaker
• 1 250-mL beaker
• 1 watch glass
• 1 paper towel

**Pre-demo Exercise:**
Write a balanced chemical equation for the reaction of copper with aqueous silver nitrate. (Be sure to indicate the states of matter.)

**Procedure:**
**Day 1:**
1. Determine and record the mass of the vial plus silver nitrate.
2. Transfer the silver nitrate crystals into the 250-mL beaker.
3. Determine and record the mass of the empty vial.
4. Add distilled water to about half fill the 250-mL beaker containing the silver nitrate crystals.

5. Stir the mixture with a glass stirring rod until the silver nitrate crystals dissolve completely. As the stirring rod is removed, rinse it with distilled water.

6. Clean the copper wire with steel wool to remove oxides and lacquer.

7. Wrap the copper wire around a test tube to form a coil with a handle.

8. Place the copper coil into the silver nitrate solution. Record the visual observations for the first few minutes of the reaction.

9. Cover the beaker with a watch glass and set aside until next day.

**Day 2:**

10. Record visual observations concerning the beaker contents.

11. Shake and remove the copper coil from the beaker solution. Use a wash bottle and rubber policeman to rinse any particles of silver back into the beaker. (Examine the copper coil.)

12. Fold and determine the mass of the piece of filter paper.

13. Set up a filtration apparatus. Decant the solution through the filter paper and then transfer the silver crystals onto the filter paper. Record correct lab techniques in the space provided.

14. Wash the silver crystals on the filter paper several times.

15. Carefully remove the filter paper and silver from the filter funnel. Place the filter paper on a clean watch glass and unfold.

16. Set the filter paper and silver aside to dry until the next day.

**Day 3:**

17. Determine the mass of the filter paper plus silver.

**Data and Observations:**
Record the following for each day:

**Day 1:**
 a. Mass of vial plus silver nitrate crystals _____
 b. Mass of empty vial _____
 c. Visual observations

 _____

 _____

 _____

 _____

**Day 2:**
 a. Mass of filter paper _____
 b. Visual observations

 _____

 _____

 _____

 _____

 c. Filtration techniques

 _____

 _____

 _____

**Day 3:**
Mass of filter paper plus silver _____

**Calculations:**

1. Determine by subtraction the actual mass of silver nitrate reacted.

2. From the mass of silver nitrate that reacted, predict the mass of silver that should have been produced (i.e., the theoretical yield).

3. Determine by subtraction the actual mass of silver produced (i.e., the actual yield).

4. Calculate the percent yield for the reaction.

5. Calculate the percent error for the yield.

**Questions:**

1. What evidence supports the assumption that all of the silver nitrate reacted?

_____

_____

2. The atom that became an ion was _____.

3. The ion that became an atom was _____.

4. The compound in the filtrate was _____.

5. The blue color in the final solution was a result of _____.

6. Why was the stirring rod rinsed in procedure step 5?

_____

_____

_____

_____

_____

7. Why is the copper wire thinner after sitting overnight in the silver nitrate solution?

_____

_____

List a correct lab technique concerning each of the following:

8. folding the filter paper

_____

_____

_____

_____

9. tip of funnel

_____

_____

10. height of solution in filter funnel

_____

_____

11. decanting (removing a solution from over a solid)

_____

_____

_____

_____

12. transferring precipitate to funnel

_____

_____

_____

_____

_____

_____

13. washing precipitate in funnel

_____

_____

14. removing filter paper plus precipitate from funnel

_____

_____

_____

_____

15. What incorrect lab technique might result in the filter paper turning blue when it dries? Explain

_____

_____

_____

_____

# G.5 Stoichiometry Calculations

There are several types of stoichiometry calculations, but all of them use the mass or moles of Substance #1 to determine the mass or moles of Substance #2. All other substances in the reaction can be ignored—they have already been accounted for when the equation was balanced.

The flowcharts in FIGURE G1 can be used to solve all types of stoichiometry problems. Start with the given amount of Substance #1 and do the calculations necessary to find Substance #2. Each boxed item in a flowchart can be used as a conversion factor:

FIGURE G1    Stoichiometry Flowchart

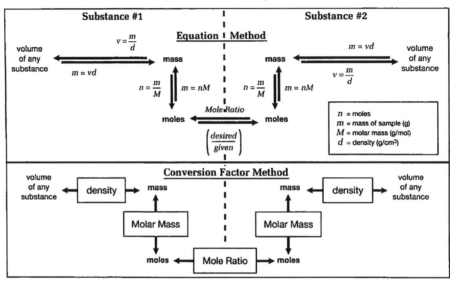

For each type of stoichiometric problem, (1) find the given quantity on the flow chart, (2) use the equations or conversion factors needed to change the given quantity to the final quantity, (3) multiply and/or divide as needed, and (4) round off the final answer. Be sure to set up the problems so that all the units cancel except the final units to the answer:

$$\text{Given amount} \times \left( \frac{\rule{2cm}{0.4pt}}{\text{(Necessary conversion factors)}} \times \rule{2cm}{0.4pt} \times \rule{2cm}{0.4pt} \right) = \text{Required amount}$$

Remember, round off only after the final calculation is completed.


# G.6 Mass-Mass Stoichiometry

Mass-mass stoichiometry simply means you are given the mass of one of the substances and are using the balanced chemical reaction to predict the required or expected mass of another substance in the reaction.

## Example:

Portland cement is prepared by heating a mixture of limestone ($CaCO_3$) and clay (aluminum silicate). When hydrated (i.e., when water is added), the resulting mixture becomes cement. What mass of calcium carbonate must react with 70.5 g of aluminum silicate to produce the Portland cement mixture of calcium oxide, carbon dioxide, aluminum oxide and calcium silicate?

*Step 1:* Write the balanced chemical equation.

$$4\,CaCO_3(s) + Al_2(SiO_3)_3(s) \rightarrow CaO(s) + 4\,CO_2(g) + Al_2O_3(s) + 3\,CaSiO_3(s)$$

$\phantom{4\,CaCO_3}$? g $\phantom{xxxxx}$ 70.5 g

*Step 2:* Convert the mass to moles.

$$n_{Al_2(SiO_3)_3} = \frac{m}{M} = \frac{70.5\,g}{282.23\,g/mol} = 0.250\ mol$$

*Step 3:* Determine the number of moles of the required substance.

$$n_{CaCO_3} = 0.250\ mol\ Al_2(SiO_3)_3 \times \frac{4\ mol\ CaCO_3}{1\ mol\ Al_2(SiO_3)_3} = 1.00\ mol\ CaCO_3$$

*Step 4:* Determine the mass of the required substance.

$$m_{CaCO_3} = n\,M = 1.00\ mol \times 100.09\ g/mol = 100.\ g\ CaCO_3$$

Or combine Steps 2, 3 and 4 using the conversion factor method:

$$70.5\ g\ Al_2(SiO_3)_3 \times \frac{1\ mol\ Al_2(SiO_3)_3}{282.23\ g\ Al_2(SiO_3)_3} \times \frac{4\ mol\ CaCO_3}{1\ mol\ Al_2(SiO_3)_3} \times \frac{100.09\ g\ CaCO_3}{1\ mol\ CaCO_3}$$

| Step 2: (molar mass conversion) | Step 3: (mole ratio conversion) | Step 4: (molar mass conversion) |

$$= 100.\ g\ CaCO_3$$

# G.7 Exercises  Mass-Mass Stoichiometry

Show all work (exactly as in the preceding example) when answering the questions below:

1. The Thermit reaction was once used for making crude welds. The Thermit mixture is composed of aluminum and iron(III) oxide. What mass of solid iron(III) oxide is required for every 40.5 g of solid aluminum?

___ Al( ) + ___ Fe$_2$O$_3$( )   →   ___ Fe( ) + ___ Al$_2$O$_3$( )

2. Iron ore (Fe$_2$O$_3$) is refined to iron (and carbon monoxide) by reacting the iron ore together with coke (pure carbon, C). What mass of coke is required for every 1.000 kg of iron ore refined?

___ Fe$_2$O$_3$( ) + ___ C( )   →   ___ Fe( ) + ___ CO( )

# G.8 Mole-Mass Stoichiometry

Mole-mass stoichiometry simply means you are given the number of moles of one of the substances and are using the balanced chemical reaction to predict the required or expected mass of another substance in the reaction.

## Example:

Roasting zinc ore (ZnS) converts it into an oxide; then it is reduced into the pure metal. (The SO$_2$ gas produced becomes an environmental problem if it is not recovered.) What mass of zinc sulfide could react with 21.0 mol of oxygen to produce zinc oxide and sulfur dioxide?

*Step 1:* Write the balanced chemical equation.

$$2\ ZnS_{(s)} + 3\ O_{2(g)} \rightarrow 2\ ZnO_{(s)} + 2\ SO_{2(g)}$$
$$?\ g \qquad 21.0\ mol$$

*Step 2:* Determine the number of moles of the required substance.

$$n_{ZnS} = 21.0\ mol\ O_2 \times \frac{2\ mol\ ZnS}{3\ mol\ O_2} = 14.0\ mol\ ZnS$$

*Step 3:* Determine the mass of the required substance.

$$m_{ZnS} = n\ M = 14.0\ mol \times 97.44\ g/mol = 1.36 \times 10^3\ g\ ZnS = 1.36\ kg\ ZnS$$

Or combine Steps 2 and 3 using the conversion factor method:

$$21.0\ mol\ O_2 \times \frac{2\ mol\ ZnS}{3\ mol\ O_2} \times \frac{97.44\ g\ ZnS}{1\ mol\ ZnS} = 1.36 \times 10^3 g\ ZnS = 1.36\ kg$$

| Step 2: | Step 3: |
|---|---|
| (molar mass conversion) | (mole ratio conversion) |

# G.9 Exercises  Mole-Mass Stoichiometry

Show all work (exactly as in the example above) when answering the questions below:

1. What mass of sodium metal must react with water to produce 0.540 mol of hydrogen gas? (Recall the rule for the formula for water in single and double replacement reactions.)

___ Na(  ) + ___ HOH(  )  →  ___ $H_2$(  ) + ___ NaOH(  )

2. Slaked lime (calcium hydroxide) may be used for whitewashing or in mortar for bricklaying. In both cases the solid slaked lime reacts with carbon dioxide in the air to produce calcium carbonate and water.  What mass of calcium carbonate will be produced by the reaction of 0.962 mol of calcium hydroxide with carbon dioxide to produce calcium carbonate and water?

___ $Ca(OH)_2$(  ) + ___ $CO_2$(  )  →  ___ $CaCO_3$(  ) + ___ $H_2O$(  )

# G.10  Mass-Mole Stoichiometry

Mass-mole stoichiometry simply means you are given the mass of one of the substances and are using the balanced chemical reaction to predict the required or expected number of moles of another substance in the reaction.

## Example:

Reacting rock phosphorus with sulfuric acid produces phosphoric acid for fertilizer production. Determine the number of moles of sulfuric acid required to react with 62.0 g of calcium phosphate.

*Step 1*: Write the balanced chemical equation.

$$3\ H_2SO_4(aq)\ +\ Ca_3(PO_4)_2(s)\ \rightarrow\ 2\ H_3PO_4(aq)\ +\ 3\ CaSO_4(s)$$
$$\text{? mol} \qquad \text{62.0 g}$$

*Step 2*: Convert the mass to moles.

$$n_{Ca_3(PO_4)_2} = \frac{m}{M} = \frac{62.0\ g}{310.18\ g/mol} = 0.200\ mol\ Ca_3(PO_4)_2$$

*Step 3*: Determine the number of moles of the required substance.

$$n_{H_2SO_4} = 0.200\ mol\ Ca_3(PO_4)_2\ \times\ \frac{3\ mol\ H_2SO_4}{1\ mol\ Ca_3(PO_4)_2} = 0.600\ mol\ H_2SO_4$$

Or combine Steps 2 and 3 using the conversion factor method:

$$62.0\ g\ Ca_3(PO_4)_2 \times \underbrace{\frac{1\ mol\ Ca_3(PO_4)_2}{310.18\ g\ Ca_3(PO_4)_2}}_{\substack{\text{Step 2:}\\ \text{(molar mass}\\ \text{conversion)}}} \times \underbrace{\frac{3\ mol\ H_2SO_4}{1\ mol\ Ca_3(PO_4)_2}}_{\substack{\text{Step 3:}\\ \text{(mole ratio}\\ \text{conversion)}}} = 0.600\ mol\ H_2SO_4$$

# G.11 <u>Exercises</u> Mass-Mole Stoichiometry

Show all work (exactly as in the preceding example) when answering the questions below:

1. In the first step in the production of sulfuric acid, sulfur is burned in air to produce sulfur dioxide. How many moles of oxygen are required to react with 160 g of sulfur?

$$\_\_\ S_8(\ )\ +\ \_\_\ O_2(\ ) \qquad \rightarrow \qquad \_\_\ SO_2(\ )$$

2. Hydrofluoric acid may be produced in the laboratory and used to etch glass. (The fumes of hydrogen fluoride from hydrofluoric acid are extremely irritating and corrosive to the skin and mucous membranes. Inhalation of the vapor may cause ulcers of the upper respiratory tract.) How many moles of hydrofluoric acid may be produced by the addition of sufficient sulfuric acid to 7.81 g of solid calcium fluoride?

$$\_\_\ H_2SO_4(\ )\ +\ \_\_\ CaF_2(\ ) \qquad \rightarrow \qquad \_\_\ HF(\ )\ +\ \_\_\ CaSO_4(\ )$$

# G.12 The Reaction of Sodium Bicarbonate and Hydrochloric Acid

**Purpose:**
✔ To apply stoichiometric calculations to a reaction between sodium hydrogen carbonate and hydrochloric acid.

**Materials:**
- 1 250-mL beaker
- 1 watch glass
- 1 hot plate
- 1 balance
- sodium hydrogen carbonate (baking soda)
- dropping bottle of dilute (1.0 mol/L) hydrochloric acid solution
- wash bottle containing distilled water

**Lab Challenge:**
Design and carry out a procedure to react 2.00 g of baking soda with an excess of hydrochloric acid to obtain the maximum amount of solid ionic compound product.

**Prelab Information:**
1. It is known that sodium hydrogen carbonate (baking soda) reacts vigorously with acids to produce carbon dioxide gas. (*Test it and see! At home, in the sink, add together baking soda and vinegar.*)
2. There are three products: one is a gas, one is a liquid, and one is a soluble ionic compound.

**Prelab Exercise:**
1. Write the balanced equation for the reaction between sodium hydrogen carbonate and hydrochloric acid. (**Hint:** *It is a type of double replacement reaction where one of the products is broken down into two simpler products.*)

  sodium hydrogen carbonate + hydrochloric acid

  ➙ \_\_\_\_\_ + \_\_\_\_\_ + carbon dioxide

2. Before designing your procedure, answer the following questions:
   a. Why is it necessary to cover the dish with the watch glass?

b. How will you know when you have added enough HCl?

c. Why is it a good idea to add an excess of HCl? How will you accomplish this?

d. After adding the acid to the baking soda, what will be found on the underside of the watch glass and what should be done about it?

e. How will you obtain the new pure ionic compound? Why is it desirable to use a low setting?

3. Now design a Procedure to obtain the new compound from 2.00 g $NaHCO_3$. Put the Procedure in "picture format." Get instructor approval of your Procedure before beginning the lab.

**Lab Safety:**

1. The hydrochloric acid used in this experiment is a fairly concentrated solution. CAUTION! Hydrochloric acid at this concentration is highly toxic by ingestion or inhalation and is severely corrosive to skin and eyes. Wear protective gloves and safety goggles. Work in a fume hood if possible.

2. Any heating to be done should be at low temperatures to avoid loss due to spattering. This also minimizes any danger due to contact with hot ejected material.

**Procedure:**

1. Carry out your approved procedure to answer the Lab Challenge.

2. Record your observations for each of the problems. This includes colors, odors, texture, etc.

3. Include all data in chart/table form so the information is easy to locate and read. Have a separate chart for each problem section.

4. Show all equations and calculations. Round off your answers to the correct number of significant digits.

**Observations:**

1. Observe any sights, sounds and smells of the reaction. Also feel the bottom of the evaporating dish immediately after adding the acid. Record all observations.

   _____

   _____

2. Observe, describe and draw the sodium chloride crystals as seen under a magnifying glass or stereomicroscope.

   _____

   _____

   _____

   _____

   _____

   _____

**Data and Results:**

1. Report all data in a clearly labeled chart.

2. What is the actual yield of sodium chloride? (Show your calculations.)

3. Using the balanced chemical equation and the initial mass of sodium hydrogen carbonate, calculate the theoretical yield of sodium chloride.

4. Determine the percent yield of sodium chloride.

5. Determine the percent error of the results.

**Post-lab Questions:**
1. Why didn't the sodium chloride boil away when the water was evaporated?

_____

_____

_____

_____

_____

_____

2. a) Look up the shape of the following crystals in the Handbook of Chemistry and Physics:

sodium chloride _____

sodium hydrogen carbonate _____

sodium carbonate _____

b) How does the shape of your crystals compare with the expected shape of solid sodium chloride?

_____

c) What does it mean if the shapes of your crystals are different from the shape of sodium chloride as stated in the handbook?

_____

_____

_____

_____

_____

3. Was the addition of hydrochloric acid to baking soda an exothermic or endothermic reaction? Explain how you know. *(Hint: Refer to your observations. Did the dish get hotter or colder after the addition of acid?)*

_____

_____

_____

4. List four different properties that could be checked to show that the new solid that was produced is sodium chloride.

_____

_____

**Conclusions:**
1. Discuss at least three things you learned including something regarding the statement given in the Purpose.

_____

_____

_____

_____

_____

2. Explain how each error would affect the amount of NaCl.

a. Error: Not enough HCl added.

   Effect: _____

b. Error: Did not rinse watch glass.

   Effect: _____

c. Error: Water not completely evaporated.

   Effect: _____

d. Error: Did not wait for fizzing to stop.

   Effect: _____

3. Include comments concerning any difficulties you encountered and what you did to solve each problem. What did you like/dislike about this lab?

_____

_____

_____

_____

_____

_____

# G.13 <u>Exercises</u> Mixed Stoichiometry

Show all work when solving the following problems. Work should include the balanced chemical equation, the quantity equations, proper unit symbols and the correct number of significant digits (use a separate sheet of paper if necessary):

1. In the electrolytic decomposition of water, 0.500 kmol of hydrogen gas were formed. How many moles of oxygen gas were formed at the same time?

2. Milk of magnesia [$Mg(OH)_{2(s)}$] is used to neutralize excess stomach acid ($HCl_{(aq)}$). 0.583 g of magnesium hydroxide will neutralize how many moles of hydrochloric acid?

3. What mass of cream of tartar (_potassium hydrogen tartrate_) is required to react with 4.20 g of baking soda (_sodium hydrogen carbonate_) in a baking recipe?

$$KHC_4H_4O_{6(aq)} + NaHCO_{3(aq)} \rightarrow CO_{2(g)} + KNaC_4H_4O_{6(aq)} + H_2O_{(l)}$$

4. A foam-producing fire extinguisher should be used for fighting gasoline fires. The foam [$Al(OH)_3$] and the carbon dioxide produced both help to smother the fire. Determine the number of grams of foam produced from 1.00 kg of baking soda.

$$\_\_ NaHCO_{3(aq)} + \_\_ Al_2(SO_4)_{3(aq)} \rightarrow \_\_ Al(OH)_{3(s)} + \_\_ CO_{2(g)} + \_\_ Na_2SO_{4(aq)}$$

5. Carbohydrates (such as $C_6H_{12}O_6$) undergo combustion with oxygen to produce carbon dioxide and water. Living things use a type of this reaction (a process called respiration) to produce energy. Determine the mass of carbohydrate consumed for every 0.300 mol of oxygen gas consumed during respiration.

6. A student obtained the following data from a reaction between a zinc strip and a copper(II) sulfate solution. What mass of copper should be produced (i.e., what is the theoretical yield of copper)?

initial mass of zinc  15.42 g
final mass of zinc   14.15 g    (**Hint:** _What mass of zinc actually reacted?_)

# Unit H
# Behavior of Gases

Unit A, *Matter, Energy and the Periodic Table*, described the three states of matter (solids, liquids and gases). Of these, gases are the most difficult to observe because many are colorless and transparent. Even so, scientists have discovered methods of measuring properties such as pressure, temperature and volume of gases. Gases have properties that are easily understood. In this unit, you will investigate the properties, theories and mathematics of gases.

## H.1 The Composition and Importance of the Atmosphere

The atmosphere of Earth is composed of elements and compounds that are usually in the gaseous state. Without these gases, we could not live on this planet. For example, the gases of our atmosphere are needed for:

- breathing ($O_2$) and cellular respiration ($CO_2$) in animals and plants.
- photosynthesis in plants ($O_2$).
- protection from harmful solar radiation, especially ultraviolet rays and ozone ($O_3$).
- transmission of heat and water vapor to moderate our climates and sustain life—water, carbon dioxide and methane ($H_2O$, $CO_2$, $CH_4$).

Although the atmosphere is a mixture of many gases, there are only two gases, nitrogen and oxygen, that make up approximately 99% of air. Even in trace amounts, however, other gases can have a tremendous impact on the environment. For example, $CO_2$ is not only involved in respiration, but is also an important "greenhouse gas" that moderates temperatures in the atmosphere. Water vapor, which varies greatly due to climatic factors, is responsible for all our weather. Many gases are a source of pollution and can affect the quality of our atmosphere. **Air pollution** can be defined as *anything in the air that causes difficulty to humans.* The gases' concentration in the air varies from one location to another. Some common sources of air pollution are:

- sulfur oxides ($SO_2$ and $SO_3$, collectively known as "$SO_x$") from oxidation of coal, oil and natural gas (fuels derived from plants and animals that had been buried and subjected to high temperatures and pressures) and industrial processes that are a major source of acid rain.
- nitrogen oxides (NO, $NO_2$ and others—"$NO_x$") from automobiles and industries, which contribute to acid fogs and rains.
- carbon monoxide (CO) from burning fossil fuels.
- hydrocarbons ($CH_4$, $C_2H_6$, etc.) that are not completely burned during fossil fuel combustion.
- fluorocarbons (freons) that attack the ozone layer.

The atmosphere is also an important source for obtaining resources. Nitrogen, oxygen, carbon dioxide and all the noble gases are removed from the air using a technique known as *fractional distillation.* In this procedure, the air is liquefied and the components separated by distillation. Many industries depend on these gases to make their products. Indeed, the gases in the air are a valuable resource needed by us all.

FIGURE H1 Composition of the Atmosphere at Sea Level

| Gas | % by volume |
|---|---|
| nitrogen ($N_2$) | 78.1 |
| oxygen ($O_2$) | 20.9 |
| argon (Ar) | 0.93 |
| carbon dioxide ($CO_2$) | 0.03 |
| neon (Ne) | 0.002 |
| helium (He) | 0.0005 |
| krypton, xenon, methane ($CH_4$), hydrogen | trace quantities |
| nitrogen oxides ($NO_x$)* and sulfur oxides ($SO_x$)* | trace quantities |
| water vapor* | trace quantities |

* Percentages of these gases vary with climatic factors and the amount of pollution.

DEMO ...

## H.2 General Properties of Gases / A Theory to Fit These Properties

Your teacher will perform a series of demonstrations illustrating some of the properties of gases. While all gases share similar properties, each gas is uniquely different from all the others. Record your observations and conclusions in the following chart.

**1. Balloon on balance:**
An inflated balloon is placed on a balance to determine its mass. The balloon is "popped" and the balloon fragments are massed again.

0.00 g

3.76 g

3.20 g

Observations: ______________________________

______________________________

______________________________

______________________________

Conclusions: ______________________________

______________________________

______________________________

______________________________

______________________________

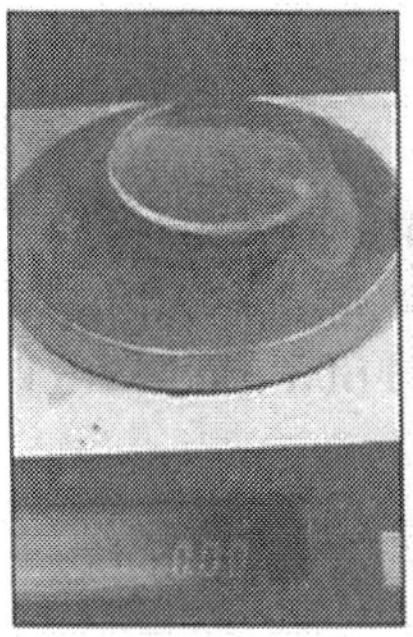

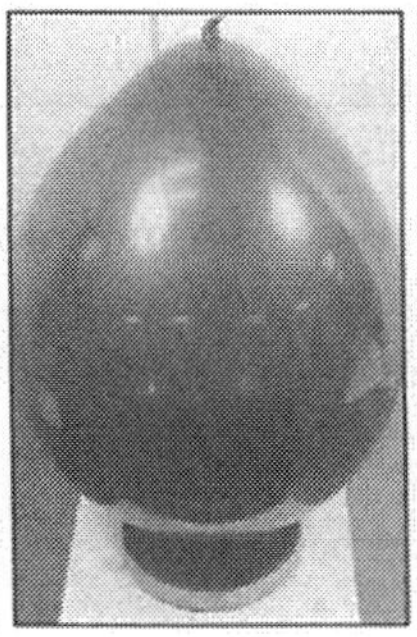

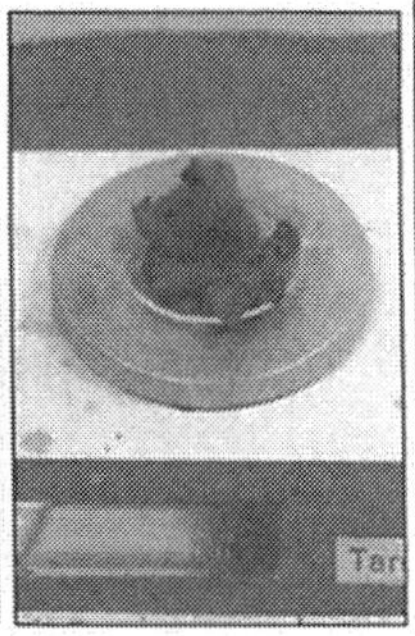

2. **Tornado tube demo:**
   A 2-L bottle is half-filled with water. A "tornado tube" is
   screwed on and a second empty 2-L bottle is attached.

   Observations: _____

   _____

   _____

   Conclusions: _____

   _____

   _____

   _____

3. **Comparison of relative gas densities:**
   Several balloons are inflated with different gases.
   (Set this up ahead of time.)

   Observations: _____

   _____

   _____

   Conclusions: _____

   _____

   _____

4. **Comparison of gas flammabilities:**
   The balloons in the previous demo are all touched with a
   burning splint taped to the end of a meter stick.

   before        after

   Observations: _____

   _____

   _____

   Conclusions: _____

   _____

   _____

   _____

   _____

## 5. Balloon in flask:

Place prepared flask on hot plate. Wait to observe changes.
(See proposed theory #1 in section H.3.)

Observations: _____

_____

_____

_____

_____

Conclusions: _____

_____

_____

_____

_____

## 6. Can on hot plate:

A juice or pop can has a small amount of water inside. The can is set on the hot plate until the water boils.* (See proposed theory #1 in Section H.3.)

*The can is then inverted into a beaker of cold water.

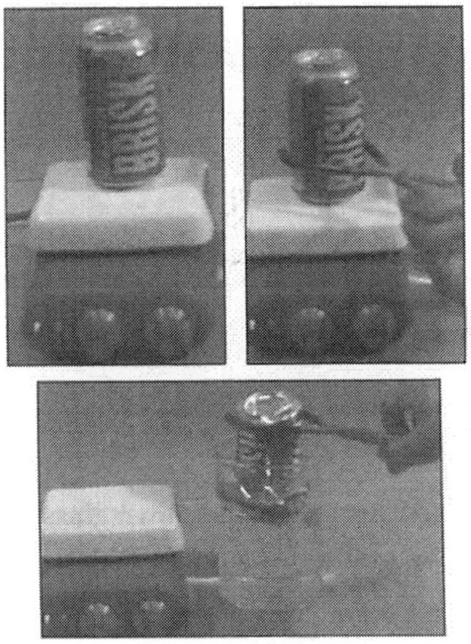

Observations: _____

_____

_____

_____

Conclusions: _____

_____

_____

_____

_____

_____

_____

7. **Visual display of several gases:**

Use bromine tubes or add a few crystals of iodine to a stoppered flask and warm slightly. (See proposed theory #2 in Section H.3.)

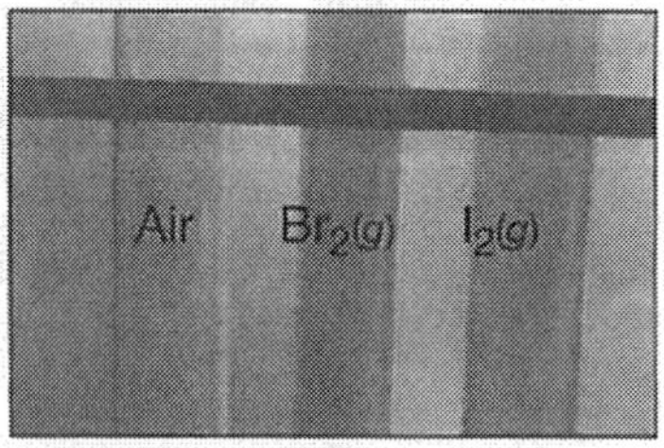

Air    Br$_2$(g)    I$_2$(g)

Observations: _____

_____

_____

Conclusions: _____

_____

_____

8. **Diffusion of gases:**

Hold an eyedropper containing ammonia next to an eyedropper containing HCl.

Add some phenolphthalein to a 50-mL beaker of water. Put ammonia in a second 50-mL beaker. Cover both beakers with a larger beaker. (See proposed theory #3 in Section H.3.)

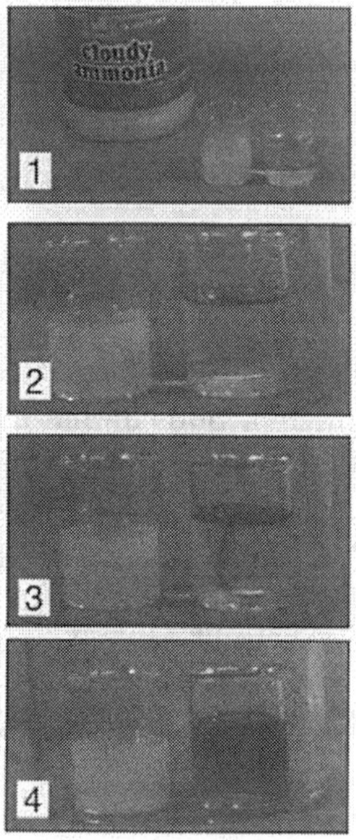

Observations: _____

_____

_____

Conclusions: _____

_____

_____

_____

9. **Water in upside-down glass:**

Partially fill a bottle with water. Put a (plastic) card over the mouth of the bottle and invert the bottle. (See proposed theory #3a in Section H.3.)

Observations: _____

_____

_____

Conclusions: _____

_____

_____

**10. Measuring gas pressures**
   (See proposed theory #3b in
   Section H.3.)

Barometer

   Observations: _____

   _____

   _____

   _____

Pressure gauge
Pressure sensor

   Conclusions: _____

   _____

   _____

   _____

   _____

   _____

**11. Gas Model Demonstrator**
   Use some kind of overhead projector simulator or a computer
   simulation to show how scientists model the behavior of gas
   molecules. (see proposed theory #4 in Section H.3.)

   Observations: _____

   _____

   _____

   Conclusions: _____

   _____

   _____

   _____

# H.3 Properties of Gases and the Ideal Gas Model

As you have just observed in the H.2 Demo, gases have a wide variety of properties.
Chemists find it useful to explain many of these properties using the **Ideal Gas Model**,
which is part of the **Kinetic Molecular Theory of Matter** (discussed further in Unit I). This
model makes several assumptions that simplify the explanations of gases and are "close
enough" for the temperatures and pressures normally encountered with the usual gases
studied in a typical chemistry laboratory. A *scientific law* is based on an observation in
experiments that has been tested and re-tested and is now accepted as true.

| Proposed Theory | Fact |
|---|---|
| 1. *The tiny molecules that make up gases are spaced so far apart from each other that the actual volume of the molecule is insignificant when compared to the space between them.* | Under normal conditions of temperature and pressure, about 99.96% of the total volume of gas is empty space. Gases, therefore, can be easily compressed. |
| 2. *No intermolecular forces exist between molecules in a **perfect gas**.* | Gases freely and spontaneously fill the entire space available to them. |
| 3. *Molecules of a gas are in constant, straight-line motion:*<br>a. *They collide with each other and the sides of the container.*<br>b. *Molecular collisions with the container wall cause pressure. Energy is exchanged in these collisions but no energy is lost. The collisions are said to be completely elastic.* | A Brownian motion apparatus can be used to show that gas molecules are in continuous motion. Particles of dust or smoke are added to the gas (air) in the apparatus. Even though the gas molecules are too small to be seen, the particles of smoke can be observed through a microscope. These particles move continuously as if the invisible gas molecules were hitting them. Since the dust particles do not settle, we can assume that these collisions are strong enough to overcome the pull of gravity on the dust particles. |
| 4. *At any given time, molecules are moving at different speeds and, therefore, have different kinetic energies. It has been determined, however, that the **average kinetic energies (AKE)** of the different gases are the same at a given temperature. In addition, the average kinetic energy of the gas molecules increases as temperature increases.* | Collisions between molecules of gas will continually cause their speed to change. However, the collisions are elastic and thus no kinetic energy is lost during these collisions. The total kinetic energy of the system is the sum of the kinetic energies of all the molecules. If the temperature of the gas is increased by adding heat, the average kinetic energy of the particles will increase proportionately. |

# H.4 <u>Exercises</u> Properties of Gases and the Ideal Gas Model

1. What molecular characteristics of a gas cause it to disperse its odor quickly?

   _____

   _____

2. What causes gas pressure?

   _____

3. Compare equal volumes of $H_2$ and $N_2$ at the same temperature and pressure. What can be said about these gases in terms of the following?

   a. The mass of each molecule. (Hint: Calculate the molar mass of each.)

   _____

   b. The average kinetic energy (AKE) of the molecules. (Hint: See Proposed Theory #4.)

c. The average velocity of each molecule.

(Hint: If $AKE_{H_2} = AKE_{N_2}$ and $KE = \frac{1}{2} mv^2$, then solve for $\dfrac{v^2_{H_2}}{v^2_{N_2}}$ )

d. The number of collisions in each container.

_____

_____

4. Use your answers in question 3 to explain what allows the pressure to be the same in each container of gas.

_____

_____

_____

5. Explain how gaseous odors, such as skunk odor, travel by describing the molecular motion of the gas. Why do such odors tend to fade and disappear? What molecular characteristics of a gas could cause it to disperse its odor more quickly?

_____

_____

_____

_____

_____

6. *Challenge Question!* Explain why a *perfect gas* will remain in the gaseous state at all temperatures and pressures. It is known that gases can be liquefied at low temperatures and high pressures. What does that suggest about gas molecules? (See Section H.30.)

_____

_____

_____

_____

_____

_____

# H.5 Preparation and Properties of Several Gases

**Purpose:**
✔ To prepare oxygen gas.
✔ To study some of the properties of oxygen.
✔ To prepare hydrogen gas.
✔ To study some of the properties of hydrogen.

## Part 1 — Oxygen

**Safety:**
* Wear goggles.
* Wash hands after completing the lab.

*Warning: Caution must be exercised in this lab. Follow all instructions carefully and heed all warnings. This reaction is very dangerous.*

**Materials:**
* 1 250-mL Florence flask
* 1 thistle tube setup (with delivery tube)
* 2 glass bottles
* 2 glass plates
* 4 test tubes (20 × 150 mm)
* 4 rubber stoppers to fit test tubes
* 1 pneumatic trough
* 1 ring clamp
* 1 ring stand
* 100 mL hydrogen peroxide (6%)
* 3-4 g manganese dioxide
* 1 Bunsen burner
* 1 crucible tongs
* 2 wood splints
* steel wool
* 1 5-cm piece of magnesium ribbon
* limewater
* Universal Indicator

c. acid

_____

_____

_____

d. base

_____

_____

**Prelab Exercise — Part 1:**
1. Define the following terms:

   a. catalyst

e. indicator

_____

_____

_____

_____

_____

_____

   b. oxide

2. Write a balanced equation for the chemical reaction that occurs when oxygen gas is prepared from hydrogen peroxide in the presence of a catalyst, manganese dioxide.

_____

_____

_____

*Safety Warning: Follow all instructions carefully. Wear goggles throughout this experiment.*

## Procedure — Part 1A — Gas Generation:

1. Set up the apparatus as shown in the photos. Be sure that the thistle tube is within 2-3 mm of the bottom of the flask.

2. Fill two gas-collecting bottles with water, cover the tops with glass plates and invert the bottles in the pneumatic trough. Slide the glass plates away after the gas bottles have been inverted and are underwater. Also submerge four test tubes into the trough.

3. Place 1 spoonful (3-4 g) of manganese dioxide into the flask. Stopper the assembly and add about 10–15 mL of 6% hydrogen peroxide down the thistle tube.

*Caution:* *Hydrogen peroxide destroys flesh—wear protective gloves and chemical-splash goggles.*

4. Let the gas bubble through the water in the pneumatic trough for the first 10 seconds. This will remove the air from the system. Then place the delivery tube into the mouth of one of the gas bottles and begin to collect the gas. (How will you know when the bottle is full?)

5. Add the 6% hydrogen peroxide *a little at a time AS NEEDED* (10-15 mL portions) down the thistle tube to keep the reaction going at a steady rate. As pressure builds up in the flask, the hydrogen peroxide may not run down the thistle tube. If this happens, stop adding the hydrogen peroxide until the pressure in the flask drops. You will not have to use all the hydrogen peroxide.

6. When the gas bottle is filled, slide a glass plate under each gas bottle and place each one upright on the desktop. Then fill each test tube with gas, stopper it and set it on the table.

7. When the bottles and test tubes have been filled, remove the delivery tube from the pneumatic trough. Remove the stopper from the generator and add water to stop the reaction. Rinse the apparatus thoroughly.

## Procedure — Part 1B — Gas Testing:

1. Light a Bunsen burner.

2. With a gas bottle nearby, hold a small piece of magnesium ribbon with crucible tongs, ignite the magnesium, slide the glass plate off the bottle and hold the burning ribbon inside the bottle. Do not look directly at the flame. Record the results.

3. Repeat step 2 with the second bottle, this time using steel wool. Record the results.

4. Insert a glowing splint into the first test tube. Record the results.

5. Insert a burning splint into the second test tube. Record the results.

6. Place about 5 mL of water into the third test tube keeping the tube covered as much as possible to prevent loss or mixing of oxygen and the air. Add a few drops of Universal Indicator. Shake the tube to mix. Match the color of the solution to a pH chart and record both the color and the pH of the solution.

7. Add limewater to the fourth test tube. Shake the tube to mix, and record the results.

## Observations — Part 1:

Record your observations for each of the tests in the chart below:

| Magnesium ribbon (in bottle) | Steel Wool (in bottle) | Glowing Splint (in test tube) | Burning Splint (in test tube) | Universal Indicator (in test tube) | Limewater (in test tube) |
|---|---|---|---|---|---|
| | | | | | |

## Questions — Part 1:

1. What changes have occurred in the manganese dioxide? What evidence supports your claim?

_____

_____

_____

_____

2. Describe three problems you experienced in collecting and studying oxygen gas in an ordinary laboratory situation.

_____

_____

_____

_____

3. Describe the test for oxygen.

_____

_____

4. Compare the combustion of the various elements in air and in oxygen.

_____

_____

## Part 2 — Hydrogen

*Warning: Follow all instructions carefully. Wear goggles throughout this experiment. Be sure there are no flames in the room when you start this experiment and do not light a match or produce a flame of any kind until you are told to do so by your teacher.*

### Materials:
- 1 250-mL Florence flask
- 1 thistle tube setup with delivery tube
- 2 glass bottles
- 2 glass plates
- 4 test tubes (20 × 150 mm)
- 4 rubber stoppers to fit test tubes
- 1 pneumatic trough
- 1 ring clamp
- 1 ring stand
- 3 mol/L $H_2SO_4$ or 6 mol/L HCl
- mossy zinc (or magnesium shavings)
- 1 Bunsen burner
- 1 crucible tongs
- 2 wood splints
- steel wool
- 1 5-cm piece of magnesium ribbon
- limewater
- Universal Indicator

### Prelab Exercise — Part 2:
Write the balanced equation for the production of hydrogen gas from the action of sulfuric acid on zinc metal.

### Procedure — Part 2A — Gas Generation:
1. Set up the apparatus as shown in the photos at the beginning of the lab. Be sure that the thistle tube is within 2-3 mm of the bottom of the flask.
2. Fill two gas-collecting bottles with water, cover the top with glass plates and invert the bottles in the pneumatic trough. Slide the glass plates away after the gas bottles have been inverted and are underwater. Also submerge four test tubes into the trough in like manner.
3. Place 6-8 pieces of mossy zinc in the flask. Stopper the assembly and add sulfuric acid to the flask through the thistle tube. *Caution:* Pour the acid slowly into the thistle tube until the level in the flask covers the end of the thistle tube. **Why?**
4. Let the gas bubble through the water in the pneumatic trough for the first 10 seconds. Fill

the two bottles and four test tubes with gas as in Part 1A, step 6.
5. Add more sulfuric acid if the bubbling stops and there is still some zinc present.
6. When the bottles and test tubes have been filled, remove the delivery tube from the pneumatic trough. Remove the stopper from the flask and pour the acid (**carefully**) into the container provided by the teacher. This will stop the reaction so it is safe to test the collected hydrogen gas.

### Procedure — Part 2B — Gas Testing:
1. Check to see that no one else around is still producing hydrogen before continuing.
2. Light a Bunsen burner.
3. With a gas bottle nearby, hold a small piece of magnesium ribbon with crucible tongs, ignite the magnesium, slide the glass plate off the bottle and hold the burning ribbon inside the bottle. Record the results.
4. Repeat step 2 with the second bottle, this time using steel wool. Record the results.
5. Insert a glowing splint into the first test tube. Record the results. ***Caution!***
6. Insert a burning splint into the second test tube. Record the results. ***Caution!***
7. Place about 5 mL of water into the third test tube, keeping the tube covered as much as possible to prevent loss or mixing of hydrogen and the air. Add a few drops of Universal Indicator. Shake the tube to mix. Match the color of the solution to the pH chart and record both the color and the pH of the solution.
8. Add limewater to the fourth test tube. Shake the tube to mix and record the results.

### Observations — Part 2:
Record your observations for each of the tests in the chart below:

| Magnesium ribbon (in bottle) | Steel Wool (in bottle) | Glowing Splint (in test tube) | Burning Splint (in test tube) | Universal Indicator (in test tube) | Limewater (in test tube) |
|---|---|---|---|---|---|
| | | | | | |

### Questions — Part 2:
1. Given the fact that you were able to collect hydrogen by displacement of water, what does this suggest about the solubility of hydrogen in water?

2. Some groups removed the stopper and waited before doing the burning splint test and found that nothing happened. Others observed a rather dramatic reaction. Explain why waiting too long might "spoil" the expected reaction.

_____

_____

_____

_____

3. Why must the end of the thistle tube be immersed in the sulfuric acid solution?

_____

_____

_____

_____

4. Why must all gas generation be stopped before a flame is lit?

_____

_____

_____

_____

**Conclusions:**

1. What did you learn in this lab? Discuss at least 3 or 4 things you learned including something regarding the statement given in the Purpose.

_____

_____

_____

_____

_____

_____

2. Can you identify any errors that actually occurred or are possible in the procedure?

_____

_____

_____

_____

3. General comments: e.g., "I liked/disliked this lab because..."; "My favorite part was..."

_____

_____

_____

_____

_____

**Mini DEMO ...**

# H.6 Cartesian Divers

On the demonstration desk is a 2-L bottle filled with water. Inside are some Beral® pipets partially filled with water and weighed down at the end. One of the pipets is open while the other has been closed by putting a screw in the open end. Increase the pressure inside the bottle either by squeezing or by using the pump cap. Explain your observations of each pipet.

| Observation: | Explanation: |
|---|---|
| Open-end Pipet: _____ | • _____ |
| _____ | _____ |
| Closed-end Pipet: _____ | • _____ |
| _____ | _____ |

**Questions:**

1. What causes the pressure to increase...

   a. When you squeeze the bottle?

   _____

   _____

   _____

   _____

   b. When you pump the FizzKeeper®?

   _____

   _____

   _____

   _____

# H.7 Measurement of Gas Pressure

Gases exert pressure when their particles collide with a surface. The number of collisions and the amount of energy associated with these collisions is constant in a given unit of time. The more kinetic energy a particle of gas possesses, the greater the impact of a collision between it and the surface of its container, the more collisions it will have, and the more pressure it will exert.

Pressure is a measurement of the force against a unit of surface area. In the metric system, the unit of force is the **pascal** (Pa), which is equal to the force of one newton per square meter of surface area.

$$\text{Pressure} = \frac{\text{Force}}{\text{Area}} = \frac{1\ N}{m^2} = 1\ Pa$$

Pascals are quite small, however, so chemists use the kilopascal (kPa) when expressing pressure units (1000 Pa = 1 kPa). The average pressure of the air at sea level is called **standard pressure** and has a value of 101.325 kPa. Sometimes it is convenient to refer to standard pressure as one **atmosphere** (1 atm).

## The Mercury Barometer

Atmospheric pressure is normally measured using a **barometer**. One kind of barometer, the mercury barometer (see FIGURE H2), was originally invented by Italian scientist Evangelista Torricelli. It is made by using a glass tube about 80 cm in length and sealed at one end. The tube is filled with mercury and inverted into a container containing mercury. The mercury column in the tube falls until it exerts the same pressure as the air in the atmosphere around it. Changes in air pressure are monitored by shifts in the level of the mercury column.

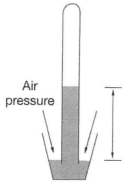

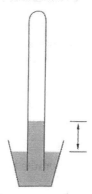

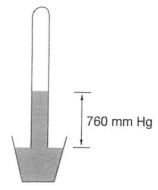

As the air pressure increases, mercury is forced up the glass tube. (high pressure)

As the air pressure decreases, mercury in the glass tube falls. (low pressure)

When measuring air pressure at standard pressure and at sea level, the mercury in the glass tube has a length of 760 mm.

If the air pressure drops, perhaps due to the passing of a low-pressure weather system, the mercury column falls. If the air pressure increases, usually indicating fair weather, the mercury column rises. The average height of a mercury column at sea level is 760 mm or 76 cm; 760 mm Hg (also referred to as 760 torr [after Torricelli]) is an equivalent pressure to 101.325 kPa.

Mercury barometers are not used in the science classroom due to the toxicity of mercury. It is also unreliable because mercury expands and contracts with temperature changes, requiring corrections to be made before reporting the final pressure.

Since not everyone lives at sea level and air pressure changes from day to day, it is necessary to be able to change from one pressure unit to another. Using the equivalent pressures for standard pressure, it is possible to set up a conversion factor from one unit to another:

Standard Pressure = 760 mm Hg (760 torr)  =  101.325 kPa  =  1 atm

$$\underline{\quad}\ \text{mm Hg} \times \frac{101.325\ \text{kPa}}{760\ \text{mm Hg}} = \underline{\quad}\ \text{kPa} \quad \textbf{and} \quad \underline{\quad}\ \text{kPa} \times \frac{760\ \text{mm Hg}}{101.325\ \text{kPa}} = \underline{\quad}\ \text{mm Hg}$$

## The Aneroid Barometer

An aneroid barometer has a vacuum canister that expands or contracts as the pressure changes. A lever touching this canister then moves and ultimately results in causing the needle to move on the dial. The needle reading on the dial indicates the prevailing air pressure.

Aneroid barometers are very useful for helping predict weather changes and are preferable to mercury barometers because they are easy to use. In addition, because air pressure depends partly on altitude, special aneroid barometers called *altimeters* are used by airplane pilots to determine the height of the plane above the earth's surface.

## Pressure Gauges/Pressure Sensors

Often at New Year's Eve or birthday parties, the celebration includes a blowout toy. A paper tube is curled under the action of a fairly weak spring. The harder you blow into the tube, the farther it uncurls. This is really a simple kind of pressure gauge. A pressure gauge is simply a tube of spring steel coiled up like the paper tube in the toy. When gas pressure is applied to the end of the tube, it uncurls and operates a pointer on the gauge dial.

An electronic pressure sensor works when the applied air pressure moves a special piece of foam inside the device. This movement is converted into an electrical signal by a transducer and reported on a digital readout.

# H.8 <u>Exercises</u>  Measurement of Gas Pressure

1. Convert the following pressures to kilopascals:
   a. 700. mm Hg    b. 850. mm Hg    c. 350. mm Hg

2. Convert the following pressures to mmHg:
   a. 100. kPa       b. 75 kPa         c. 125 kPa

3. Convert the following pressures to atm:
   a. 850. mm Hg    b. 75 kPa

4. Atmospheric pressure changes from day to day. What would a drop in the air pressure readings indicate about the weather?

   _____

   _____

   _____

5. Assume that the atmospheric pressure increases from 750 mm Hg to 765 mm Hg. Make an approximate sketch of the initial and final views of a mercury barometer.

**LAB ...**

# H.9 The Effect of Pressure on the Volume of Gas (Boyle's Law)

**Purpose:**
✔ To study the effect of pressure on the volume of gas and manipulate the data to obtain a straight-line graph.

**Materials:**
- 1 pressure gauge
- 1 50-mL syringe (or whatever is available)
- graph paper (or may be done using a graphing program)

**Introduction:**
In this experiment, a fixed amount of gas is trapped in a syringe and the syringe is attached to a pressure gauge to form a closed system. The gas is manually compressed. The volume of the gas and its pressure are then measured at various compressions. The pressure exerted on the gas is caused by atmospheric pressure and by the pressure resulting from the force of the manual compression.

**Procedure:**

1. Write all data in the table below.

2. Record today's atmospheric pressure in mmHg and kPa.

3. Obtain the internal gauge volume from the instructor.

4. Set the volume of the syringe to 50.0 mL and attach the syringe to the pressure gauge. Record the syringe volume and the gauge pressure.

5. Decrease the syringe volume by 5.0 mL. Record the new syringe volume and gauge pressure.

6. Repeat step 5 until the pressure readings are off scale.

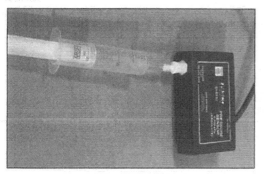

**Data and Results:**

Fill in the chart below. Complete all calculations.

**Questions:**

1. What is the effect of increasing the pressure on this volume of gas?

_____

2. What conclusion can be made regarding total pressure × total volume (PV)?

_____

3. Plot a graph of the total pressure in kPa on the horizontal axis and the volume of the gas in mL on the vertical axis. Describe the shape of the line that is obtained.

_____

_____

4. Plot a graph of reciprocal pressure (1/P) in $kPa^{-1}$ on the horizontal axis and the volume on the vertical axis. Describe the shape of the line that is obtained.

_____

_____

5. Make a general statement about the relationship between the pressure and volume of a gas at a constant temperature, in words and mathematically.

_____

_____

_____

_____

_____

_____

| Gauge Volume (mL) | Syringe Volume (mL) | Total Volume (mL) | Gauge Pressure (kPa) | Atmospheric Pressure (kPa) | Total Pressure (kPa) | $\dfrac{1}{Pressure}$ $(kPa^{-1})$ | P x V |
|---|---|---|---|---|---|---|---|
| | | | | | | | |
| | | | | | | | |
| | | | | | | | |
| | | | | | | | |
| | | | | | | | |
| | | | | | | | |
| | | | | | | | |

Today's atmospheric pressure = _____ mmHg = _____ kPa

6. Would the PV results be too high or too low if the syringe leaked at high pressure? Explain.

_____

_____

_____

**Conclusions:**

1. What did you learn in this lab? Discuss at least 3 or 4 things you learned including something regarding the statement given in the Purpose.

_____

_____

_____

_____

_____

_____

2. Can you identify any errors that actually occurred or are possible in the procedure?

_____

_____

_____

_____

3. General comments: e.g., "I liked/disliked this lab because..."; "My favorite part was..."

_____

_____

_____

_____

# H.10 Boyle's Law

Robert Boyle was the first to investigate pressure-volume relationships of gases (1627–1691). Boyle was one of the first scientists to believe that scientific study must be based on laws that have been empirically determined, that is, proven through observation. **Boyle's Law** deals with changes in pressure and volume when the temperature (T) and number of molecules (n) are held constant. It states that *the volume of a quantity of gas at a particular temperature is inversely proportional to the pressure applied to the gas*. Thus

$$V \propto \frac{1}{P} \quad \text{(where } \propto \text{ means "is proportional to")}$$

which is consistent with your experimental findings. In mathematics, a proportion is converted into an equation by the use of a constant, $k$.

$$V \propto \frac{1}{P} \quad \text{becomes} \quad V = \frac{k_1}{P} \quad \text{or} \quad PV = k_1$$

In science, the $k$ value usually holds the secret to an explanation (or theory) of the relationship. Here, $k$ has the same value as long as the temperature and the same quantity (mole) of gas is maintained. Boyle's only attempt at an explanation was that since gases could be compressed, they must consist of a void, or *empty space that contained particles*. The **Kinetic Molecular Theory (KMT)**, proposed 200 years later by Maxwell and Boltzmann, can be used to explain Boyle's Law. The Ideal Gas Model discussed in Section H.3 is part of the KMT.

The KMT states that the pressure exerted by a gaseous system is caused by the collision of the molecules with the walls of the container. If the volume of the container is decreased at constant temperature as shown in FIGURE H3, the molecules will collide more frequently with the container's walls. The pressure in the smaller volume is therefore greater.

**FIGURE H3 Boyle's Law and the Kinetic Molecular Theory**

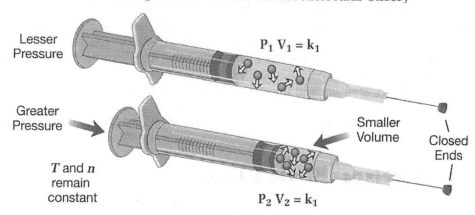

The product of the pressure and volume—$P_1V_1$ or $P_2V_2$—remains nearly constant at the temperatures and pressures typically encountered in the laboratory, provided the temperature is unchanged and the system does not leak. This greater pressure is caused by the molecules colliding with the container walls more frequently. At higher pressures and lower temperatures, deviations from Boyle's Law occur due to the gas molecules being in closer contact with each other, allowing intermolecular attractions to influence their behavior.

Since $P_1V_2 = k_1$ and $P_2V_2 = k_1$ (for the same system), then the equation for Boyle's Law becomes

$$P_1V_1 = P_2V_2 \text{ (at constant T and n)}$$

where

$P$ = pressure (any pressure unit may be used)

$V$ = volume (any volume unit may be used)

$T$ = temperature

$n$ = number of moles of gas

## Example:

One mole of a gas occupies a volume of 22.4 L at standard pressure. What volume will it occupy if the pressure is increased to 150.0 kPa? Assume that no temperature change occurs.

*(List unknowns, then the given data; state formula, rearrange equation in terms of the unknown, substitute and solve.)*

$V_1 = 22.4 \text{ L}$     $P_1 V_1 = P_2 V_2$     which rearranges to     $V_2 = \dfrac{P_1 V_1}{P_2}$

$V_2 = \text{ ?}$     $V_2 = \dfrac{(101.325 \text{ kPa})(22.4 \text{ L})}{(150.0 \text{ kPa})}$

$P_1 = 101.325 \text{ kPa}$     $V_2 = 15.1 \text{ L}$

$P_2 = 150.0 \text{ kPa}$

## Boyle's Law and Diving

Divers soon learn the importance of Boyle's Law. The relationship between pressure and volume described in Boyle's Law affects the spaces in our body that are filled with air, such as our ears, sinuses, lungs and digestive tract.

The air inside these body cavities is pushing out while the air outside the body is pushing in.   The walls of the body cavities are like fragile light bulbs. Under normal circumstances, they are able to withstand atmospheric pressure because the gas inside the body is at approximately the same pressure as outside the body.

Have you ever experienced a "funny" sensation when you came down very quickly in an elevator or an airplane? The deep-sea diver experiences the same sensation. His ears experience pressure against the eardrum, and his body attempts to compensate by decreasing the volume of the middle ear cavity. Another way to compensate is to bring more air into the inner ear through the Eustachian tube. This can be done by yawning, swallowing or chewing gum.

The sinuses, lungs, stomach and intestines experience similar problems during descent or ascent in the water, an airplane or an elevator in a tall building. These organs tend to be able to correct the problem and equalize the pressure. Most problems are only temporary.

# H.11 <u>Exercises</u> Boyle's Law

1. If 2000. L of hydrogen gas at a pressure of 80.0 kPa is compressed into a cylinder with a volume of 10.0 L while keeping the temperature constant, what pressure will the gas exert in the cylinder?

2. A gas is confined in a syringe (i.e., a cylinder with a moveable piston). When the volume of the cylinder is 750. mL the pressure is 150. kPa. What will the volume of the cylinder be when the pressure has risen to 250. kPa?

3. An open air-filled can is lowered upside down into the water. If the volume of air in the can is 5.00 L, what will the volume of air be at 55.0 m deep? (There is an additional 1 atm of pressure for every 11.0 m of water.) Assume standard pressure at the start. Hint: Draw a picture.

4. Modern jets regularly fly at heights over 10 000 m, yet passengers do not get the "bends." Explain why this is true.

5. In the Cartesian Diver Mini-Demo H.7, one way to make the diver descend is to squeeze the bottle. How does squeezing the bottle increase the pressure?

6. A hyperbaric chamber is a device used to raise the internal air pressure and has room for several people at once. How could a doctor use this chamber to treat a person who has ascended from a deep dive too quickly and is experiencing the "bends?"

# H.12 The Effect of Temperature on the Volume of a Gas (Charles' Law)

**Purpose:**
✔ To study the effect of temperature on the volume of a confined gas while pressure remains constant.
✔ To show how the data can be graphed to obtain an approximation of absolute zero.

**Materials:**
- 1 18 × 150 mm test tube
- 1 thermometer (−10 to 150°C)
- 1 sealed glass tube (10-15 cm long)
- 1 Bunsen burner
- 1 centimeter ruler
- vegetable oil to cover glass tube

length of air column | Air

**Procedure:**
1. Set up the apparatus as shown in the diagram.
2. Carefully heat to 125°C. Stop heating and wait for the temperature to stop rising.
3. Notice that there is a column of air trapped in the glass tube. The volume of this air is proportional to the length of the air column. ($V_{cylinder} = \pi r^2 h$ and $\pi$ and r do not change for the glass tubing, only the length. Therefore, $V_1 = \pi r^2 h_1$, $V_2 = \pi r^2 h_2$, etc.)
4. Hold a ruler alongside the test tube to measure the length of the air column. Record both the length and the temperature.
5. Take length and temperature readings approximately every 10°C beginning around 120-130°C.
6. Continue taking readings until the temperature drops 60 to 70 degrees from the original temperature.

**Data and Results:**

| Length (cm) | Temp (°C) |
|---|---|
|  |  |
|  |  |
|  |  |
|  |  |
|  |  |
|  |  |
|  |  |
|  |  |
|  |  |
|  |  |

**Questions:**
1. Plot a graph of your data. Put temperature on the y axis and length on the x axis. If the graph is not a straight line, try using temperature on the y axis and 1/length on the x axis. *Extrapolate* the data on the straight-line graph back to zero length (volume) (*i.e., extend the line formed by the data back to where it crosses the x axis*). Use a graphing program to construct your graph.

2. As the gas cools, the volume of the gas decreases. Obviously the gas volume cannot shrink to less than zero. Therefore, the point where the line intersects the y axis represents the coldest possible temperature that can exist.

   a. What is the *name* given to this temperature? (This can be found in Section H.4.)

b. What is *your value* for the temperature at zero volume?

_____

c. What is the *literature value* for this temperature? (This can be found in Section H.10.)

_____

d. Suggest three reasons for any difference in the experimental value and the literature value.

_____

_____

_____

_____

_____

3. Use your straight-line graph to develop a mathematical statement about the relationship between volume and temperature at constant pressure.

$$y = a \ x + b$$
$$\downarrow \quad \downarrow \ \downarrow \quad \downarrow$$
$$= k$$

4. It should be obvious that there is a simple relationship between volume and temperature at constant pressure. However, this is mathematically difficult because of the need to deal with negative temperatures. Lord Kelvin solved this problem by developing a new temperature scale with only positive numbers.

The Kelvin temperature scale assigns **absolute zero** a value of zero and its degrees are the same size as Celsius degrees.

a. Based on the information given above, what Kelvin temperature would correspond to the normal freezing point of water?

_____

b. What Kelvin temperature would correspond to the normal boiling point of water?

_____

c. How do you convert a temperature in degrees Celsius units to its corresponding temperature in degrees Kelvin?

_____

5. Write a general statement of the temperature-volume relationship for gases at constant pressure.

_____

_____

_____

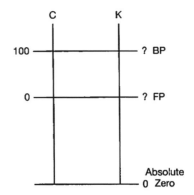

**Error Discussion:**

6. a. Suppose the oil plug is "sticky" and does not move as far as it should. Will that make the length reading of the gas inside the tube too long or too short? How does that affect the absolute zero value?

_____

_____

_____

b. Just like the air inside the tube contracts when cooled, the oil also contracts as it cools. This allows more oil to move inside the glass tube. How would the absolute zero value be affected? Explain.

_____

_____

_____

**Conclusions:**

1. What did you learn in this lab? Discuss at least 3 or 4 things you learned including something regarding the statement given in the Purpose.

_____

_____

_____

_____

2. Can you identify any errors that actually occurred or are possible in the procedure?

_____

_____

_____

_____

3. General comments: e.g., "I liked/disliked this lab because..."; "My favorite part was..."

_____

_____

_____

_____

# H.13 Charles' Law

You have just rediscovered another **gas law** or mathematical equation that predicts the behavior of gases. J.A. Charles, a French physicist who was the first to do precise measurements relating the volume of a gas and its temperature, did this work in the eighteenth century. Charles was the first to determine that, when the pressure (P) and the number (n) of molecules are held constant, the volume increases proportionately with its temperature. More specifically, Charles' Law states that for every degree Celsius increase in temperature, the volume of a gas increases by 1/273 of its original volume. Later, Lord Kelvin, a Scottish physicist, used Charles' Law to introduce the Kelvin scale of temperatures and the relationship between volume and temperature. This relationship is often expressed as:

$$V \propto T_K \qquad \text{which becomes} \qquad V = k_2 T_K \qquad \text{or} \qquad \frac{V}{T_K} = k_2$$

where $T_K$ is the temperature in Kelvins

$k_2$ used here has a different value from the $k$ used before, as the temperature is different, and the number of moles of the gas could also be different.

To put it another way, there is a "bottom" to the temperature scale: when the temperature is decreased, the volume decreases; when the volume decreases to zero, the temperature is as low as it can get. This temperature is called **absolute zero** and is equal to 0 K or –273.15°C. This naturally leads to an equation relating the Celsius temperature to the Kelvin temperature:

$$T_K = T_C + 273.15°C$$

T = 373 K

Since $\frac{V_1}{T_1} = k_2$ and $\frac{V_2}{T_2} = k_2$

T = 423 K

and assuming the system does not leak and the pressure is constant, then the equation for Charles' Law becomes:

$$\frac{V_1}{T_1} = \frac{V_2}{T_2} \quad \text{(at constant } P \text{ and } n\text{)}$$

where:
T = temperature (MUST BE KELVIN)
V = volume (any volume unit may be used)
P = pressure
n = number of moles

The kinetic-molecular theory can be used to explain Charles' Law. When the temperature of a gas is increased, the average kinetic energy of the molecules also increases. As a result, more forceful and frequent collisions occur. As shown above, even though the external pressure has not changed, the increase in temperature after heating causes an increase in internal pressure, and the piston in the cylinder moves up. This causes an increase in volume until the pressure inside the container is once again equal to the pressure outside the container. Similarly, a decrease in temperature would cause the piston to move down.

Charles' Law holds true for most gases at the temperatures and pressures typically encountered in the laboratory. If, however, the pressure is very high or the temperature is lowered to approach the point where the gas will liquefy, the observed volumes are different from those predicted by Charles' Law. As with Boyle's Law, successful application of the model is restricted.

## Example:

One mole of a gas occupies a volume of 22.4 L at standard temperature (0.0°C). What volume will it occupy at 50.0°C?

*Step 1:* Convert $T_2$ to Kelvins:

$$T_K = T_C + 273.15°C = 50.0°C + 273.15°C = 323.2 \text{ K}$$

*Step 2:* State formula, rearrange equation in terms of the unknown, substitute and solve:

$V_1 = 22.4$ L $\qquad \dfrac{V_1}{T_1} = \dfrac{V_2}{T_2}$ which rearranges to $\quad V_2 = \dfrac{V_1 T_2}{T_1}$

$V_2 = ? \qquad\qquad V_2 = \dfrac{(22.4 \text{ L})(323.2 \text{ K})}{(273.2 \text{ K})}$

$T_1 = 273.2$ K $\qquad V_2 = 26.5$ L

$T_2 = 323.2$ K

## Charles' Law and Ballooning

Up, up and away! Well, make sure that you know what you are doing! The first ballooning flight took place on November 21, 1783, when a hot air balloon built by Etienne Montgolfier carried Pilatre de Rosier and the Marquis d'Arlandes aloft near Paris. The balloon was filled with air, and a fire in the balloon basket heated the air in the balloon, causing it to expand. As the air warmed, its volume increased, thereby causing the density to decrease (the gas did not increase in mass). The balloon rose to about 900 meters before the fire went out and the gas cooled, bringing the balloon back down after 20 minutes in the air.

Jacques Charles was apparently not overly impressed. He envisaged longer flights and higher altitudes and suggested the use of hydrogen as the balloon gas. Hydrogen, being much less dense than air, required no heating. However, it was potentially dangerous because hydrogen is extremely flammable and one small spark would cause an explosion.

Charles filled a balloon, which he is reported to have named "Charlière," with hydrogen, and took it up himself on December 1, 1873. He soared to a height of about 3000 meters.

Ballooning became a hit and led to the development of the great airships. This technology continued until the tragic explosion of the Hindenburg as it was landing in New Jersey in 1937, during a thunderstorm. The huge hydrogen bag exploded, sending many of the passengers and crew to their deaths.

So why is ballooning so popular again? The answer is simple —helium. Helium is a light and nonreactive noble gas, thus decreasing the risk of ballooning. Up, up and away!

## Temperature Inversions

Visible and ultraviolet rays arriving from our Sun pass right through our atmosphere and strike the Earth's surface. Some are absorbed, and some are changed to infrared rays and released as heat. As such, it is absorbed by the carbon dioxide and water vapor of our atmosphere, thereby providing a warm blanket of air over the surface of the planet. Thus the carbon dioxide and the water vapor trap the heat. The glass of a greenhouse traps sunlight, but the energy reflected off the plants and the floor cannot pass through the glass. Thus this effect is often called the **greenhouse effect** (FIGURE H4).

Carbon dioxide and water vapor in our atmosphere are responsible for trapping energy and causing the greenhouse effect around our planet. Scientists estimate that our planet's average yearly temperature would be about 40°C less than it is without the greenhouse effect. Life, as we know it, would cease to exist.

As this air warms up, its volume tends to increase. Since its mass remains constant, its density tends to decrease with increasing temperatures.

$$\text{density} = \frac{\text{mass}}{\text{volume}}$$

Because the atmosphere is heated by energy reflected from the earth's surface, temperature normally decreases as you move away from the surface. However, it is possible for denser, cooler air to become trapped under less dense, warmer air. Such a situation is called a thermal or temperature inversion. Thus warm air (smoke, exhaust) formed at the surface rises, but when it hits the warm air above, it stops. Thus pollutants accumulate. (See FIGURE H5 below.) This accumulation accentuates the problem because the pollutants reflect the sunlight back into space. Thus as conditions continue, the temperature inversion may last for several days, producing hazardous health conditions. The effects are particularly dangerous for the elderly, children and anyone with respiratory problems.

## Charles' Law and Toothaches

Sometimes an ice cube stops a toothache. But when the tooth warms up again — watch out! If there is tooth decay in the interior of the tooth, gases are produced which attack the nerve, causing the ache. Cold temperatures slow the gases down and although they continue to collide, they do so with less energy and less pressure so the ache disappears. As the gases heat up again, the ache returns.

FIGURE H4
Greenhouse Effect

FIGURE H5   A Temperature Inversion

SMoke (pollution) + fOG = SMOG

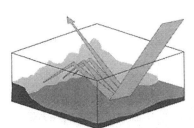

Gases in the atmosphere absorb infared radiation (heat) to warm the air around our planet.

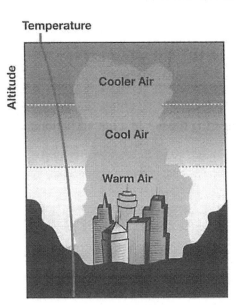

Normal Conditions

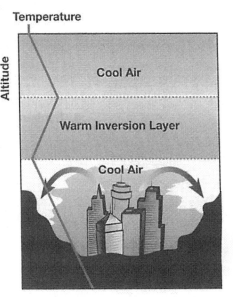

Temperature Inversion

# H.14 Exercises  Charles' Law

1. A gas storage tank has a spring closure that maintains a constant pressure while permitting the volume to adjust to changes in temperature. What will be the volume of the gas if 25.0 L of a gas at 20.0°C is heated to 30.0°C?

2. A helium-filled balloon has a volume of 10 000. L at 20°C. Determine the volume of the gas at 25°C.

3. An industrial gas storage tank with adjustable pressure has a volume of 100.0 L when the gas temperature is 55.0°C. Calculate the temperature of the gas if the volume drops to 75.0 L with no loss in pressure.

4. Several helium-filled balloons are purchased for a December birthday party. When the customer takes them from the store to the car, the balloons collapse. Explain what happened.

5. Explain how heating the gas in a hot air balloon causes the balloon to float upward.

6. Explain why an aerosol can explodes when it is thrown into a fire.

## H.15  Fire Syringe

Your teacher will show you a special thick-walled glass tube with a tight-fitting piston to match.  A small piece of cotton is placed inside at the bottom of the tube.   Now the piston will be rammed forcefully into the syringe.

**Questions:**
1. What did you observe?

_____

_____

2. a. Is this process enothermic or exothermic?

_____

b. In terms of attractions between molecules, what causes this energy change to occur?

_____

_____

c. State a rule relating P and T for gases.

_____

# H.16 The Combined Gas Law

Charles' Law and Boyle's Law can be combined and used to solve problems in which both the temperature and pressure may vary.  The **Combined Gas Law** involves simultaneous changes in pressure, volume, and temperature when the number of molecules remains constant.

$$\frac{PV}{T} = k \qquad \text{therefore} \qquad \frac{P_1 V_1}{T_1} = \frac{P_2 V_2}{T_2}$$

## Example:

Find the volume of a gas at 110.0 kPa and 35.0°C if its volume at 98.0 kPa and 15.0°C is 7.50 L.

*Step 1:* List all variables. Convert temperatures to Kelvins.

$P_1$ = 98.0 kPa           $P_2$ = 110.0 kPa
$V_1$ = 7.50 L             $V_2$ = ?
$T_1$ = 15.0°C + 273.15 = 288.2 K     $T_2$ = 35.0°C + 273.15 = 308.2 K

*Step 2:* State formula, rearrange equation in terms of the unknown, substitute and solve.

$$\frac{P_1 V_1}{T_1} = \frac{P_2 V_2}{T_2} \qquad \text{becomes} \qquad V_2 = \frac{P_1 V_1 T_2}{P_2 T_1} = \frac{(98.0 \text{ kPa})(7.50 \text{ L})(308.2 \text{ K})}{(110.0 \text{ kPa})(288.2 \text{ K})}$$

$$= 7.1 \text{ L}$$

# H.17 Exercises  The Combined Gas Law

1. A balloonist fills a balloon with 25 000. L of helium gas. The temperature at ground level is 25.0°C and the barometric pressure is 1.000 atm or 101.3 kPa. At 3500 m, the temperature has dropped to 5.0°C and the barometric pressure is 0.900 atm or 91.2 kPa. What is the volume of the balloon's gasbag at this altitude?

2. The gases from a smokestack at an industrial plant emerge at a temperature of 250.°C and a pressure of 110. kPa. If 1.00 L of this gas is allowed to cool to 18°C and adjust to 100.5 kPa, what will be the new volume?

3. Hot exhaust gases are often used in a chemical plant to heat chemical reactions before the gases are discharged to the atmosphere. If 10.0 L of gas at 300°C and 3.00 atm expand to 125 L at 1.00 atm during the heat exchange process, what is the temperature of the gas that is released to the atmosphere?

4. On a day when the temperature is 24°C and the barometric pressure is 100.0 kPa, a balloon is inflated using 5.0 L of air. When the balloon is brought into a cold chamber at the same pressure, the volume drops to 4.0 L. What is the temperature of the cold chamber?

# H.18 Avogadro's Hypothesis

Recall the Cartesian Diver H.6 Mini-Demo? One of the methods used to increase the pressure inside the bottle was to pump air into the bottle. This works because the pump adds air molecules to the container. The more molecules in a container, the more collisions and the greater the pressure. In a similar way, a balloon is inflated when you blow into it, because the more molecules of gas present, the greater the volume. It is apparent that both the pressure and the volume of a gas are related to the number of gas molecules present.

In 1811, Amedeo Avogadro, an Italian physicist, was studying how pressure and volume are related to the number of molecules. He proposed a hypothesis to accompany Dalton's Atomic Theory (1804) and to explain the work of the French chemist Joseph-Louis Gay-Lussac. Gay-Lussac had determined empirically that the volumes of gases that combine, or are produced in chemical changes, are always in small whole-number ratios. Dalton proposed that in chemical reactions, atoms, or "compound atoms," react in fixed simple whole-number proportions. Avogadro saw that the gas-volume ratios of Gay-Lussac and the atom or compound atom ratios of Dalton were identical. This led to **Avogadro's Hypothesis** that *equal volumes of gases at the same temperature and pressure contain the same number of molecules* ("compound atoms"). In other words, *the volume of a gas depends on the number of molecules in the container as long as the temperature and pressure are constant.* If the gas volume ratio in a chemical reaction was to equal the atom or "compound atom" ratio, this had to be true.

$$V = k_3 n$$

For example,

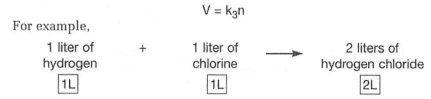

| 1 liter of hydrogen | + | 1 liter of chlorine | → | 2 liters of hydrogen chloride |
|---|---|---|---|---|
| 1L | | 1L | | 2L |

Thus Avogadro speculated that one volume of hydrogen contained the same number of molecules as one volume of chlorine, whereas two volumes of hydrogen chloride contained twice as many molecules.

For this to be so, hydrogen and chlorine must be **diatomic** molecules (*two atoms per molecule*). If they were not, then the reaction could not be balanced.

$$H_2(g) + Cl_2(g) \longrightarrow 2\,HCl(g)$$

Avogadro's ideas about molecules and atoms were not accepted for many years. He introduced the term molecule, and made the writing of molecular formulas and the balancing of chemical equations possible. Molecular and atomic masses became possible as well.

# H.19 <u>Exercises</u> Avogadro's Hypothesis

1. It is known that one volume of hydrogen gas reacts with one volume of chlorine gas to form two volumes of hydrogen chloride gas.

   a. Which diagram (model) best illustrates this experimental result? (Assume ⚪ represents a hydrogen atom and ⚫ represents a chlorine atom.) _____

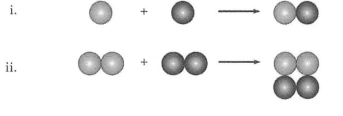

i.

ii.

iii.

b. What does this say about the number of atoms in one molecule of hydrogen? of chlorine? of hydrogen chloride?

_____

_____

_____

2. It is known that sulfur dioxide molecules are 32 times heavier than hydrogen molecules. If 1.0 L of sulfur dioxide has a mass of 4.0 g at a certain temperature and pressure, what would be the mass of 1.0 L of hydrogen gas at the same temperature and pressure?

_____

# H.20 Calculations of Gases at STP—Molar Volume

Because of the low density of gases, it is much more convenient to measure volumes rather than masses of gases. If Avogadro's Hypothesis is correct, it should be possible to obtain a definite number of gaseous molecules by measuring a definite volume of gas. Since temperature and pressure are very important factors in gas volume measurements, scientists often refer to "standard temperature and pressure" or **STP**, which conventionally is 0°C and 101.325 kPa (normal atmospheric pressure at sea level). Experimentally it is found that the volume of one mole of almost any common gas at STP is approximately 22.4 L. Thus the **molar volume** of many gases **at STP** is **22.4 L/mol**, which allows quick calculations of number of moles in a given volume.

The number of moles of a sample can be determined by:

$$\text{\# moles} = \frac{\text{volume}}{\text{molar volume}}$$

or if n = # moles of gas, v = volume of gas sample and V = molar volume.

| **Equation Method** |
|:---:|
| $n_{\text{any gas}} = \dfrac{v}{V}$  or  $n_{\text{any gas}} = \dfrac{v}{22.4 \text{ L/mol}}$ |
| $v = n_{\text{any gas}}\, V$  or  $v = n_{\text{any gas}} \times 22.4 \text{ L/mol}$ |

| **Conversion Factor Method** |
|:---:|
| $n_{\text{any gas}} = v \times \dfrac{1 \text{ mol}}{22.4 \text{ L}}$ |
| $v = n_{\text{any gas}} \times \dfrac{22.4 \text{ L}}{1 \text{ mol}}$ |

Below is a generalized method to use for solving problems using moles:

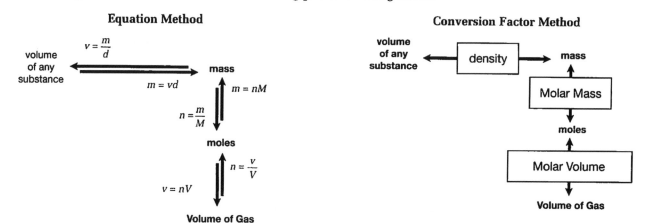

| Example #1 | Solving Process |
|---|---|
| Calculate the number of moles of oxygen gas contained in a volume of 112 L at STP. | **Equation Method** $$n_{O_2} = \frac{v}{V} = \frac{112\ L}{22.4\ L/mol} = 5.00\ mol\ O_2$$ |
| | **Conversion Factor Method** $$112\ \cancel{L}\ O_2 \times \frac{1\ mol\ O_2}{22.4\ \cancel{L}\ O_2} = 5.00\ mol\ O_2$$ |

| Example #2 | Solving Process |
|---|---|
| Calculate the volume that 0.200 mol of hydrogen gas occupies at STP. | **Equation Method** $$v_{H_2} = nV = 0.200\ mol \times 22.4\ L/mol = 4.48\ L\ H_2$$ |
| | **Conversion Factor Method** $$0.200\ \cancel{mol}\ H_2 \times \frac{22.4\ L\ H_2}{1\ \cancel{mol}\ H_2} = 4.48\ L\ H_2$$ |

| Example #3 | Solving Process |
|---|---|
| Calculate the mass of oxygen gas present in a volume of 896 L at STP. | **Equation Method** $$n_{O_2} = \frac{v}{V} = \frac{896\ L}{22.4\ L/mol} = 40.0\ mol$$ $$m_{O_2} = nM = (40.0\ mol)(32.00\ g/mol) = 1.28 \times 10^3\ g = 1.28\ kg\ O_2$$ |
| | **Conversion Factor Method** $$896\ L\ O_2 \times \frac{1\ \cancel{mol}\ O_2}{22.4\ L\ O_2} \times \frac{32.00\ g\ O_2}{1\ \cancel{mol}\ O_2} = 1.28 \times 10^3\ g = 1.28\ kg\ O_2$$ |

| Example #4 | Solving Process |
|---|---|
| Calculate the volume occupied at STP by 40.0 g of methane. | **Equation Method** $$n_{CH_4} = \frac{m}{M} = \frac{40.0\ g}{16.05\ g/mol} = 2.49\ mol$$ $$v_{CH_4} = nV = (2.49\ mol)(22.4\ L/mol) = 55.8\ L\ CH_4$$ |
| | **Conversion Factor Method** $$40.0\ \cancel{g}\ CH_4 \times \frac{1\ \cancel{mol}\ CH_4}{16.05\ \cancel{g}\ CH_4} \times \frac{22.4\ L\ CH_4}{1\ \cancel{mol}\ CH_4} = 55.8\ L\ CH_4$$ |

# H.21 <u>Exercises</u> Calculations of Gases at STP

1. Calculate the number of moles of helium gas used to inflate a 2.00 L balloon at STP.

2. An exhausted cross-country skier inhales 2.50 L of oxygen at STP. Calculate the mass of oxygen inhaled.

3. What is the volume at STP of 20.0 t of sulfur dioxide gas released as a pollutant into the air by a tar-sands plant. (1 t = 1000 kg)

4. One liter of dry ice (solid carbon dioxide) has a mass of 1.56 kg. What volume of gaseous carbon dioxide will be produced at STP if this mass of dry ice is allowed to sublime (from a solid to a gas)?

# H.22 The Ideal Gas Law

The properties of gases discussed so far can be summarized as follows:

**Boyle's Law:**

$$V = k_1 \left( \frac{1}{P} \right) \quad \text{(volume is proportional to inverse pressure)}$$

**Charles' Law:**

$$V = k_2 T \qquad \text{(volume is directly proportional to Kelvin temperature)}$$

**Avogadro's Hypothesis:**

$$V = k_3 n \qquad \text{(volume is directly proportional to the number of moles of gas molecules)}$$

It is extremely useful to combine these laws and hypothesis into a single law, called the **Ideal Gas Law,** which has the form

$$V = \frac{k_1 \, k_2 \, k_3 n T}{P} \qquad \text{or} \qquad V = \frac{RnT}{P} \qquad \text{or} \qquad PV = nRT$$

where: $P$ = pressure in kilopascals (kPa)
$V$ = volume in liters (L)
$n$ = number of moles of gas (mol)
$R$ = universal gas constant = 8.314 kPa $\cdot$ L $\cdot$ mol$^{-1}$ $\cdot$ K$^{-1}$
$T$ = absolute temperature in Kelvins (K)

One of the most useful applications of the **Ideal Gas Law** is the calculation of the volume, pressure, temperature or number of moles of gas present at conditions other than 0°C (273.15 K) and 101.325 kPa (i.e., STP). Recall that the molar volume of many gases at STP is stated to be 22.4 mol/L. This is an important property of gases, but is too restricted to be very useful in the real world where standard conditions of temperature and pressure are seldom found.

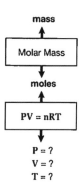

### Example:

Hydrogen gas can be generated by decomposing water in a Hoffman apparatus. What mass of hydrogen is produced if the gas occupies a volume of 50.0 mL (0.0500 L) at 20.00°C and 94.01 kPa?

*Step 1:* Calculate the number of moles of hydrogen.

$$n_{H_2} = \frac{PV}{RT} = \frac{(94.01 \text{ kPa})(0.0500 \text{ L})}{(8.314 \text{ kPa} \cdot \text{L} \cdot \text{mol}^{-1} \cdot \text{K}^{-1})(293.15 \text{ K})} = 0.00193 \text{ mol } H_2$$

*Step 2:* Convert number of moles to mass.

$$m_{H_2} = nM = 0.00193 \text{ mol } H_2 \times \frac{2.02 \text{ g } H_2}{1 \text{ mol } H_2} = 0.00390 \text{ g } H_2$$

# H.23 <u>Exercises</u> The Ideal Gas Law

1. A weather balloon has a capacity of 10 000. L at 100 kPa and 20.00°C. Cesium metal is reacted with water to fill the balloon with hydrogen gas. How many moles of $H_2$ must be generated to fill it?

2. An almost empty natural gas storage tank contains 2.65 kg of methane gas at 650.5 kPa and 18.0°C. What is the volume of the storage tank?

3. An average bungalow contains about 700. m³ of air. How many moles of air does this correspond to if the temperature is 20.00°C and the pressure is 100.5 kPa? (Note: 1 m³ = 1000 L)

4. What mass of neon is in a 160.0 L neon sign if at −10.0°C the gas pressure is 3.00 kPa?

5. A crude thermometer can be made by sealing a known quantity of gas such as nitrogen in a container and measuring the volume and pressure of the gas. If 28.2 g of nitrogen is found to occupy a volume of 20.23 L at 102.0 kPa, what is the temperature in degrees Celsius?

# H.24 Dalton's Law of Partial Pressures

When two or more gases are introduced into a container, each gas contributes part of the total pressure in the system. Dalton explained this behavior of gases in 1801 when he developed his **Law of Partial Pressures** in which he stated that in a mixture of gases, *the total pressure exerted by the mixture is equal to the sum of the partial pressures exerted by the separate components.*

Dalton's Law is written mathematically as follows:

$$P_{total} = p_{gas\ 1} + p_{gas\ 2} + p_{gas\ 3} + \cdots$$

Consider the following model of three gases in a rigid container (FIGURE H6). Recall that each gas has the same average kinetic energy at the same temperature. Therefore the collisions from each gas molecule, on average, will provide the same pressure. The more gas molecules of one kind, the greater the pressure due to that gas.

If the total pressure inside the container is 90.0 kPa, then the partial pressures of each gas will be:

6 ● molecules = 60% of 90.0 kPa = 54.0 kPa

3 ◉ molecules = 30% of 90.0 kPa = 27.0 kPa

1 ○ molecules = 10% of 90.0 kPa = 9.0 kPa
_____
**10** molecules     100%     = 90.0 kPa

*In effect, each gas behaves independently of the other gases in the mixture.* Most mixtures of gases closely obey Dalton's Law.

In laboratory experiments such as the one you did earlier to generate oxygen and hydrogen (H.5 Lab), gases are collected by water displacement. Since the gas bubbles through the water, the gas becomes saturated with water vapor. This water vapor contributes to the total pressure of the system. The total pressure of the system includes the partial pressure of the gas and the partial pressure of the water vapor.

If a gas is collected by water displacement, the pressure exerted by the gas may be determined by measuring the atmospheric pressure with a barometer and subtracting the water vapor pressure at the particular temperature of the gas mixture.

## FIGURE H6
**Ten molecules of 3 different types moving around in a rigid container**

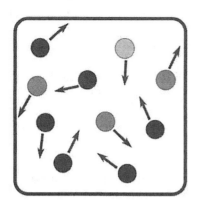

## FIGURE H7 Gas Collecting Apparatus

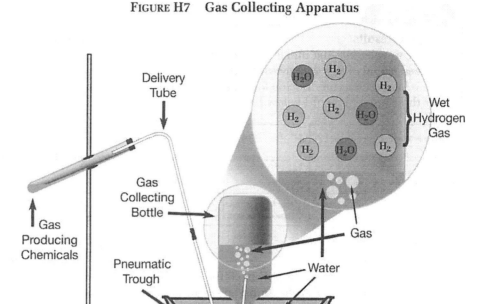

**FIGURE H8**
**Water vapor pressures at various temperatures**

$$P_{atmosphere} = p_{dry\ gas} + p_{water\ vapor} \quad or \quad p_{dry\ gas} = P_{atmosphere} - p_{water\ vapor}$$

| Temp (°C) | Pressure (kPa) | Temp (°C) | Pressure (kPa) |
|-----------|----------------|-----------|----------------|
| 0 | 0.61 | 30 | 4.2 |
| 5 | 0.87 | 35 | 5.6 |
| 10 | 1.2 | 40 | 7.4 |
| 15 | 1.7 | 45 | 9.6 |
| 18 | 2.1 | 50 | 12.3 |
| 19 | 2.2 | 55 | 15.7 |
| 20 | 2.3 | 60 | 19.9 |
| 21 | 2.5 | 70 | 31.2 |
| 22 | 2.6 | 80 | 47.3 |
| 23 | 2.8 | 90 | 70.1 |
| 24 | 3.0 | 100 | 101.3 |
| 25 | 3.2 | 105 | 120.8 |

**DEMO ...**

# H.25 Molar Mass of a Gas—Syringe Method

**Purpose:**
✔ To apply the Ideal Gas Law to determine the molar mass of an unknown gas.

**Materials:**
- 140 cm³ syringe
- syringe cap
- nail
- unknown gas

**Procedure:**
Determine the mass of the empty syringe.
1. With the syringe piston pushed in completely, cap the end of the syringe.
2. Pull back on the piston and insert the nail in the hole that has been provided.

3. Mass the entire assembly.

Determine the mass of an unknown gas.
4. Your teacher will help you fill the syringe with gas to the volume where the nail is in the syringe.
5. Cap the assembly and determine its mass.

**Data and Results:**

In order to calculate the molar mass of this gas, you will need a total of five data measurements. (The first two are labeled for you. Decide for yourself what the other three are and record below.)

| | | | |
|---|---|---|---|
| 1. Mass of empty syringe | | 4. | |
| 2. Mass of syringe with gas | | 5. | |
| 3. | | Molar Mass of Gas (Show calculations) | |

**Questions:**

1. Why was it necessary to pull back the syringe piston before massing the empty syringe? (*Test it yourself on the balance with the syringe piston in and the syringe piston pulled out.*)

_____

_____

_____

_____

2. How would the molar mass results be affected under the following conditions? Explain your answers.

a. The gas put into the syringe was slightly cooler than the recorded room temperature.

_____

_____

b. The true volume of the syringe is slightly smaller than the recorded volume.

_____

_____

c. Some air is mixed in with the unknown gas (assuming the unknown gas is carbon dioxide).

_____

_____

**Conclusions:**

1. What did you learn in this lab? Discuss at least 3 or 4 things you learned including something regarding the statement given in the Purpose.

2. Can you identify any errors that actually occurred or are possible in the procedure?

3. General comments: e.g., "I liked/disliked this lab because..."; "My favorite part was..."

# H.26 <u>Exercises</u> Dalton's Law of Partial Pressures

1. Suppose the air pressure on a given day is 755 mmHg. Use the percent composition of the atmosphere in FIGURE H1 to calculate the partial pressure of nitrogen and oxygen on that day.

2. A mixture of gases contains $H_2$, $O_2$ and $CO_2$. The total pressure of the gases is 95.5 kPa. The partial pressure of oxygen is 300. mmHg. The partial pressure of hydrogen is 24.6 kPa. What is the partial pressure of carbon dioxide in mmHg and kPa?

3. Hydrogen is collected by water displacement at a temperature of 18°C. The air pressure on that day is 744 mmHg. What is the pressure due to dry hydrogen gas? (Hint: See FIGURE H7 and use FIGURE H8.)

# H.27 Going Further—Gas Law Stoichiometry

In Unit G, Section G.5, stoichiometry problems were limited to mass and mole relationships in chemical reactions. Using the Ideal Gas Law, calculations involving masses and volumes of gases at a variety of temperatures and pressures can also be performed.

## Example:

Antoine Lavoisier was able to produce oxygen by heating the calx of mercury [mercury(II) oxide]. What volume of oxygen could be produced at 25.0°C and 95.00 kPa when 56.0 g of mercury(II) oxide are heated?

*Step 1:* Write the balanced equation for the reaction. Show what is given and what is to be found.

$$2\ HgO_{(s)} \longrightarrow 2\ Hg_{(l)} + O_{2(g)}$$
$$56.0\ g \qquad\qquad\qquad ?\ L$$

*Step 2:* Calculate the number of moles of $HgO_{(s)}$.

$$n_{HgO} = \frac{m}{M} = \frac{56.0\ g}{216.59\ g/mol} = 0.259\ mol\ HgO$$

*Step 3:* Calculate the number of moles of $O_{2(g)}$ produced using the mole ratio.

$$n_{O_2} = 0.259\ mol\ HgO \times \frac{1\ mol\ O_2}{2\ mol\ HgO} = 0.129\ mol\ O_2$$

*Step 4:* Calculate the volume of oxygen gas.

$$V = \frac{nRT}{P} = \frac{(0.129\ mol\ O_2)(8.314\ L \cdot kPa \cdot mol^{-1} \cdot K^{-1})(298.2\ K)}{(95.00\ kPa)} = 3.37\ L\ O_2$$

Or combine steps 2, 3 and 4 into one problem.

$$\frac{\left[ 56.0\ g\ HgO \times \dfrac{1\ mol\ HgO}{216.59\ g\ HgO} \times \dfrac{1\ mol\ O_2}{2\ mol\ HgO} \right] (8.314\ L \cdot kPa \cdot mol^{-1} K^{-1})(298.2\ K)}{(95.00\ kPa)} = 3.37\ L\ O_2$$

This flowchart may be useful in solving gas stoichiometry problems:

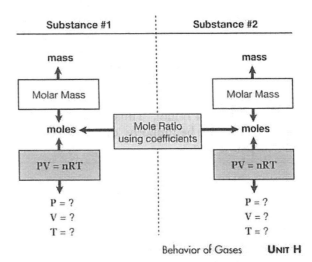

| Substance #1 | | Substance #2 |
|---|---|---|
| mass | | mass |
| ↑ | | ↑ |
| Molar Mass | | Molar Mass |
| ↓ | | ↓ |
| moles ← | Mole Ratio using coefficients | → moles |
| ↑ | | ↑ |
| PV = nRT | | PV = nRT |
| ↓ | | ↓ |
| P = ? | | P = ? |
| V = ? | | V = ? |
| T = ? | | T = ? |

# H.28 Exercises Gas Law Stoichiometry

1. What volume of carbon dioxide would be produced at 20.0°C and 96.0 kPa if 1.00 L of gasoline was burned completely to yield carbon dioxide and water vapor? (Assume 1.00 L of gasoline is 703 g of octane, $C_8H_{18}(l)$.)

2. In the electrolytic decomposition of water, what maximum volume of oxygen gas could be produced at 15.0°C and 100.5 kPa if 250 g of water are decomposed?

3. Hydrogen gas can be produced by the action of sulfuric acid on zinc. What mass of hydrogen will be produced if 15.0 g of zinc are reacted with excess sulfuric acid at 0.0°C and 101.325 kPa?

# H.29 Real Gases

So far it has been *assumed* that all gases have the same molar volume at STP (i.e., 22.4 L/mol) and that all gases obey the **Ideal Gas Law** (PV = nRT). However, it has been proven otherwise: different gases have volumes that vary by a few percentage points. See FIGURE H9.

Although the molar volumes shown in FIGURE H9 are, on the whole, very close to 22.4 L/mol, it is obvious that differences do exist. In fact, every gas would have a unique molar volume at STP if it could be measured with enough precision. However, with the exception of the last three gases in the table, the molar volumes are, to one decimal place, very close to 22.4 L/mol. Thus the assumption made earlier that the number of moles of gas at STP could be found by dividing the gaseous volume by 22.4 L/mol appears to be an acceptable one.

**FIGURE H9  Molar Volumes and Boiling Points of Real Gases at STP**

| Gas | Formula | Measured Molar Volume (L/mol) | Boiling Point (°C) | (K) |
|---|---|---|---|---|
| hydrogen | $H_2$ | 22.43 | −253 | 20 |
| helium | He | 22.43 | −269 | 4 |
| neon | Ne | 22.43 | −246 | 27 |
| krypton | Kr | 22.42 | −152 | 121 |
| (ideal gas) | --- | 22.414 | --- | --- |
| carbon monoxide | CO | 22.40 | −192 | 81 |
| nitrogen | $N_2$ | 22.40 | −196 | 77 |
| argon | Ar | 22.39 | −186 | 87 |
| oxygen | $O_2$ | 22.39 | −183 | 90 |
| methane | $CH_4$ | 22.36 | −161 | 112 |
| xenon | Xe | 22.30 | −107 | 166 |
| carbon dioxide | $CO_2$ | 22.26 | −78.5 | 194.7 |
| hydrogen chloride | HCl | 22.25 | −84.9 | 188.3 |
| ammonia | $NH_3$ | 22.09 | −33.4 | 239.8 |
| chlorine | $Cl_2$ | 22.06 | −34.6 | 238.6 |
| sulfur dioxide | $SO_2$ | 21.89 | −10.0 | 263.2 |

The volume, 22.4 L, is obtained if the ideal gas law is solved for the volume of one mole of gas at STP.  If gases deviate from 22.4 L/mol at STP, then these gases must not obey the ideal gas law.  In fact, no real gas is found to obey the ideal gas law precisely over a reasonably large range of pressures, temperatures and volumes.  Scientists often refer to an **ideal gas** as *a hypothetical gas that would obey the Ideal Gas Law.*  The molar volume of an ideal gas, 22.414 L/mol at STP, is included in FIGURE H9.

In an *ideal gas*, the *molecules* themselves have *no volume* and there are *no intermolecular forces.*  Thus no matter how high the pressure became or how small the volume of an ideal gas became, the Ideal Gas Law would be followed.  In real gases, however, both molecular volume and intermolecular forces are important factors that depend on the nature and conditions of the gas.  A real gas equation has been developed which compensates for molecular volumes and intermolecular forces, but it is mathematically complex:

$$\left(P + \frac{n^2a}{V^2}\right)(V - nb) = nRT$$

where "a" is related to molecular attractions and "b" is related to the size of the molecules.

In general, gases that are easily condensed, such as ammonia and sulfur dioxide, have strong attractions between molecules, and their molar volumes are smaller than predicted by the Ideal Gas Law.  However, gases that are not easily condensed, such as the noble gases and hydrogen, tend to have less intense attractions between molecules, and their molar volumes are much closer to the value predicted by the Ideal Gas Law.

# H.30 Exercises Real Gases

1. In terms of intermolecular attractions and particle motion, explain what happens to gas particles:

   a. when the gas is cooled.

   b. when the gas is compressed.

2. What is the best way to liquefy a gas? Explain.

3. Explain the differences between a real gas and an ideal gas:

| | Intermolecular Attractions | Volume of Gas Particles | Is Liquefaction Possible? | Other |
|---|---|---|---|---|
| Real Gas | | | | Usually behaves nearly like an ideal gas |
| Ideal Gas | | | | Purely hypothetical |

4. If an ideal gas is only hypothetical, why do scientists use the concept?

5. Refer to FIGURE H9 and compare the boiling points and molar volumes of the gases. What generalization can be made concerning the boiling points and their molar volumes? (In Unit I you will study how boiling points are related to intermolecular attractions.)

# Unit I
## Liquids, Solids and Phase Changes

### 1.1 The Kinetic-Molecular Theory

Matter in its various forms is all around us. What is it at one temperature that makes some things solid, others liquid, and still others gas? What happens to matter during heating, cooling and phase changes? These topics and others will be discussed in this unit.

The **Kinetic-Molecular Theory (KMT)** is an explanation of the behavior of matter based on the motion (kinetic energy) of the particles (molecules) that make up the matter. The theory is summarized below:

A. All matter is composed of particles. (By now, you should accept the concepts of atoms, ions and molecules.)

B. Particles have an attraction for each other.

C. Particles are moving. (That is, they possess kinetic energy. This kinetic energy causes a disruption of the attractions between the molecules.)

D. These attractions and molecular motions (disruptions) are opposed to each other.

E. The strength of the attractions and the degree of molecular motion determines the state of matter of a substance.

   1. **Solid** — *The strength of the attractions is much greater than the disruptions caused by molecular motions.*
- Highly organized, tightly packed particle arrangement
- Only vibrational movement is allowed.

   2. **Liquid** — *The strength of the attractions is approximately equal to the disruptions caused by molecular motions.*
- Semi-organized groups and clusters of particles, fairly tightly packed
- Particles are free to move relative to each other

   3. **Gas** — *The strength of the attractions is much less than the disruptions caused by molecular motions.*
- Totally random particle movement
- Particles able to move rapidly in any direction

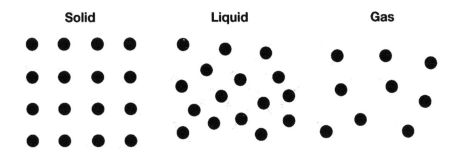

| Properties | Solids | Liquids | Gases |
|---|---|---|---|
| Volume and Shape | Definite volume Definite shape | Definite volume Shape of the container | Takes the shape and volume of its container |
| Compressibility | Very small | Small, but more than the solid (except water) | Large |
| Density | High | High, but usually less than the solid | Low |
| Thermal Expansion | Very small | Small | Moderate |

# I.2 <u>Exercises</u> The Kinetic-Molecular Theory

Use the Kinetic-Molecular Theory outlined in Section I.1 to explain the following properties:

1. The density of a gas is low, but the solid form is high.

 

 

2. Liquids do not compress easily, while gases are readily compressed.

 

 

3. Liquids take the shape of their container, but leave an air space at the top. By contrast, a gas is found everywhere in the container.

 

 

 

4. Solids expand when heated.

 

 

5. The pressure of a gas increases when the temperature increases and decreases when the temperature decreases. *(**Hint**: What causes gas pressure?)*

_____

_____

_____

_____

# I.3 Particle Motion and Temperature

While it is impossible to see the movement of particles, scientists have accumulated evidence that indicates that particles are, indeed, moving. This movement may consist of the whole particle moving from place to place, a tumbling action of the molecule, or just a vibrational motion as the particles "shake" within the same average position. Particle motion increases (*molecules speed up*) as the temperature increases, and decreases (*molecules slow down*) when the temperature goes down. Imagine for a moment that the temperature drops more and more until the *particle motion stops completely*. This temperature is *the lowest temperature possible* and is called **absolute zero**.

FIGURE I2 — A Comparison of Temperature Scales

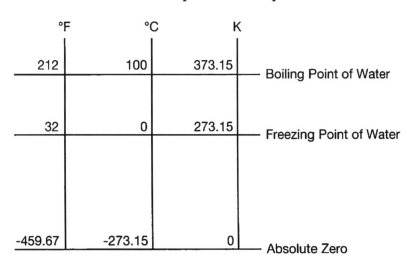

From this it is seen that $K = C + 273.15$

# I.4 <u>Exercises</u> Particle Motion and Temperature

1. If you have ever been in a hurry to make ice cubes or have seen ice forming in a puddle, you would have noticed that only part of the water was solid while the rest was a liquid at the same time. How is this evidence that not all molecules are moving at the same speed at the same time?

_____

_____

_____

_____

2. Some students mistakenly think that the freezing point is the same as absolute zero. Explain their error.

_____

_____

3. What is a "fixed point" on the temperature scale and why is it needed?

_____

_____

_____

4. Use the fixed points on the Fahrenheit and Celsius temperature scales to determine the ratio of F/C. Your teacher will show you how this ratio can be used to develop an equation to convert Fahrenheit temperatures to Celsius (and vice versa).

# 1.5 Explaining States of Matter

Up until now, the room temperature state of matter for molecular substances (i.e., solid, liquid or gas) was either known empirically (from experience in the lab) or was given to you. All ionic substances were previously generalized empirically as being solids at room temperature, but molecular substances were found to be solids, liquids and gases at room temperature (see D.16 LAB). Since ionic compounds are all solids at room temperature, there is not much interest or incentive at this level of chemistry to explain and predict their state of matter. However, an *empirical* way of knowing the state of matter of molecular substances becomes frustrating and pressures science students and scientists into developing a *theoretical* way of knowing *why* matter behaves the way it does. A scientific theory concerning states of matter of molecular substances would be able to both explain and predict molecular states of matter at room temperature. The currently accepted theory concerning states of matter involves a vision of *attractive forces between molecules* called **intermolecular forces** (IMFs).

History in science usually involves a complex interaction of empirical (experimental) and theoretical advances. In an evolving pattern with several scientists from around the world, new, less restricted theories were built over old theories. The history of what we now call intermolecular forces illustrates the scientific enterprise—the visions and the unending search for new versions of "truth."

The early empirical and theoretical work concerning intermolecular forces centered around **capillary action** (Alexis Clairault, France—1743 and Carl Gauss, Germany—1830), **viscosity** (James Maxwell, Britain—1868) and **condensation** (Ludwig Boltzmann, Austria—1886–1893). Most of this early work involved *condensed phase phenomena (solids and liquids)*. You might also recall from your earlier courses a study of the **meniscus, capillary action**, and perhaps the use of the terms **adhesion** and **cohesion**. These are all examples of properties that depend on IMFs, which will be demonstrated in the next section.

In 1873, a Dutch physicist, Johannes Diderik van der Waals, empirically challenged an assumption of the Kinetic-Molecular Theory that there were no attractive forces between gas molecules. Van der Waals gathered evidence concerning deviations from the "ideal" behavior of gases to suggest that there were intermolecular forces. This is the concept that will be studied in the next few sections.

**LAB ...**

# 1.6 Evidence for Intermolecular Forces (IMFs) in Solids and Liquids

**Purpose:**
✔ To observe a few of the physical properties of liquids and solids that illustrate intermolecular forces in substances.
✔ To observe that a change in energy accompanies evaporation and boiling (as well as all other phase changes)

**Safety:**
- Wear goggles
- Tie back long hair
- Wash hands after completing the lab

**Directions:**
On the lab tables are 12 stations all showing different properties of substances. Do the indicated procedure and answer the accompanying questions.

*Station 1—Observe the nature of various molecular substances at room temperature.*

Explain why some substances are solids, some liquids and some gases at room temperature.

_____

_____

_____

_____

*Station 2—Briefly open the valve of the gas cylinder. Spray on the counter top. Notice what happens to the temperature when the gas is allowed to expand rapidly.*

Explain your results.

_____

_____

_____

*Station 3—Pass a beaker of cold water slowly through the flame of the burner. Notice the condensation forming on the outside of the beaker. Explain what happens.*

_____

_____

_____

*Station 4—Observe the capillary tubes. (Hold tubes against a white background to see the differences in liquid heights.) Look carefully. **Capillary action** is the movement of a liquid up a slender tube.*

What accounts for the differences?

_____

_____

_____

_____

_____

*Station 5—Observe the level of liquids in the graduated cylinders. Is the surface of the liquid level curved up or curved down?*

What are their shapes? Why do the liquids curve that way? Is this **adhesion** (one substance "sticking to" another) or **cohesion** (one substance "sticking to" itself)?

_____

_____

_____

_____

**Station 6**—*Observe what happens when each of the flasks is swirled. Rank the liquids in order of increasing* **viscosity** *(resistance to flow).*

_____

Why is one liquid more viscous than another? Is viscosity a result of **adhesion** or **cohesion**?

_____

_____

_____

_____

**Station 7**—*Hold the aerosol can in your hand. Does it appear to be at or near room temperature? If so, begin to shake it.* **DO NOT SPRAY THE CONTENTS**!

What do you notice? Why does it happen?

_____

_____

_____

_____

**Station 8**—*Put a few drops of rubbing alcohol on the back of your hand. Wave your hand around a bit.*

What do you notice? Why does it happen?

_____

_____

_____

_____

**Station 9**—*Hold the pulse glass in your hand.* **DO NOT SQUEEZE.** *Depending on the temperature of your hand, the liquid will either rise or fall. (Find one person with warm hands and one with cold.)*

Explain your results.

_____

_____

_____

_____

_____

_____

**Station 10**—*Observe models of the following solids:*

| Metals | Ionic Compounds | Network Covalent Solids | Molecular Solids |
|---|---|---|---|
| copper | zinc sulfide (wurtzite) | diamond | carbon dioxide |
| magnesium | cesium chloride | graphite | |
| | calcium carbonate | | |
| | sodium chloride | | |

graphite

magnesium

copper

zinc sulfide

cesium chloride

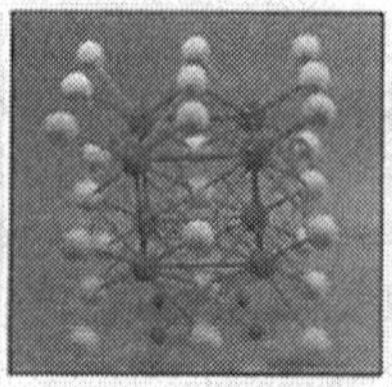

calcium carbonate

sodium chloride

carbon dioxide

Do you observe any repeating patterns? What does that suggest about bonding in solids?

_____

_____

_____

_____

*Station 11—Observe a piece of tin metal.*

What do you see? (Each section is a crystal of tin.)

_____

_____

*Carefully flex the tin. (Not too much, please!)*
What do you hear? Explain your observations.

_____

_____

_____

**Station 12**

Describe what you see.

_____

_____

Explain why the bird keeps on drinking. (Only scientific explanations count!)

_____

_____

_____

_____

_____

_____

_____

_____

_____

_____

_____

# I.7  Understanding Intermolecular Attractions

Intermolecular attractions are those forces of attraction that one molecule has for another molecule. It is these attractions that must be overcome in order for a solid to become a liquid and a liquid to become a gas. Therefore, melting points and boiling points are useful as indicators of the relative strength of the intermolecular forces. The stronger the attraction, the more energy (motion) is needed to change from a condensed phase to an expanded phase, and the higher the boiling point.

Consider for a moment the three substances in FIGURE I3 (*the dotted lines show **interparticle** attractions*):

## FIGURE I3  Relating Intermolecular Attractions to the State of Matter

The solid gray circle represents a complete mix of positive and negative charges inside the molecule. The circles fading from white to black represent a partial separation of charges within the molecule. The ions represent total charge separation.

| Generalized Diagram | Type of Bonds Between Atoms | States of Matter (at room temp) | Attractions Between Particles | Strength of Interparticle Attractions |
|---|---|---|---|---|
|  | Nonpolar Molecules | Gases, liquids and low MP (melting point) solids | London Dispersion Forces | Weakest |
|  | Polar Molecules | A few gases, higher BP (boiling point) liquids, and solids | Dipole-Dipole Attractions | Moderate |
|  | Ions | Solids | Ionic | Strongest |

Since opposite charges attract, a reasonable guess as to the strength of attractions would be that nonpolar covalent substances have the weakest attractions because they are uncharged; polar covalent substances have intermediate-strength attractions due to their partial charges; and ionic substances have the strongest attractions because they possess completely positive and completely negative charges. This shows that the strength of the intermolecular force (and also the type of force) is a direct result of the kind of bonding within the molecule. The types of intermolecular forces and what causes them will be explained in the next few sections.

# I.8  Bonding Between Molecules— Intermolecular Forces

Intermolecular forces are collectively classified as *van der Waals forces* — forces of attraction between electrically neutral molecules or atoms, which cause a substance to change to a liquid or solid. Van der Waals forces are named after the Dutch scientist Johannes Diderik van der Waals (1837–1923), Professor of Physics at Amsterdam University. Van der Waals forces are believed to be present between all chemical species—atoms, molecules and ions. Van der Waals forces vary considerably in magnitude, and this has led to some convenient subclassifications called London dispersion forces and dipole-dipole forces.

*Van der Waals forces:*

1. London dispersion forces
2. Dipole-dipole forces (Hydrogen bonds will be shown to be a special case of dipole-dipole attractions.)

# 1.9 London Dispersion Forces

Atoms and molecules are normally viewed as being electrically symmetrical. However, it must be remembered that the diagrams as drawn represent a probability picture—that is, the region where electrons are most likely to be found. In this respect, it is much like looking at the propeller of an airplane in rapid motion. If we stop the propeller we no longer see the propeller as a solid circle but its individual parts. In the same way, if we could stop the electron for an instant we would be able to see its location.

Stationary Fan

Studied by Fritz London (hence the term London dispersion forces), these instantaneous changes in charge density in any given direction from the nucleus result in a *temporary* dipole. If one nonpolar species is near another, these temporary dipoles may result in a weak, transient attraction with its nearest neighbors.

Spinning Fan

| FIGURE 14 | FIGURE 15 |
|---|---|
| **Electron Shift Within Atoms and Molecules** | **Comparing Covalent Bonds and London Dispersion Forces** |

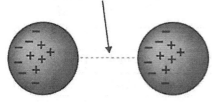

Intermolecular force (IMF) called London dispersion

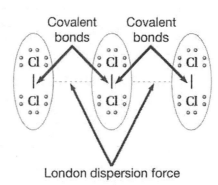

Temporary dipoles are caused by the shift of the electron cloud rather than an electronegativity difference.

London dispersion force

Many substances have nonpolar molecules (e.g., $CO_2$, $H_2$, $Cl_2$ and the monatomic noble gases). Each of these substances has its own boiling point. Therefore, there must be a force of intermolecular attraction that does not depend on polarity.

Consider the case of chlorine, which condenses from vapor to liquid when cooled to –35°C and solidifies at –101°C. While humans consider such temperatures very low, they are still a long way above absolute zero (–273.15°C).

The two chlorine atoms in each chlorine molecule share two bonding electrons. Because these shared electrons are in the valence energy level of both atoms at the same time, they are simultaneously strongly attracted by both nuclei. The atoms show a strong tendency to stay together, held by the covalent bond.

Now consider that the chlorine nuclei in one molecule may, and in fact do, attract all of the other electrons in neighboring molecules. All electrons are thus simultaneously attracted by all neighboring nuclei. Because these electrons are much farther out than the valence energy level, they are not very strongly attracted by these nuclei, but if chlorine molecules are moving slowly enough, these attractions will pull the molecules together (i.e., cause condensation).

Two factors influence the strength of the London dispersion forces:

1. The number of electrons in the molecules. *In general, the **more electrons** the molecules of a substance have, the **stronger** the **London dispersion forces**.*

2. The shapes of the molecules. *Shape affects how closely the molecules may approach each other in solid and liquid states. The closer the molecules can get, the stronger the attraction will be.*

London dispersion forces are much weaker than covalent bonds for two reasons:

1. The simultaneous attraction of electrons is much further from the nuclei.

2. There are significant repulsion or shielding effects from inner electrons.

All molecules have London dispersion forces, and if they are polar, they have dipole-dipole forces as well. (See next section for a discussion of dipole-dipole forces.) The London dispersion forces are usually far more significant in cases where both types of van der Waals forces exist.

A measure of comparative strengths of intermolecular forces for substances is a comparison of their boiling points. This works fairly well since the stronger the intermolecular forces are holding the molecules together in liquid phase, the more heat will be required to cause them to separate. FIGURE I6 compares the boiling points of the noble gases to the number of electrons they have.

FIGURE I6
Variation of the Boiling Points of the Noble Gases with Number of Electrons

| Element | Number of Electrons | Boiling Point (°C) | (K) |
|---------|---------------------|--------------------|-----|
| He | 2 | –269 | 4 |
| Ne | 10 | –246 | 27 |
| Ar | 18 | –186 | 87 |
| Kr | 36 | –152 | 121 |
| Xe | 54 | –107 | 166 |
| Rn | 86 | –62 | 211 |

## I.10 Exercises    London Dispersion Forces

Further confirm the trend illustrated in FIGURE I6 by comparing the boiling points of another group of nonpolar molecules, the halogens.

| Element | | Number of Electrons | Boiling Point | |
|---------|--|---------------------|---------------|--|
| | | | (C) | (K) |
| 1. | $F_2$ | | | |
| 2. | $Cl_2$ | | | |
| 3. | $Br_2$ | | | |
| 4. | $I_2$ | | | |

5. Using the data from FIGURE I6, plot a graph of boiling point versus number of electrons for the *noble gases. (Use graph paper or a spreadsheet program.)*

6. State a generalization relating London dispersion forces to the number of electrons in atoms or molecules. Based on this generalization, explain why Ar, boiling point −186°C, and $F_2$, boiling point −188°C, are very nearly the same.

|      | Polarity | Number of Electrons | IMFs | B.P. (°C) |
|------|----------|---------------------|------|-----------|
| Ar   |          |                     |      |           |
| $F_2$ |          |                     |      |           |

_____

_____

_____

**DEMO ...**

# I.11 Effects of Electrical Charges On Molecular Liquids

**Predemo Information:**
It is well known that when a glass rod is rubbed with silk, the glass rod obtains a positive charge and that a black plastic strip rubbed with cat's fur obtains a negative charge. (These definitions are attributed to Benjamin Franklin and are responsible for the electron's charge being "negative.") These charged rods will attract opposite charges to them as a result of electrostatic attractions. In the following demonstration, these rods will be used to investigate the effects that electrostatic charges have on two molecular liquids, water and hexane, $C_6H_{14}$.

**Predemo Exercise:**
Predict the polarity of water and hexane using the rules presented in Unit C.

Water =

Hexane =

**Materials:**
- 1 black plastic strip
- 2 50-mL burets
- 1 clear plastic strip
- 1 piece of silk
- 1 piece of fur
- 2 buret clamps
- 2 large beakers
- 2 ring stands
- hexane
- water

**Procedure:**
1. Fill one buret with water and the other with hexane and open the stopcocks, allowing the liquids to drain into the beakers. (Leave about 30 cm of space between the buret tips and the beakers.)

2. Rub the black plastic strip with cat's fur and hold it close to the stream of water. (*This rod is negatively charged.*) Record observations.

_____

3. Hold the charged black plastic rod close to the stream of hexane. Record observations.

_____

4. Repeat steps 2 and 3 with the clear plastic strip rubbed with silk. (*This strip is positively charged.*) Record observations.

_____

_____

5. Now hold the black plastic strip on one side of the stream and the clear plastic strip on the other side. Record observations.

_____

_____

**Post-Demo Exercise:**
1. a. In Procedure Step 2, you observed water attracted to the negatively charged strip. What does this say about water molecules?

_____

b. In Step 4, you observed water attracted to the positively charged strip. What does this say about water molecules?

_____

c. In Step 5, you tested water with both negatively and positively charged strips, simultaneously. What would it mean if the water had split into two different streams? What does it mean if the water is in a "tug-of-war" between the two strips?

_____

2. Propose an explanation of the different effects the charged rods had on the streams of water and hexane.

_____

_____

_____

_____

_____

3. Propose an explanation of the similar effects the differently charged rods had on the stream of water.

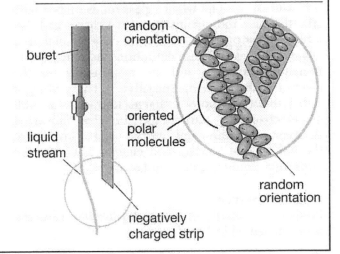

buret

liquid stream

random orientation

oriented polar molecules

random orientation

negatively charged strip

## I.12  Dipole-Dipole Forces

If the molecules of a substance are polar, the presence of molecular dipoles is believed to cause simultaneous intermolecular attractions.  The positive side of one molecule should attract the negative side of a neighboring molecule, which attracts the next, and so on, out to the limits of that substance.  Note in FIGURE I7 that the central polar molecule is simultaneously attracted to the polar molecules surrounding it.

FIGURE I7   Simultaneous Dipole-Dipole Forces

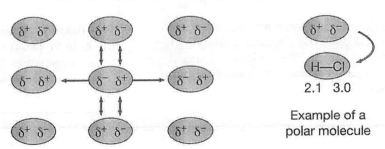

2.1   3.0

Example of a polar molecule

All bonding in this unit is defined in terms of simultaneous attractions. These definitions are not the original, historical definitions presented by the scientists. The similar definitions given for all of the bond types are typical of the unity that is sought in all scientific fields.

## I.13  Exercises    Dipole-Dipole Forces

Compare the boiling points of the hydrogen halides given in FIGURE I8 below to the boiling points of the halogens given in the previous exercise.

FIGURE I8    The Boiling Points of the Hydrogen Halides

| Hydrogen Halide | Electronegativity of Halogen | Number of Electrons | Boiling Point (°C) | (K) |
|---|---|---|---|---|
| HF | 4.0 | 10 | ???? | ???? |
| HCl | 3.0 | 18 | -83.7 | 189.5 |
| HBr | 2.8 | 36 | -67.0 | 206.2 |
| HI | 2.5 | 54 | -35.4 | 237.8 |

1. Explain why the boiling point increases from HCl to HI.

_____

_____

2. Explain why the boiling points of the hydrogen halides are all significantly higher than the noble gases containing the same number of electrons.

_____

_____

3. Use the number of electrons in each molecule of the hydrogen halide series to predict the boiling point of HF.

## I.14  Hydrogen Bonding

The four compounds in the preceding exercise are similar in that they are all hydrogen halides and they are all polar. Each compound is molecular in that intermolecular attractions involve van der Waals forces. The generalization about increasing van der Waals forces with increasing number of electrons holds up when HCl (hydrogen chloride), HBr (hydrogen bromide) and HI (hydrogen iodide) are compared. In addition, since these molecules are all polar, their intermolecular attractions include both London dispersion forces and dipole-dipole forces. With this additional dipole-dipole force, the hydrogen halides all have higher boiling points than their pure halogen counterparts with the same number of electrons.

But hydrogen fluoride, HF, does not fit into the predicted trend. Instead of having a boiling point lower than −83.7°C, thus fitting into the trend, HF has the highest boiling point of all four compounds, 19.4°C. Examination of the electronegativities of the halogens reveals that the HF molecule is the most polar. However, molecular polarity alone could not account for the magnitude of the reversal in the trend. The existence of an additional intermolecular force is suggested.

A very special case of dipole-dipole force occurs between molecules in which one contains hydrogen in a highly polarized bond and the other contains lone-pair valence electrons representing regions of high electron density. The attraction of the highly positive hydrogen to the available lone pair of valence electrons on fluorine, oxygen or nitrogen is called a **hydrogen bond** (see FIGURE I9).

FIGURE I9   Hydrogen Bonds (Generalized) (X = N, O, F)

Hydrogen bonds arise for the following reasons:

1. *Hydrogen atoms contain only one electron.* When covalently bonded to a highly electronegative atom, the **electron cloud density** moves away from the hydrogen and toward the other atom. This makes the hydrogen end of the molecule extremely positive.

2. *Fluorine, oxygen and nitrogen have a higher electronegativity than all other elements. They also have the smallest atomic radii of nonmetals.* When the electron cloud is shifted toward these atoms, that end of the molecule becomes very highly negative.

These two factors come together to make a molecule, or part of a molecule, "***super polar***," resulting in an enhanced dipole-dipole attraction. The hydrogen atom's positively charged nucleus can interact easily with unshared electrons on another neighboring molecule. In many ways it is similar to a covalent bond except that hydrogen bonds are longer and weaker than similar full covalent bonds. (The hydrogen bond has about 10% the strength of a covalent bond.)

FIGURE I10   Atomic Radius, Electronegativity, and Polarity

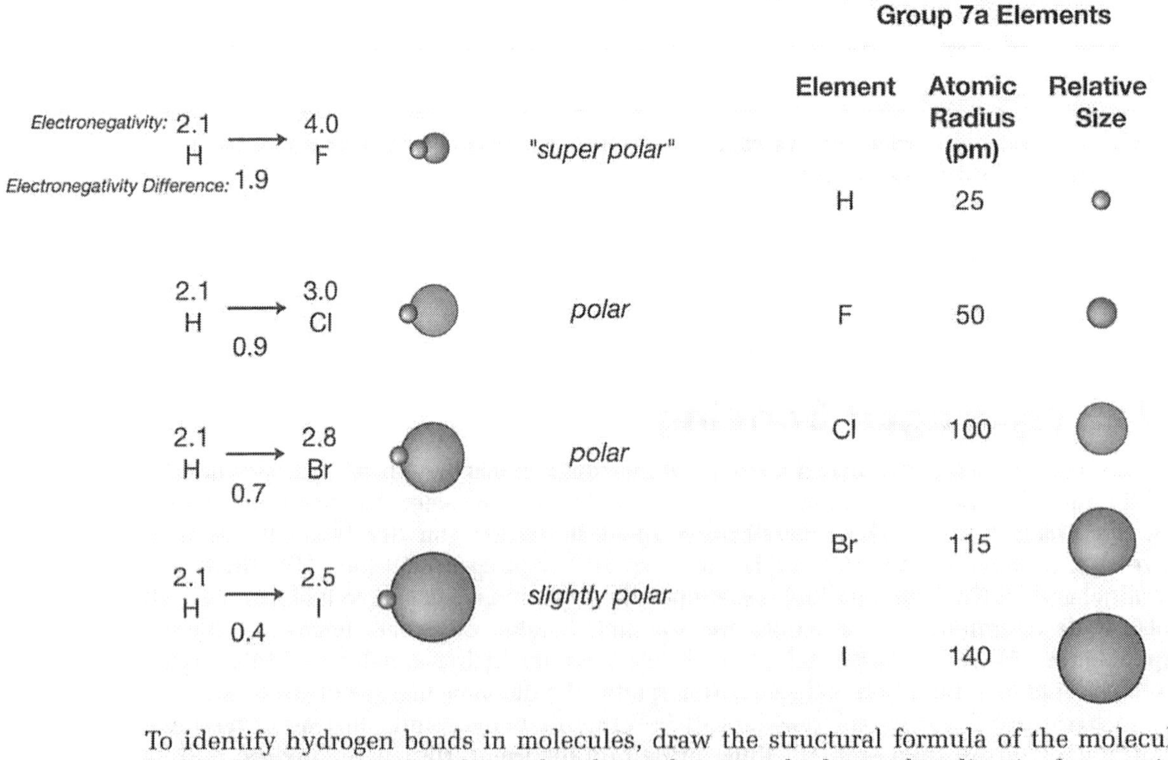

**Group 7a Elements**

| Element | Atomic Radius (pm) | Relative Size |
|---------|--------------------|--------------| 
| H | 25 | |
| F | 50 | |
| Cl | 100 | |
| Br | 115 | |
| I | 140 | |

Electronegativity: 2.1 H → 4.0 F   Electronegativity Difference: 1.9   "*super polar*"

2.1 H → 3.0 Cl   0.9   *polar*

2.1 H → 2.8 Br   0.7   *polar*

2.1 H → 2.5 I   0.4   *slightly polar*

To identify hydrogen bonds in molecules, draw the structural formula of the molecule and look for O–H, F–H and N–H bonds. In diagrams, hydrogen bonding is shown with dotted lines to indicate that it is a weaker bond type than covalent bonds, which are shown as solid lines. Hydrogen bonding should be thought of as continuing from molecule to molecule in three dimensions out to the limits of the sample.

1. **H–F Bond**: the only example is hydrogen fluoride.

$$\text{H}\!-\!\ddot{\underset{\cdot\cdot}{\text{F}}}\colon \cdots\cdots\cdots \text{H}\!-\!\ddot{\underset{\cdot\cdot}{\text{F}}}\colon \qquad \text{or} \qquad \text{H}\!-\!\text{F} \cdots\cdots\cdots \text{H}\!-\!\text{F}$$

2. **O–H Bond**: One or more O–H bonds may occur in a molecule.

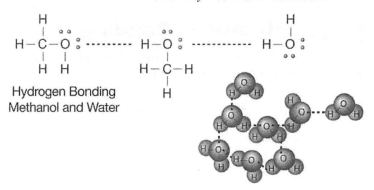

Hydrogen Bonding
Methanol and Water

3. **N–H Bond**: One or more N–H bonds may occur in a molecule.

(urea)

*Note that in urea there are multiple places where hydrogen bonding can occur. For example, each NH$_2$ group links with O and with another NH$_2$ group. Try drawing it yourself.*

## Properties of Hydrogen-Bonded Substances

Hydrogen bonding affects physical and chemical properties in various ways. Some of these effects include:

1. **Higher than expected melting and boiling points:**

   a. $H_2O$ is a liquid at room temperature, which boils at 100°C, whereas $H_2S$ (hydrogen sulfide), which has more electrons, is a gas at room temperature and boils at –62°C.

   b. Ethanol, $C_2H_5OH$, boils at 78.5°C whereas dimethyl ether, $CH_3OCH_3$, boils at 23°C. Both compounds have the same number of electrons.

2. **Increased solubility between substances mutually involving hydrogen bonding:**

   Water, $H_2O$, methanol, $CH_3OH$ and ethanol, $C_2H_5OH$, are soluble in each other in any proportion. All three compounds exhibit hydrogen bonding.

3. **Shape and stability of certain chemical structures:**

   a. *Expansion of water upon freezing:* When water changes to ice, hydrogen bonding between molecules directed by the v-shape of the water molecules leaves hexagonal holes. The resulting structure is less dense than water. The structure would not be possible without the stabilizing effect of hydrogen bonding. (The difference is similar to a deck of cards all jumbled in a pile versus a "house of cards" with a completely open structure.)

   b. *Biochemical processes:* Hydrogen bonding between molecules and within molecules has significant effects upon structurally large protein molecules. The behavior and stability of protein molecules are related to their shape, which in turn is related to the hydrogen bonding present. DNA's alpha helix shape ("spiral staircase") is also a result of hydrogen bonding.

4. **Physical properties, such as the high surface tension of water, capillary action, and the pronounced meniscus of water in a graduated cylinder.**
   - **Surface Tension** — a force that causes the surface of a liquid to behave as if it had a skin
   - **Capillary Action** — the tendency of a liquid to rise inside tiny tubes or fine pores
   - **Meniscus** — the curved surface of a liquid

# I.15  <u>Exercises</u> Hydrogen Bonding

1. Substances that are able to hydrogen-bond could be thought of as being "super polar." What is meant by the term "super polar"?

_____

_____

_____

_____

_____

2. Hydrogen chloride, HCl, shows a "hint" of hydrogen bonding. Explain why this might be so.

_____

_____

_____

_____

_____

3. Explain why H atoms bonded to N, O and F atoms form molecules with such strong intermolecular forces.

_____

_____

_____

_____

4. Why are the boiling point, increased solubility of substances, and surface tension of water dependent on hydrogen bonding, whereas color and chemical reactivity are not?

_____

_____

_____

_____

5. Using FIGURE I11 as an example, draw a diagram of the hydrogen bonding that can occur between water and ammonia.

6. Explain why $CH_3F$ and $CH_3OCH_3$ do not hydrogen-bond whereas $CH_3NH_2$ and $C_2H_5OH$ will readily hydrogen-bond. (*Hint: Draw the Lewis diagrams for each of the molecules.*)

# I.16  Intermolecular Forces Are Cumulative

Nonpolar molecules are capable of London Dispersion forces only between their molecules. Polar molecules will have dipole-dipole attractions, as well as a London Dispersion effect. "Super polar" molecules link together using hydrogen bonds, dipole-dipole attractions and London Dispersion forces. Assuming that several molecules are **isoelectronic** (*contain equal numbers of electrons*), the nonpolar molecule would have the lowest boiling point, followed by the polar molecule, and the polar molecule containing hydrogen bonds would have the highest boiling point.

FIGURE I12 — A Summary of Intermolecular Forces

| Polarity of Molecule | Van der Waals Force Type Present | | |
|---|---|---|---|
| | London Dispersion | Dipole-Dipole | Hydrogen Bonds |
| Nonpolar | ✓ | | |
| Polar | ✓ | ✓ | |
| Polar with OH, NH, FH | ✓ | ✓ | ✓ |

**DEMO ...**

# I.17 Evaporation Race

**Purpose:**
✔ To compare the rate of evaporation of several liquids to the intermolecular forces present.

**Materials:**
• Dropper bottles containing water, ethanol, acetone and hexane.

**Procedure:**
In quick succession, squirt equal amounts of each liquid onto the chalkboard. Time how long it takes for each liquid to evaporate completely. (Alternatively, have two lab partners each squirt two liquids: one should do $H_2O$ and ethanol consecutively; the other acetone and hexane together.) Compare evaporation times to the intermolecular forces present in the molecules.

**Questions:**

1. Which two substances have the longest evaporation times? Explain why.

_____

_____

_____

_____

2. Explain why the other two substances evaporate so quickly.

_____

_____

_____

_____

_____

3. Acetone and hexane have similar evaporation times. Explain why.

_____

_____

_____

_____

_____

_____

_____

_____

_____

_____

|  | Water | Ethanol | Acetone | Hexane |
|---|---|---|---|---|
| Time needed to completely evaporate |  |  |  |  |
| Molecular Structure |  |  |  |  |
| Polarity of Molecules |  |  |  |  |
| IMFs Present (& Electron Count) |  |  |  |  |

## I.18  Exercises   Intermolecular Forces Are Cumulative

1. Both Kr (boiling point, −152°C) and HBr (boiling point, −67°C) are isoelectonic. Explain what factors could affect intermolecular bonding to cause the difference in boiling points between Kr and HBr.

|        | Polarity | Number of Electrons | IMFs | B.P. (°C) |
|--------|----------|---------------------|------|-----------|
| Kr     |          |                     |      |           |
| HBr    |          |                     |      |           |

2. The boiling point of $Cl_2$ is –35°C and the boiling point of $C_2H_5Cl$ (monochloroethane) is 13°C. Does the explanation proposed for question #1 apply here? Explain.

|           | Polarity | Number of Electrons | IMFs | B.P. (°C) |
|-----------|----------|---------------------|------|-----------|
| $Cl_2$    |          |                     |      |           |
| $C_2H_5Cl$|          |                     |      |           |

| Relationship of Boiling Point to the Number of Electrons and the Type of Intermolecular Force | | | | | |
|---|---|---|---|---|---|
| Molecular Substance with Phase at Room Temperature | Number of Electrons and Polarity of Molecule | Boiling Point (°C) | Types of Intermolecular Forces | | |
| | | | London Dispersion | Dipole-Dipole | Hydrogen Bonding |
| $F_{2(g)}$ | 18 / NP | –188 | X | | |
| 3.  $Cl_{2(g)}$ | | –35 | | | |
| 4.  $Br_{2(l)}$ | | 59 | | | |
| 5.  $I_{2(s)}$ | | 184 | | | |
| 6.  $ClF_{(g)}$ | | –101 | | | |
| 7.  $BrF_{(g)}$ | | –20 | | | |
| 8.  $BrCl_{(s)}$ | | 5 | | | |
| 9.  $ICl_{(s)}$ | | 97 | | | |
| 10.  $IBr_{(s)}$ | | 116 | | | |

| Molecular Substance with Phase at Room Temperature | Number of Electrons and Polarity of Molecule | Boiling Point (°C) | Types of Intermolecular Forces | | |
|---|---|---|---|---|---|
| | | | London Dispersion | Dipole-Dipole | Hydrogen Bonding |
| 11. $CH_4(g)$ | | −162 | | | |
| 12. $C_2H_6(g)$ | | −87 | | | |
| 13. $C_3H_8(g)$ | | −45 | | | |
| 14. $C_4H_{10}(g)$ | | −0.50 | | | |
| 15. $C_5H_{12}(l)$ | | 36 | | | |
| 16. $CF_4(g)$ | | −129 | | | |
| 17. $CCl_4(l)$ | | 77 | | | |
| 18. $CBr_4(s)$ | | 189 | | | |
| 19. $CH_3F(g)$ | | −78 | | | |
| 20. $CH_3Cl(g)$ | | −24 | | | |
| 21. $CH_3Br(g)$ | | 3.6 | | | |
| 22. $CH_3I(l)$ | | 43 | | | |
| 23. $CH_3OH(l)$ | | 65 | | | |
| 24. $C_2H_5F(g)$ | | −38 | | | |
| 25. $C_2H_5Cl(g)$ | | 13 | | | |
| 26. $C_2H_5Br(l)$ | | 38 | | | |
| 27. $C_2H_5I(l)$ | | 72 | | | |
| 28. $C_2H_5OH(l)$ | | 78 | | | |

Use the preceding table to answer questions 29 to 35

29. Compare the boiling points of $BrF(g)$ and $C_3H_8(g)$. Account for the difference in boiling points.

| | Polarity | Number of Electrons | IMFs | B.P. (°C) |
|---|---|---|---|---|
| BrF | | | | |
| $C_3H_8$ | | | | |

_____

_____

_____

30. Dimethyl ether, $(CH_3)_2O(g)$, has a boiling point of –24.9°C. Compare with the boiling point of ethanol, $C_2H_5OH(l)$, and account for the difference. (*Hint: Draw the structural formulas for each compound.*)

| | Polarity | Number of Electrons | IMFs | B.P. (˚C) |
|---|---|---|---|---|
| $(CH_3)_2O$ | | | | |
| $C_2H_5OH$ | | | | |

_____

_____

_____

31. As the number of electrons in a substance increases, in general, the boiling point increases. Explain this in terms of number of electrons and the strength of intermolecular forces.

_____

_____

_____

_____

_____

32. Methanol, $CH_3OH$, and ethanol, $C_2H_5OH$, each have the least number of electrons but the highest boiling point in their respective series. Account for this.

_____

33. Explain the difference in boiling point between $C_2H_6$ and $CH_3F$.

| | Polarity | Number of Electrons | IMFs | B.P. (˚C) |
|---|---|---|---|---|
| $C_2H_6$ | | | | |
| $CH_3F$ | | | | |

_____

_____

_____

34. Explain the difference in boiling point between $Cl_2$ and $C_4H_{10}$.

| | Polarity | Number of Electrons | IMFs | B.P. (˚C) |
|---|---|---|---|---|
| $Cl_2$ | | | | |
| $C_4H_{10}$ | | | | |

_____

_____

_____

_____

_____

_____

35. (Challenge Question!) Explain the difference in boiling point between BrCl and $C_2H_5Br$.

| | Polarity | Number of Electrons | IMFs | B.P. (°C) |
|---|---|---|---|---|
| BrCl | | | | |
| $C_2H_5Br$ | | | | |

_____

_____

_____

_____

Refer to the graphs in FIGURE I14 when answering questions #36, 37 and 38.

36. The hydrogen compounds of Groups 5A, 6A, and 7A elements have consistently increasing van der Waals forces (except for the first hydrogen compounds) with increasing numbers of electrons. Explain why the boiling points of $NH_3$, $H_2O$ and HF are much higher than expected.

_____

_____

37. Explain why $CH_4$, the first member of the Group 4A hydrogen compounds, does not have the unexpectedly high boiling point displayed by the first hydrogen compound of the other groups.

_____

_____

38. The boiling points of the hydrogen compounds of the Group 4A elements are considerably lower than the boiling points of the other hydrogen compounds. Give a reason for this effect.

_____

_____

_____

_____

# 1.19 Radial Paper Chromatography

**Purpose:**

✔ To see further evidence of intermolecular forces.

✔ To relate intermolecular forces to separation processes.

**Materials:**

- filter paper
- cup
- water
- several overhead projector markers of different colors.

**Procedure:**

The teacher will describe the procedure to you in class. Write the procedure in picture form. Use as many pictures as needed.

**Observations:**

Record your description of what happened to the filter paper. When the paper is dry, staple it to your lab report.

**Questions:**

Include answers to these questions on your report:

1. What colors separated from each original color? (e.g.,"The green separated into __ and __.")

2. What does it mean if there is more than one color present after separation?

3. Why do the colors separate at all? How does this give evidence for the existence of intermolecular forces?

4. What practical application might this separation technique have?

**Excursion:**

For extra credit, you may want to look up the method of chromatography and report on "Thin Layer Chromatography," "Column Chromatography" or "Gas Chromatography."

# I.20 Going Further—Graphical Comparisons of Intermolecular Forces

The relative strength of London dispersion forces, dipole-dipole interactions and hydrogen bonding may be illustrated by comparing the boiling points on a graph. Assume that, if no intermolecular force exists in a substance, then its melting point and boiling point would be 0 K (absolute zero). It follows, then, that the boiling points serve as a good comparison of strengths of intermolecular attractions.

Compare, for example, the boiling points of the isoelectronic substances $Br_2$ (70 electrons and boiling point 59°C or 332 K) and ICl (70 electrons and boiling point 97°C or 370 K) (see FIGURE I13).

**FIGURE I13**
**IMFs of Various Substances**

| Substance | BP (K) | Number of Electrons | Polarity | Force(s) Between Molecules |
|:---:|:---:|:---:|:---:|:---:|
| $Br_2$ | 332 | 70 | NP | London Dispersion |
| ICl | 370 | 70 | P | London Dispersion Dipole-Dipole |

Since the two molecules are isoelectronic, they should have the same dispersion force and a similar boiling point. The higher boiling point of ICl is due to an *additional* dipole-dipole force. This is shown graphically in FIGURE I15.

**FIGURE I14**
**Boiling Points for Hydrogen Compounds of Group 4A, Group 5A, Group 6A, and Group 7A**

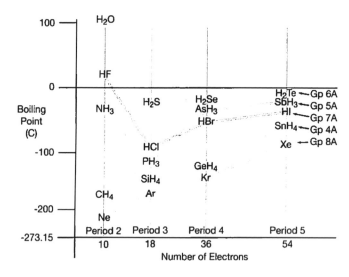

**FIGURE I15**
**Boiling Points of $Br_{2(l)}$ and $ICl_{(s)}$**

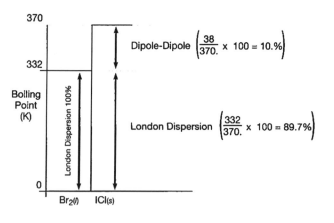

# I.21 Exercises Graphical Comparisons of Intermolecular Forces

First, fill in the information in the table below for the four substances listed. Then, using the first three molecules as a guide, label the intermolecular forces and the percentage contribution of each for the fourth molecule on the right side of the graph.

| Substance | Structural Formula | BP (K) | Number of Electrons | Polarity | Force(s) Between Molecules |
|---|---|---|---|---|---|
| 1. $C_5H_{12}$ | H H H H H<br>\| \| \| \| \|<br>H–C–C–C–C–C–H<br>\| \| \| \| \|<br>H H H H H | 309 | | | |
| 2. $C_3H_7Cl$ | H H H<br>\| \| \|<br>H–C–C–C–CC<br>\| \| \|<br>H H H | 320 | | | |
| 3. $C_4H_9OH$ | H H H H<br>\| \| \| \|<br>H–C–C–C–C–O<br>\| \| \| \| \\<br>H H H H   H | 391 | | | |
| 4. $C_3H_6(OH)_2$ | H H H<br>\| \| \|<br>H–C–C–C–H<br>\| \| \|<br>O H O<br>\\   \|   \\<br>H       H | 487 | | | |

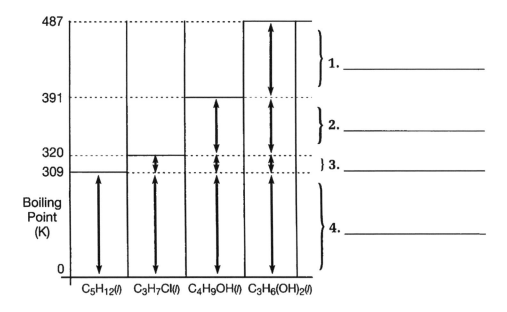

5. What two assumptions are being made in this graph?

_____

_____

_____

_____

# 1.22 The Polymer Lab

## Purpose:
✔ To investigate what happens when water is added to the polymer.

## Background:
Polyacrylamide is a long-chain molecule (polymer) formed by joining together *thousands* of acrylamide (monomer) molecules. It has the molecular structure shown below.

The dashed lines indicate the possible hydrogen bonds between polyacrylamide and water molecules. Only a few of the possible hydrogen bonds are shown.

Because polyacrylamide has so many places where water molecules can be hydrogen-bonded, there is a tremendous capacity to absorb and hold water. In fact, polyacrylamide is able to hold more than 10 times its weight in pure water. Scientists make the most of this unique property in such applications as stay-dry diapers and as "Soil Moist®," a substance added to soil to help retain moisture and prevent overwatering.

**Acrylamide**

$CH_2 = CH$
$C = O$
$N-H$
$H$

**Polyacrylamide**

$CH_2 - CH - CH_2 - CH - CH_2 - CH$
$C = O \quad C = O \quad C = O^n$
$N-H \quad N-H \quad N-H$
$H \quad H \quad H$

$O-H \quad O-H \quad O-H$
$H \quad H \quad H$

$H$
$H-O$
$O-H$
$H$

## Materials:
• sealable plastic bag
• teaspoonful of Ghost Crystals
• 250-mL beaker
• 200 mL water

## Procedure:
1. Open the sealable plastic bag containing the polyacrylamide crystals.

2. Add 200 mL (approximately 1 cup) of water to the bag. If you want to add some color to the experiment, add some food coloring to the bag. Zip shut.

3. Observe what happens to the crystals in the bag and record your observations.

_____

_____

4. Check the bag and record any additional observations over the next 10 minutes.

_____

_____

_____

## Conclusions:
Write a short paragraph explaining what happened to the polymer crystals in the water, why you think it happened, and what this polymer might be *used for* in the home.

_____

_____

_____

_____

_____

_____

_____

_____

## Questions:
Write down three questions after completing this experiment that you would like answered. What are **your** explanations?

_____

_____

_____

_____

_____

_____

_____

_____

# I.23  Ionic Bonding

Recall from Section C.9 that metals lose electrons to form positive ions, and nonmetals gain electrons to form negative ions. Simultaneous electrostatic forces of attraction among oppositely charged ions hold ions together in ionic compounds. The *overall force of attraction among oppositely charged ions* is called an **ionic bond.**

Ionic bonding produces an orderly three-dimensional arrangement of ions into ionic crystals as illustrated in FIGURE I16. Note that in the NaCl crystal lattice, every ion is closest to, and simultaneously attracted by, six ions of opposite charge. Each $Na^+$ ion is simultaneously attracted to six $Cl^-$ ions. Each $Cl^-$ ion is simultaneously attracted to six $Na^+$ ions. It is the simultaneous attraction of one ion to several others that greatly enhances the strength of the ionic bond.

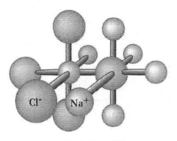

NaCl or $Na^+Cl^-$
sodium chloride *(table salt)*

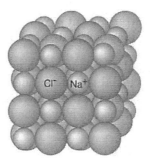

**FIGURE I16**
**NaCl (sodium chloride) Ionic Crystal Lattice**

There are several features associated with ionic bonding that collectively lead to the stable ionic crystal:

1. The formation of ions involves an electron transfer that usually produces ions with the most stable electronic configuration of a noble gas. Note that the process of electron loss is not spontaneous, and energy is required to remove an electron from a neutral metallic atom. When an atom of a metal closely approaches an atom of a nonmetal, an electron transfer results in ions having a more stable electron condition. But while energy is lost when the nonmetal atom gains an electron in forming the negative ion, that energy alone is not enough to stabilize most ionic compounds.

2. *An energy release* (**lattice energy**) *occurs when positive and negative ions form the regular three-dimensional arrangement found in ionic crystals.* It is this lattice energy that holds the crystal together. In general, the stronger the lattice energy, the higher the melting and boiling points of the ionic compound and the harder the crystal.

3. The forces which hold crystals together are not concentrated between the individual ions. That is, the bonding force involves all of the ions.

## Properties of Ionically Bonded Substances

1. **High melting points and boiling points:**

   Due to the strong, three-dimensional, electrostatic attraction between ions, a large amount of energy is required to break the bonds.

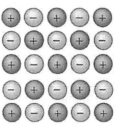

2. **Brittle:**
   Displacing the ions slightly puts ions of the same charge next to each other. The crystal cleaves (*breaks apart*) due to the repulsion of like charges.

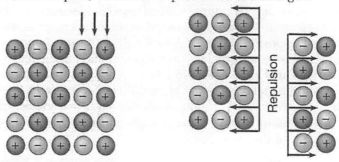

Arrangement of one layer of          Arrangement of ions
ions before displacement             after displacement

3. **Soluble in polar solvents such as water:**
   Ions in the crystal are surrounded by the oppositely charged end of the polar molecule. When the molecule-ion attractions are stronger than the attractions between ions, the ion leaves the crystal—it is "hydrated" or "dissolved."

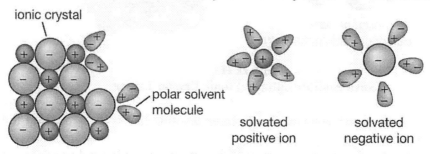

4. **Ionic solutions and melted ionic salts conduct electricity, but ionic solids do not:**
   Conduction occurs when a charged particle is free to move. In the solid state, the ions are restricted. When dissolved or melted, the ions become mobile.

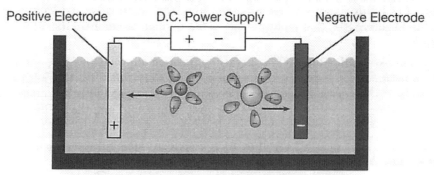

Charged Particles are free to move in the solution.

## I.24   Exercises   Ionic Bonding

1. What evidence suggests that ionic compounds are extremely strong?

   _____

   _____

2. Use ionic bonding structure to answer the following questions:

a. Why do ionically bonded substances have higher melting and boiling points than molecular substances?

_____

_____

_____

_____

b. If ionic bonds are so strong, how is it possible for ionic compounds to dissolve in water?

_____

_____

_____

c. What particle conducts the electricity in ionic solutions?

_____

_____

_____

d. Why is it possible for solutions of ionic compounds to conduct electricity whereas ionic solids do not conduct electricity?

_____

_____

_____

_____

_____

e. If an ionic compound (such as rock salt) is gently tapped with a hammer, the crystal may break with a smooth face. Explain why.

_____

_____

_____

# I.25 Metallic Bonding

As with all types of chemical bonding, metallic bonding is caused by simultaneous attraction of two or more nuclei for the same electrons. The unique character of metallic bonding results from metals having low electronegativities and few valence electrons. Having few valence electrons, atoms of metals have vacant valence orbitals. When metallic atoms are very close to one another, the loosely held valence electrons have a continuum of unoccupied orbitals through which they can move. This leads to a picture of metals described as an array of positive ions immersed in a "sea of electrons."

The atoms in the metallic structure become positive ions because their valence electrons are easily lost. The resulting positive ions have fixed positions but the electrons are free to move within the metal. This kind of arrangement allows the electrons to experience simultaneous electrostatic attractions to more than one nucleus. This leads, therefore, to a more stable situation than the free atoms in which the electron is attracted to only one nucleus. The extra attraction counterbalances and overcomes the repulsion forces between the nuclei.

### FIGURE I17    Metallic Bonding

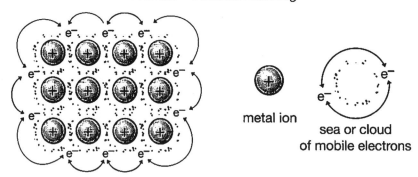

metal ion

sea or cloud
of mobile electrons

Therefore, the metallic bond is the net attraction of the positive metal ions for the total free electron cloud.

## Properties of Metals

1. **Electrical conductivity:**
   Since the valence electrons can move anywhere within the metal, electrons can "flow" from one part of the metal to another.

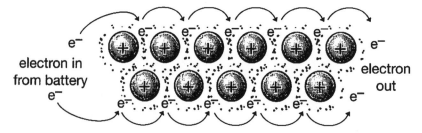

electron in
from battery
e⁻

electron
out

2. **High melting and boiling points:**
   This is due to the relatively strong electrostatic attractions between stationary positive ions and valence electrons. It explains why all metals except mercury are solid under ordinary conditions, and why most have comparatively high melting points.

3. **Ductility and malleability:**
   If the metal atoms are displaced (hammered, stretched, etc.), the electron cloud shifts to remain a part of the metallic crystal.

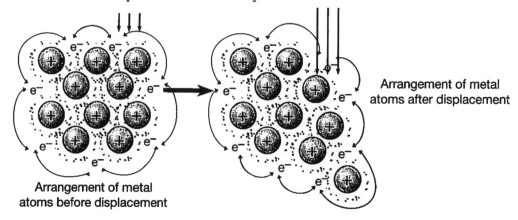

Arrangement of metal
atoms after displacement

Arrangement of metal
atoms before displacement

4. **Luster:**
Light reflects off the mobile electron cloud, like a spotlight off the sequins in a costume.

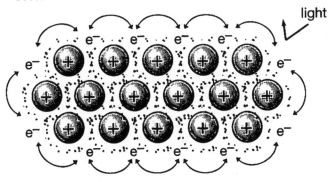

# I.26 Exercises   Metallic Bonding

1. If metal atoms do not have enough electrons to achieve a stable octet, what allows metallic bonds to be so strong?

_____

_____

_____

_____

_____

_____

2. Explain how metals can be flexible (*malleable and ductile*).

_____

_____

3. What particle in metals is responsible for its conductivity?

_____

4. Metals can conduct electricity whether in the solid or liquid state.  Yet ionic compounds only conduct when dissolved or molten. How is this possible?

_____

_____

_____

_____

_____

_____

# I.27 Network Covalent Bonding

An additional class of substances includes a small number of very hard and high-melting-point substances such as diamond ($C_n$), silicon carbide (SiC, carborundum) and silicon dioxide ($SiO_2$, present in most rock as a type of quartz). Associated with such substances must be a rigid structure—a structure in which all atoms are linked to other atoms by inflexible bonds, as in the superstructure of a bridge. The bonds would have to be very strong and very directional in a three-dimensional network.

**FIGURE I18  Network Covalent Bonding**

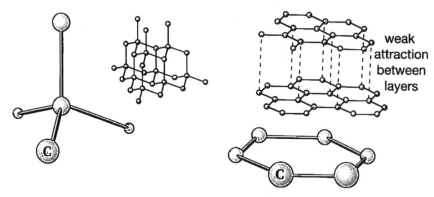

weak attraction between layers

Diamond space model          Graphite  space model

The covalent bond is the force bonding atoms in network solids. The exceptional strength and hardness of a diamond is a result of each atom being bound in three dimensions to four other atoms, and so on. As shown in FIGURE I18, there is a tight three-dimensional network where the bonds of each atom are directed to the corners of a tetrahedron. Atoms are held in rigid positions, resulting in the high melting point of network solids. Electrons are not free to move, thus there is no electrical conductivity. The overall structure can be described as a giant macromolecule, where every atom is simultaneously attracted to neighboring atoms by covalent bonds.

# I.28 Exercises  Network Covalent Bonding

1. What gives network-covalent-bonded substances generally the highest melting point, highest boiling point and greatest hardness?

_____

_____

_____

_____

2. Molecular compounds have covalent bonds, yet they are usually gases, liquids and low-melting-point solids.  What is the difference between molecular substances and network-covalent substances? (**Hint:** *Consider the diagram below in your answer.*)

H —Cl·····H —Cl·····H —Cl

molecular compound

network solid

3. Explain why most network-covalent-bonded substances do not conduct electricity.

_____

_____

_____

_____

4. While most network solids have a 3-dimensional structure, graphite is composed of layers of carbon atoms covalently bonded in a 2-dimensional network. (See FIGURE I18.) Three of carbon's valence electrons are involved in "normal" covalent bonds while the fourth electron lies above and below the layers and is dispersed throughout the layer much like the electrons in metals. The layers are held together with London Dispersion forces.

a. Explain why graphite is able to conduct electricity while most other network solids do not.

_____

_____

_____

b. Graphite is often mixed with clay and used to make pencil lead. It is also used as a dry lubricant for locks, for Pinewood Derby cars, and even in certain types of motor oil. Explain why graphite is so easily rubbed off and what makes it so useful as a lubricant for metal parts.

_____

_____

_____

_____

_____

_____

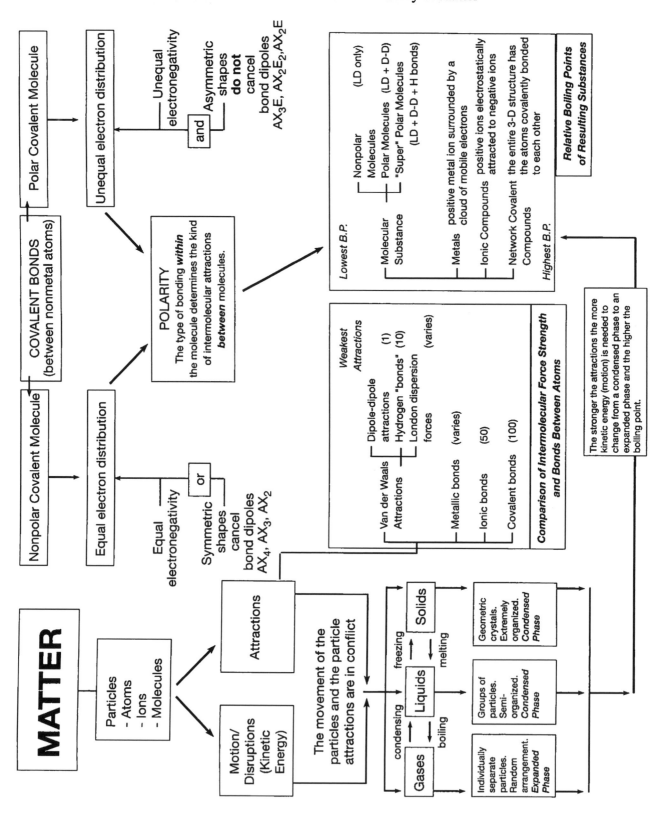

# I.29 Going Further The Relative Magnitudes of Bonding Forces

Any comprehensive comparison of the relative magnitudes of intermolecular forces must consider various effects such as molecular size, number of electrons and molecular shape. However, if it is assumed that changes in molecular size are reflected by changes in number of electrons, some useful generalizations should be made.

Six types of bonding, in decreasing order of strength of attraction, with an approximate ratio of strength, are shown as follows:

Covalent > Ionic > Metallic > Dispersion (total) > Hydrogen > Dipole-dipole
(100)    (50)    (varies)     (varies)      (10)       (1)

Metallic bonding varies over such a wide range that it cannot be classified in this way, even approximately. The boiling points of metallic elements vary from 357°C for mercury (Hg) to 5660°C for tungsten (W). However, for a metal with a relatively low boiling point (1000°C), metallic bonding will often be weaker than the ionic bonding in simple binary ionic compounds.

*As long as it is assumed that any prediction is only approximate*, the following rules can be used to compare probable properties of different substances if the bonding in the substances is known.

1. Network covalent compounds and elements will be highest in boiling points and hardness. Every atom is held in place by covalent bonding.

2. Ionic compounds will have bonding strong enough to hold ions in a solid crystal at room temperature, but they melt and boil much easier than networks and are softer.

3. Molecular compounds and elements can be compared as follows:

   a. If the molecules of a substance have hydrogen bonding (as well as London dispersion and dipole-dipole), the substance can be expected to have a much higher boiling point than any substance with molecules of even approximately the same size that have only van der Waals bonding.

   b. In comparing two molecular substances where both have only London dispersion forces, the molecules with the greatest number of electrons usually have stronger attraction, and that substance can be expected to have a higher boiling point.

   c. In comparing two molecular substances which have molecules of very similar electron count, but where one has polar molecules (London dispersion + dipole-dipole) and the other has nonpolar molecules (London dispersion only), the polar substance will usually have the higher boiling point.

On the previous page is FIGURE I19, which summarizes both the attractions and the repulsions of the Kinetic Molecular Theory.

# I.30 Exercises  A Summary of Bonding Forces

Complete the following table by providing the name of the intermolecular bond type. The bond types (not in order) are metallic, dipole-dipole, hydrogen, ionic, covalent network and London Dispersion.

| Bond Type | Characteristics of Formulation | Some General Properties | Examples |
|---|---|---|---|
| 1. | The simultaneous attraction by covalent bonds of an atom by adjacent atoms within a 3-D lattice of atoms | Very hard; very high melting point; insoluble in most ordinary solvents; nonconductors of electricity. | $C_{(s)}$ (diamond), $SiO_{2(s)}$ (quartz), $SiC_{(s)}$ (carborundum) (memorize these three) |
| 2. | The simultaneous attraction of an ion by its surrounding ions of opposite charge within an ionic crystal lattice | Crystalline solids under ordinary conditions; high melting and boiling points; dissolve in polar liquids to form conducting solutions; electrical conductors in liquid phase. | $NaCl_{(s)}$, $Ca(OH)_{2(s)}$, $CuSO_{4(s)}$, $NH_4Cl_{(s)}$, $NaHCO_{3(s)}$, $KNO_{3(s)}$ |
| 3. | The simultaneous attraction of free valence electrons by metallic cations | Lustrous, malleable, good electrical conductors; wide range of melting points. | $Al_{(s)}$, $Fe_{(s)}$, $Cu_{(s)}$, $Zn_{(s)}$, $Ca_{(s)}$, $Na_{(s)}$, $Ag_{(s)}$, $Pb_{(s)}$, $Hg_{(l)}$ |
| 4. | The simultaneous attraction of electrons of one molecule by their own nucleus and by the nuclei of adjacent molecules | Relatively low melting solids, gases or liquids because of relatively weak intermolecular forces | $H_{2(g)}$, $CO_{2(g)}$, $He_{(g)}$, $I_{2(s)}$, $CH_{4(g)}$, $S_{8(s)}$, $CCl_{4(l)}$, $HBr_{(g)}$, $CHCl_{3(l)}$ |
| 5. | The simultaneous attraction of a hydrogen ion (proton) by the electron pair of adjacent N, O or F atoms | Relatively high melting solids, gases or liquids because of relatively strong intermolecular attraction | $H_2O_{(l)}$, $HF_{(g)}$, $C_2H_5OH_{(l)}$, $H_2O_{2(l)}$, $CH_3NH_{2(g)}$, $CH_3COOH_{(l)}$ |
| 6. | The simultaneous attraction of a molecular dipole by the surrounding molecular dipoles | A weak intermolecular force that exists in addition to the stronger dispersion forces; low melting solids, liquids, and gases. | $H_2S_{(g)}$, $C_2H_3Cl_{(l)}$, $C_2H_5F_{(g)}$, $IBr_{(s)}$, $CH_3I_{(l)}$ |

Complete the following table by providing the name of the intermolecular bond type that corresponds with the diagram below that number. The bond types represented are metallic, dipole-dipole, hydrogen, ionic, covalent network, and London dispersion.

| Bond Type | 7. | 8. | 9. | 10. | 11. | 12. |
|---|---|---|---|---|---|---|
| | | | | | | |
| Diagram of bond type | $:\ddot{X}\text{-H}\cdots:\ddot{X}\text{-H}$  X = N, O, F | | | | | |

13. Write the type of intermolecular bonding under each compound below.  List the compounds in order of increasing boiling point.  (*For what intermolecular forces is it necessary to count the number of electrons?*)

$NaCl$     $Na$     $C_3H_8$     $C_2H_5OH$     $SiO_2$     $C_2H_3Cl$

_____

_____

_____

_____

_____

_____

_____

# I.31 The Many Forms of Sulfur

**Purpose:**
✔ To study some of the various allotropes of sulfur.
✔ To study some of the different crystalline shapes and investigate some of the molecular changes that occur in sulfur to cause the different shapes.

**Background:**
Sulfur has some unique properties listed below:

|        | Type of Solid | How Formed | Molecular Arrangement | |
|--------|---------------|------------|------------------------|--|
| Part 1 | Rhombic (orthorhombic) | Dissolved sulfur in olive oil. Evaporated solvent. | $S_8$ | |
| Part 2 | Monoclinic | Heated sulfur to golden yellow liquid. Somewhat viscous. Cooled slowly. | $S_8$ | |
| Part 3 | Amorphous | Heated sulfur to dark red-brown liquid. Very viscous. Cooled rapidly. | $S_4$ | |
| Part 4 | Sublimed or Flowers of Sulfur | Heated sulfur to black liquid. Very runny. Cooled vapor rapidly. | $S_2$ | |

**Safety:**
• Some people are allergic to sulfur compounds.
• Wear goggles.
• Wash hands.

**Materials:**
• flowers of sulfur
• 1 100-mL beaker
• 2 sheets bathroom tissue
• test tube
• 1 250-mL beaker
• adhesive tape
• test tube holder
• filter paper
• stapler
• Bunsen burner
• large pan or tray

**Procedure:**
1. **Rhombic, octahedral crystals:**
   a. This is prepared by your teacher.
   b. Observe the crystals under a microscope or magnifying glass.  Describe what you see.  Draw the crystals.

2. **Monoclinic, prismatic crystals:**
   a. Fill a test tube 3/4 full of sulfur and melt the sulfur at as low a temperature as possible.  (*Caress the tube with the flame!*)  During the heating, move the tube from side to side in the flame.  Don't allow the liquid to get much darker than a pale straw-yellow color.  Pour the molten sulfur into a folded filter paper in a beaker.  Watch the sulfur as it cools.  As soon as a crust has formed about halfway across the surface, carefully unfold the filter paper and examine the crystals under a microscope or magnifying glass.  Varying the focus on the microscope will bring the various layers of crystals into view.
   b. Describe what you see.  Draw the crystals.

3. **Amorphous sulfur** (plastic sulfur):

   a. Using the same test tube as before, again fill the tube 3/4 full of sulfur and heat slowly until melting is complete. Then heat more strongly and observe how the sulfur changes in color and fluidity (viscosity); you can observe fluidity by holding the tube nearly horizontal. Finally, heat the sulfur to boiling and pour the sulfur into a shallow tray of cold water.

   b. Feel the sulfur. Observe the sulfur under the microscope. Draw the strands of plastic sulfur. Describe what you see. (*The plastic strands of sulfur will slowly change color and flexibility over the next few days from brown and flexible to brittle and yellow as the amorphous sulfur changes to the more stable rhombic crystals.*)

4. **Flowers of sulfur** (sublimed sulfur):

   a. Use the same test tube, which should still have some sulfur deposited on its sides. (DO NOT ADD MORE SULFUR.) Roll about 20 cm of bathroom tissue around the top of the test tube and tape it to the tube to create a semi-porous paper column. Close the top of the paper column by putting one staple in the top of the column perpendicular to the column. Heat the tube until the sulfur boils and is well vaporized. Then plunge the test tube into a beaker of water. This will crack the tube and cause sublimation of the sulfur vapors. Solid sulfur will collect in the paper. Cool the tube and remove the paper for examination.

   b. Draw and describe the results.

**Observations:**

Put all your descriptions and drawings into the following chart:

| | Word Description of Solid | Diagram of Solid | Drawing of Ideal Crystal |
|---|---|---|---|
| Part 1 | | | |
| Part 2 | | | |
| Part 3 | | | Not applicable |
| Part 4 | | | Not applicable |

**Questions:**

1. **Allotropes** are *different forms of the same element in the same state of matter.* Name or give the formula for the allotropes for each of these elements: carbon, oxygen and phosphorus.

   _____

   _____

   _____

2. An **amorphous solid** is *a solid whose particles have no orderly structure.* They lack well-defined faces and shapes. Give two examples of substances, other than sulfur, that form an amorphous solid.

   _____

3. Consider the different molecular structures of sulfur as given in the Data and Observations section at the beginning of the lab.

   a. What types of intermolecular forces are present between sulfur molecules? *(HINT: Look at the chemical formula for sulfur and decide whether it is nonpolar, polar or "super" polar.)*

   _____

   _____

   _____

   b. Explain why both the dark red-brown liquid sulfur and the golden yellow liquid sulfur were more viscous than the black liquid sulfur. (*HINT: Find the chemical formulas for the different kinds of sulfur in the Background section.*)

   _____

   _____

   _____

   c. Explain why the dark red-brown liquid sulfur was more viscous than the golden yellow liquid sulfur. (*HINT: Both molecules have the same kind of intermolecular force, and this force is influenced by two different factors. What factor must dominate here?*)

   _____

   _____

4. Explain how the rate of cooling in Part 3 caused an amorphous solid to be formed rather than a crystalline solid. (*HINT: What must happen for crystals to form? What prevented this organization from occurring? See also question 3c.*)

_____

_____

_____

_____

_____

_____

_____

_____

_____

_____

_____

_____

_____

_____

_____

_____

_____

_____

## I.32 The Heating and Cooling Curves of a Substance

As has been shown, all matter has particles, which are moving and are attracted to each other. What happens to these particles when matter changes from one form to another?

To understand what happens, assume there is a given solid below its melting point that is being heated at a constant rate. When it has turned completely to a gas, the system is then cooled at a constant rate. The graph in FIGURE I20 is a "temperature history" of what happens to the substance.

FIGURE I20
**Hypothetical Heating/Cooling Curve**

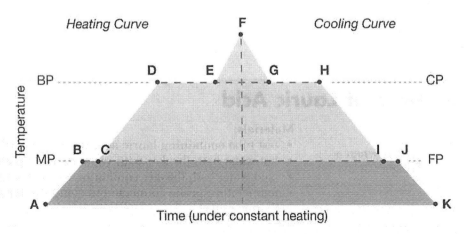

A true crystalline solid will have an organized geometrical arrangement of its particles, and its particles will be vibrating or "*shaking in a set position.*" Along line segment AB, this solid is being heated so the vibrations increase in strength until they reach a temperature where the crystal begins to break apart. This temperature is called the **melting point** (MP). During melting (segment BC), the temperature remains constant because all additional energy is being used to break apart the crystal rather than increase the average kinetic energy of the system. Line segment CD shows the liquid warming up as a result of increased motions of the semi-organized particles. Boiling (BP) occurs along segment DE. Again the temperature remains constant because the added energy is used to overcome completely all remaining *interparticle* attractions. (Typically the boiling segment takes longer than melting because there are more attractions to overcome.) Finally, segment EF shows the gas warming up from the increased motion of the gas particles.

The cooling portion (CP) of the graph is really the opposite of what occurs during heating. Segment FG shows the gas cooling off. Segment GH shows the temperature remaining constant during condensation. HI is the cooling of the liquid. Freezing (FP) occurs during IJ. Again the temperature remains constant. Finally, JK represents the cooling of the solid.

# I.33  <u>Exercises</u>   The Heating and Cooling Curves of a Substance

1. Since the melting point is the temperature at which the crystal breaks apart, what is happening to the particles at the freezing point during the freezing process?

   _____

   _____

2. How does the melting point compare to the freezing point for a given substance?

   _____

3. Suppose a substance is exactly at the melting point. Both solid and liquid are present. What determines whether the substance melts or freezes?

   _____

   _____

4. The temperature remains constant during melting and boiling because energy is being used to break bonds in the system. Explain why the temperature stays constant during freezing and condensation.

   _____

   _____

**Mini LAB ...**

# I.34  The Cooling Curve of Lauric Acid

**Purpose:**

✔ To investigate the changes that occur when a substance undergoes a phase change.

**Materials:**
- test tube containing lauric acid ($C_{11}H_{23}COOH$)
- hot water bath (beaker with water on a hot plate)
- cold water bath (beaker containing water and ice)
- temperature probe connected to computer (or a thermometer)

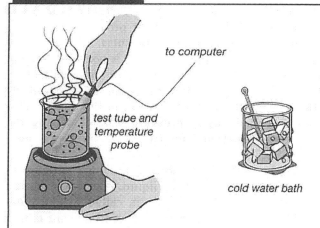

to computer

test tube and
temperature
probe

cold water bath

**Procedure:**

Do a formal lab report on your own paper. The computer will record the data for you. Otherwise, record your data and observations in a suitable chart you have prepared.

1. Put your test tube of lauric acid into the hot water bath until it melts. (The water bath should be no more than 60–65°C.)

2. Prepare an ice water bath to cool the sample.

3. Place the temperature probe into the hot test tube, then wait 30 seconds. (This will bring the probe to the temperature of the sample.)

4. Place the test tube assembly and probe into the ice water bath and begin recording data. Stir continuously and carefully with the probe.

5. Allow the experiment to proceed until the temperature begins to decrease dramatically a second time. Stop recording data.

6. Each member of the group should prepare a graph of the results.

**Questions:**

Answer the following questions in your formal lab report.
1. What do you suppose was happening to the molecules during:

a. the steep parts of the curve?

_____

b. the flat parts of the curve?

_____

2. Do you think that heat was still being lost from the tube during the flat part of the curve? How could you test your hypothesis?

_____

_____

_____

_____

_____

3. What was the freezing point of your sample? If you were to reheat the sample, at what temperature would it melt?

_____

_____

4. Sketch a temperature-time graph for the heating of water from −20°C to 60°C, assuming that heat is added to the water at a constant rate

# 1.35  Phase Changes

## Melting / Freezing

Now you understand that melting and freezing are really the same processes going in opposite directions. One process absorbs energy, the other releases energy. The melting point is the same temperature as the freezing point because they both represent the temperature where the vibrations are strong enough to break the crystal apart or weak enough to allow the particles to come together. The two processes can be represented together in one equation as follows:

$$\text{solid} + \text{heat} \underset{\text{freezing}}{\overset{\text{melting}}{\rightleftarrows}} \text{liquid}$$

## Vaporization / Condensation

A general term, used to describe *the process of changing from a liquid to a gas* is **vaporization** and includes both evaporation and boiling. Which process is occurring depends on the temperature and pressure conditions acting on the substance.

The term **vapor** is applied to *the gaseous form of a substance that is normally a liquid or a solid* at that temperature. Tiny submicroscopic pockets of vapor are continuously being formed within the body of the liquid as a result of the random collisions of the particles of a liquid. As expected, this vapor will exert a force within the liquid. This *internal pressure of the trapped gas* is called **vapor pressure**. Since raising the temperature causes harder collisions, vapor pressure increases as the temperature increases.

Normally these vapor particles collide with other slower moving particles to recombine as a liquid. If this vapor forms at the surface of the liquid, however, there is a possibility that *the gas could escape from the liquid*. This is called **evaporation**. Evaporation will occur until the liquid has completely vaporized or, if a liquid is in a closed container, when the vapor pressure within the liquid is equal to the gas pressure above the liquid.

**Boiling** will occur when the internal vapor pressure is greater than or equal to the external pressure (air pressure) acting on the surface of the liquid. At that boiling temperature, *vapor within the body of the liquid has enough energy to escape attractions of other particles in that state.*

The difference between evaporation and boiling is this:

- In *evaporation*, the vapor pressure has not yet reached the external pressure so only surface molecules can escape the liquid.

- In *boiling*, the vapor pressure is greater than or equal to the external pressure so *any* molecule can escape the liquid.

From the definition given for boiling you see that the temperature at which a liquid boils depends on the air pressure acting on its surface. (See FIGURE I21) At low air pressures, the liquid does not need much heating for its vapor pressure to reach air pressure, so the boiling point is lower. At high air pressures, the liquid must be heated quite vigorously for the vapor pressure to equal the air pressure. Therefore, the boiling point is higher. Since a liquid can be made to boil at many different temperatures, it is often convenient to refer to the **normal boiling point**. This is *the temperature at which a liquid will boil when the air pressure is at standard atmospheric pressure* (1 atm = 760 mmHg = 101.325 kPa = 14.7 psi).

### FIGURE I21
### Vapor Pressure Curves

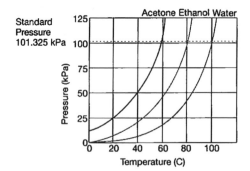

By now you should realize that boiling and condensing are opposite processes, just like melting and freezing, and that boiling absorbs energy (*endothermic process*) while condensation releases energy (*exothermic process*). In addition, it should be obvious that the boiling point and the condensation temperature are the same for a given substance.

These processes can be represented in one equation:

$$\text{liquid} + \text{heat} \underset{\text{condensing}}{\overset{\text{boiling}}{\rightleftarrows}} \text{gas}$$

## Sublimation / Deposition

**Sublimation** is *the change of a solid directly to the gaseous phase without passing through the liquid phase.* For some substances the forces of attraction between particles are very weak and random molecular collisions will cause vaporization of the solid. Sublimation occurs when the vapor pressure of the solid is greater than or equal to the air pressure acting on the surface of the solid. **Deposition** is the name given to the reverse process although sublimation is often used for the reverse process as well.

$$\text{solid} + \text{heat} \underset{\text{deposition}}{\overset{\text{sublimation}}{\rightleftarrows}} \text{gas}$$

**Mini DEMO**

# I.36  Boiling Water in a Syringe

**Purpose:**

✔ To show that water can boil at a temperature significantly lower than 100°C.

**Materials:**

- large syringe (60 mL or larger)
- cap for syringe (or syringe needle and a rubber stopper)
- beaker to hold water
- hot tap water

**Procedure:**

Add hot tap water to the syringe until the syringe is about 1/4 full of water. Cap the syringe. Pull back on the syringe piston. Discuss your observations in class.

**Comments:**

1. Pulling back on the syringe decreases the pressure inside the container. When the internal pressure equals the vapor pressure of the water, bubbling begins.

2. While some of the bubbles may be dissolved gases escaping (similar to carbon dioxide bubbles leaving a carbonated beverage), most of the bubbles are caused by water vapor inside the liquid trying to get out—the definition of boiling!

# Unit J
## Solutions

Knowledge of the properties and uses of solutions is important in the study of chemistry. Many substances used in laboratories are much easier to store and use in solution form. Many chemical reactions happen only when the reactants are in solution.

## J.1  Solutes and Solvents

**Solutions** are homogeneous mixtures—that is, solutions are uniform throughout the mixture on a molecular scale. The substance in solution with which the chemist is most concerned is called the **solute**, the "stuff" which is dissolved. The **solvent** is the substance that causes the solute to be dissolved and is the carrier for the solute. Most common solutions use water as the solvent and are called **aqueous solutions**.

| Solute | Solvent | Examples |
|--------|---------|----------|
| gas | gas | air |
| gas | liquid | ammonia solution, carbonated beverages, $O_2$ in water |
| gas | solid | hydrogen in palladium (an element) |
| liquid | liquid | antifreeze, wine, beer |
| liquid | solid | dental amalgam (mercury in silver) |
| solid | liquid | salt water, sugar solutions |
| solid | solid | metal alloys (silver in gold) |

## J.2  Concentration of Solutions

Whether you are cooking in the kitchen, making a garden spray or analyzing samples in a medical laboratory, solutions of known concentrations are being used. Rather than determine the mass of specific quantities of reactants for chemical reactions, it is more convenient to *dissolve the chemicals* to make solutions of known concentration. The chemicals may then be dispensed by *measuring specific volumes of solution*.

The concentration of a solution describes the amount of solute relative to the volume of solution. A solution of high concentration is called **concentrated**, while a solution of low concentration is said to be **dilute**. A solution may be diluted by increasing the amount of solvent in the solution.

In order to determine the amount of solute in a measured volume of solution, the concentration of the solution and the solution volume must be known. Concentrations of solutions are commonly measured in terms of molar concentration. The **molar concentration** of a solution is defined as the number of moles of solute dissolved in a liter of solution. This definition is commonly expressed as the formula:

$$\text{molar concentration of solute} = \frac{\text{amount of solute in moles}}{\text{volume of solution in liters}} \text{ or } C = \frac{n}{v} = \frac{mol}{L}$$

The units for molar concentration are mol/L. When the single word *concentration* is used in the text, it is assumed that *molar concentration* is meant.

# J.3 <u>Exercises</u> Concentration of Solutions

1. Define the following terms:

   a. solute _____

   b. solvent _____

   c. solution _____

   d. concentration _____

2. What units are used to measure molar concentration?

   _____

# J.4 Solution Problem-Solving

As with problems in Units F and G, solution problems can be solved by either of two methods: by equations (Method 1) or by the conversion-factor technique (Method 2). The examples and problems that follow show many applications of, and the convenience of, working with solutions. The examples shown will be solved by both calculation methods.

Method 1 — Equation Method: only two formulas with their variations are needed to solve most solution problems (see FIGURE J1). Start with the given amount and use the equations appropriate to determine the unknown quantity.

Method 2 — Conversion Factor Method: many people find it easier and faster to use molar mass and molar concentration in such a way that the ratios allow the units to cancel. This way the multiple calculations involved in doing solution problems can be set up as one problem and the units can be used to double-check the accuracy of the setup (see FIGURE J2).

FIGURE J1    Equation Problem-Solving

| Equations | Flowchart |
|---|---|
| $n = \dfrac{m(g)}{M(g/mol)}$ <br><br> and <br><br> $C = \dfrac{n}{v}$ <br><br> **Note:** If the Equation Method is used, the formula should be verified each time by substituting the correct units into the formula and making sure that the correct units are obtained in the answer. | |

## Figure J2  Conversion Factor Problem-Solving

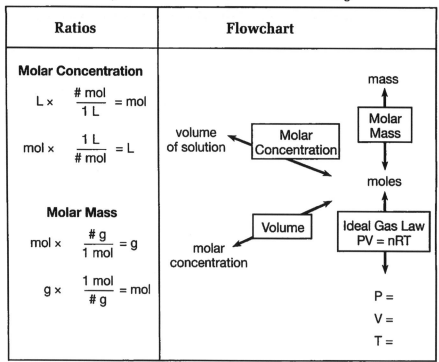

| Ratios | Flowchart |
|---|---|
| **Molar Concentration**<br><br>$L \times \dfrac{\text{\# mol}}{1\ L} = \text{mol}$<br><br>$\text{mol} \times \dfrac{1\ L}{\text{\# mol}} = L$<br><br><br>**Molar Mass**<br><br>$\text{mol} \times \dfrac{\text{\# g}}{1\ \text{mol}} = g$<br><br>$g \times \dfrac{1\ \text{mol}}{\text{\# g}} = \text{mol}$ | |

## Calculating Concentration from Moles and Volume

If 0.900 mol of table salt, NaCl, is dissolved to give 500. mL of a laboratory solution, what is the molar concentration of the solution?

In this case the definition for molar concentration is used:

$$C = \frac{n}{v} = \frac{0.900\ \text{mol}}{0.500\ L} = 1.80\ \frac{\text{mol}}{L}$$

## Calculating Concentration from Mass and Volume

An antacid solution may be prepared by dissolving 15.0 g of sodium bicarbonate (baking soda) in sufficient water to make 250. mL of solution.  Determine the molar concentration of the antacid solution.

Method 1:  $n_{NaHCO_3} = \dfrac{m}{M} = \dfrac{15.0\ \text{g}}{84.01\ \text{g/mol}} = 0.179\ \text{mol}$

$C = \dfrac{n}{v} = \dfrac{0.179\ \text{mol}}{0.250\ L} = 0.714\ \dfrac{\text{mol}}{L}$

Method 2:  $C = 15.0\ \text{g}\ NaHCO_3 \times \dfrac{1\ \text{mol}\ NaHCO_3}{84.01\ \text{g}\ NaHCO_3} \times \dfrac{1}{0.250\ L} = 0.714\ \dfrac{\text{mol}}{L}\ NaHCO_3$

Regardless of what method you choose, be sure to follow the step-wise sequence shown on the flowchart.

## Calculating Mass from Volume and Concentration

This type of calculation is most commonly used by chemists and technicians in preparing solutions of known concentration.

What mass of washing soda, $Na_2CO_3 \cdot 10\ H_2O$, is necessary to make 400. mL of 0.500 mol/L solution?

Method 1: $n_{Na_2CO_3 \cdot 10 H_2O} = Cv = 0.500 \frac{mol}{L} \times 0.400 \, L = 0.200$ mol

$m_{Na_2CO_3 \cdot 10 H_2O} = nM = 0.200 \, mol \times 286.19 \frac{g}{mol}$

$= 57.2$ g of $Na_2CO_3 \cdot 10 H_2O$

Method 2: $m_{Na_2CO_3 \cdot 10 H_2O} = 0.400 \, L \times \frac{0.500 \, mol}{1 \, L} \times \frac{286.19 \, g}{1 \, mol}$

$= 57.2$ g of $Na_2CO_3 \cdot 10 H_2O$

## Calculating Volume from Mass and Concentration

Sodium hydroxide, commonly known as caustic soda, has many uses in the laboratory and in industry. What volume of 0.600 mol/L NaOH can be prepared from 4.8 g of solute?

Method 1: $n_{NaOH} = \frac{m}{M} = \frac{4.8 \, g}{40.00 \, g/mol} = 0.12$ mol

$v_{NaOH} = \frac{n}{C} = \frac{0.12 \, mol}{0.600 \, mol/L} = 0.20$ L of solution

Method 2: $v_{NaOH} = 4.8 \, g \, NaOH \times \frac{1 \, mol \, NaOH}{40.00 \, g \, NaOH} \times \frac{1 \, L}{0.600 \, mol \, NaOH}$

# J.5  Exercises  Solution Problem-Solving

1. Copper(II) sulfate, an important copper salt, is used in copper electroplating cells, and to kill algae in swimming pools and water reservoirs. What is the molar concentration of an electroplating solution in which 1.50 mol of copper(II) sulfate are dissolved in enough water to make 2.00 L of solution?

2. When 11.0 g of glacial (pure) acetic acid is dissolved in water to make 250. mL of vinegar solution, what is the molar concentration of the vinegar?

3. Sodium bicarbonate is used medicinally to counteract excess stomach acidity. How many moles of solid sodium bicarbonate would be needed to make 100. mL of a 0.660 mol/L solution suitable for use as an antacid?

4. A toilet bowl cleaner may be prepared by mixing sodium bicarbonate (baking soda) and sodium hydroxide (lye). What mass of sodium bicarbonate must be added to a 2.50 L bowl to obtain a necessary 0.150 mol/L solution?

5. Sodium phosphate may be used to remove scale deposits from a car radiator. What volume of a 0.075 mol/L solution would contain the necessary 1.10 mol of sodium phosphate to remove the radiator scales?

6. Chlorine bleach in its solution form usually is sold as a 5 to 6 percent solution of sodium hypochlorite; (e.g., as in Clorox and Purex). How many liters of 0.800 mol/L solution would contain 119.2 g of NaOCl?

DEMO ...

# J.6 Preparation of a Solution

Chemists and technicians must constantly prepare solutions. As techniques and instrumentation become more complex, the need for proper methods becomes more essential if accuracy is to be maintained.

**Purpose:**

✔ To prepare 100.0 mL of 0.0350 mol/L aqueous solution of $NiCl_2 \cdot 6H_2O$.

✔ To demonstrate correct techniques for the preparation of a solution.

**Lab Safety:**

- Wear goggles.
- Tie back long hair.
- Nickel compounds are toxic and should be handled carefully.
- Wash hands.

**Materials:**

- 100-mL volumetric flask
- 250-mL beaker
- funnel (short stem)
- stirring rod
- centigram balance
- wash bottle
- scoopula
- distilled water
- $NiCl_2 \cdot 6H_2O$ (or another colored compound)
- meniscus finder
- eyedropper

Calibration Mark →

**Predemo Information:**

In general, the steps to be followed in preparing a solution are:

1. Calculate the mass of solute required.

2. Use a balance to obtain the required mass of solute.

3. Dissolve the required mass of solute in less than the final volume of water.

4. Transfer the solution to a volumetric flask.

5. Bring the solution up to final volume.

6. Stopper and invert several times to mix.

(*Note: These steps are outlined in more detail in the procedure.*)

**Predemo Exercise:**

Calculate the mass of solute required to prepare 100.0 mL of a 0.0350 mol/L aqueous solution of $NiCl_2 \cdot 6H_2O$.

**Procedure:**

1. a. Obtain and record mass of a clean dry 250 mL beaker to 0.01 g.

   b. Make a note of the mass of a beaker plus the required mass of solute.

   c. Add $NiCl_2 \cdot 6H_2O$ until the desired amount of solid is obtained. (Use a tapping action on the scoopula to control the addition of the $NiCl_2 \cdot 6H_2O$.)

2. Add about 60 mL of distilled water to the solute in the beaker. Stir to get the solute to dissolve more rapidly. (When the stirring rod is removed, use a wash bottle containing distilled water to rinse the solution from the stirring rod into the solution in the beaker.)

3. a. Put a clean, short-stemmed funnel into a clean, 100-mL volumetric flask.

   b. Pour the solution from the beaker through the funnel into the volumetric flask. (When pouring, hold the stirring rod onto the lip of the beaker to avoid loss of some solution down the side of the beaker.)

   c. Use the wash bottle to rinse any remaining solution from the beaker, stirring rod and funnel. Do not use an excessive amount of wash water. Remove the funnel from the volumetric flask. (The solution should not have been increased in volume to the point where it was touching the stem of the funnel.)

4. a. Use distilled water from the wash bottle to bring the solution volume up to just below the 100.0 mL line on the volumetric flask.

b. Use an eyedropper, distilled water and meniscus finder to bring the bottom of the meniscus up to the 100-mL line on the volumetric flask. (The dark line on the meniscus finder should be kept just barely below the meniscus in order to get a black meniscus against a white background.)

c. Stopper the volumetric flask. Mix the solution thoroughly by inverting (not shaking) the volumetric flask several times. Leave the volumetric flask stoppered.

**Questions:**

1. Look at the markings on a 100-mL volumetric flask. Note the calibration line on the neck and where "TC 20°C" is written on the flask. This means that the flask is calibrated *To Contain* the correct amount of liquid at room temperature (20°C). Explain how these markings are important.

_____

_____

_____

_____

_____

2. Why was a volumetric flask used to prepare the solution rather than a graduated beaker or graduated cylinder?

_____

_____

_____

_____

_____

_____

3. Which parts of the following materials had to be dry when initially used in preparation of the solution? List the following materials under the appropriate heading: $NiCl_2 \cdot 6H_2O$, scoopula, 250-mL beaker, stirring rod, funnel, volumetric flask and the volumetric flask stopper.

| Had to Be Dry | Could Be Wet |
|---|---|
|  |  |
|  |  |
|  |  |

4. Why was it necessary to rinse the equipment in step 3 and step 4?

_____

_____

_____

_____

_____

5. Why was the final solution mixed?

_____

_____

_____

_____

_____

_____

_____

6. Why should the final solution be left stoppered?

_____

_____

_____

# J.7 Pipetting Techniques

Relatively large volumes of liquids are crudely measured using beakers or graduated cylinders. Precise measurements of these large volumes can be made using volumetric flasks. This demonstration will use pipets to deliver small volumes very precisely.

**Purpose:**

✔ To demonstrate correct pipetting techniques.

✔ To practice correct pipetting techniques.

**Predemo Information:**

Pipetting is a common technique for measuring out a particular volume of a liquid. A pipet measures a small volume (usually 25 mL or less) to high precision (0.1 mL to 0.01 mL).

Two basic types of pipets are:

Graduated pipets (Mohr pipets)
(have a scale and measure incremental volumes)

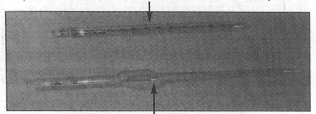

Delivery pipets (Volumetric pipets)
(deliver a specific volume only)

Pipets typically have the marking "TD 20°C" on the upper part of the tube to indicate that these devices are calibrated To Deliver the specified volume of liquid at room temperature. This includes any droplets left inside or the tiny amount of liquid in the tip after delivery.

**Materials:**
- graduated pipet (any volume)
- delivery pipet (any volume)
- pipet filter

**Lab Safety:**
- Wear goggles.
- Tie back long hair.
- Wash hands after completing lab.

**Procedure:**

The correct technique for pipetting a sample is outlined below:

1. Clean and rinse the pipet. When taking samples of a liquid with a pipet, the pipet is first rinsed with distilled water into a waste  beaker. Since the first sample taken is diluted by the film of water already inside the pipet, drain the first sample into a waste beaker. This is known as *rinsing with the sample solutions.* This procedure should be used whenever a pipet is first used for a given day or whenever a pipet is used with a different solution.

2. Hold the pipet near the top between the thumb and the last three fingers of one hand, leaving the index finger free. (This grip allows for quick finger action and does not cover the calibrated line on the pipet.) Squeeze the pipet bulb closed with the other hand.

3. Apply the pipet bulb to the large end of the pipet, and release the pressure on the bulb. This should draw liquid up into the pipet. (The bulb should be held against the pipet only firmly enough to make an air seal. Do not force the pipet entirely into the bulb. Pipetting should never be done using the mouth for suction.  Even tiny amounts of some chemicals can be poisonous if taken into the mouth. To slow the rise of the liquid into the pipet, press the end of the pipet onto the bottom of the beaker. To increase the rate of rise, tilt or raise the pipet.)

4. When the liquid level rises above the calibrated mark on the pipet, remove the bulb and quickly place the index finger over the end of the pipet. This step will be successful if:

   a. the bulb has not been forced onto the pipet;

   b. the hand holding the pipet is high on the pipet, poised for action.

   c. the index finger rather than the thumb is used:

      i. the thumb action is slower.

      ii. when the thumb is used, the fingers will often cover the calibrated line.

5. Gradually roll the index finger, breaking the air seal and allowing liquid to flow out of the pipet. Allow the level to drop until the bottom of the meniscus is exactly on the calibrated mark. Hold the level there by pressing harder with the index finger.

6. Place the tip of the pipet against the inside wall of the receiving container and allow the contents to flow out of the pipet. (For delivery pipets, simply remove the index finger. For graduated pipets, stop the flow again when the bottom of the meniscus drops to the graduation mark desired.)

7. When a delivery pipet drains, a small amount of liquid remains in the tip. (A delivery pipet is calibrated to correct for liquid remaining after the pipet tip has touched the inside of the receiving container.)

8. Repeat the procedure several times. If working in pairs, take turns. Pipetting is a skill that must be practiced.

**Questions:**

1. What are the two types of pipets?

2. Explain why a pipet is labeled TD rather than TC.

3. When is a pipet used instead of a graduated cylinder?

4. Why must the pipet be rinsed with the sample solution before pipetting an acceptably accurate volume?

5. List two reasons why the index finger, rather than the thumb, is used for stoppering the pipet.

6. List two techniques for slowing the rise of the liquid in the pipet.

7. Why is the pipet tip placed against the inside of the receiving container?

8. How might the accuracy of the pipet be
   checked? (*Optional*)

_____

_____

_____

_____

_____

_____

## J.8  Solving Dilution Problems

Most solutions obtained for laboratories are purchased in concentrated form. Some solutions are prepared in concentrated form in the laboratory for later use. The solutions are then diluted to yield solutions of known concentrations as required. **Dilution** is the process of adding solvent to a solution to decrease the concentration. When a solution is diluted, only the amount of solvent is increased. Therefore, the number of moles of solute in the initial (concentrated) solution is equal to the number of moles of solute in the final (diluted) solution.

initial moles of a solute = final moles of a solute

$$n_{iniital} = n_{final}$$

$$n = Cv = \frac{mol}{\cancel{L}} \times \cancel{L} = mol$$

$$C_{iniital}\,v_{initial} = C_{final}\,v_{final}$$

$$C_i v_i = C_f v_f$$

The above equation may be used to solve several types of dilution problems.

### Example 1:

Concentrated commercial hydrochloric acid is prepared by dissolving hydrogen chloride gas in water. The molar concentration of concentrated hydrochloric acid is 12.4 mol/L.

 What volume of concentrated (38%) hydrochloric acid must a laboratory technician use in order to prepare 2.00 L of 0.250 mol/L $HCl_{(aq)}$.

$$C_i v_i = C_f v_f$$

$$v_i = \frac{C_f v_f}{C_i} = \frac{(0.250\ mol/L)(2.00\ L)}{(12.4\ mol/L)} = 0.0403\ L = 40.3\ mL$$

### Example 2:

Concentrated (glacial) acetic acid is 99.5% pure and has a concentration of 17.4 mol/L.

 What is the concentration of a 5% vinegar solution prepared from concentrated acetic acid if 200. mL of concentrated acetic acid is diluted to fill a 4.00-L bottle containing vinegar?

$$C_i v_i = C_f v_f$$

$$C_f = \frac{C_i v_i}{v_f} = \frac{(17.4\ mol/L)(0.200\ L)}{(4.00\ L)} = 0.870\ mol/L$$

| Name | Chemical Formula | Percent Concentration (by Mass) | Molar Concentration |
|---|---|---|---|
| Hydrochloric acid | $HCl_{(aq)}$ | 38% | 12.4 mol/L |
| Phosphoric acid | $H_3PO_{4(aq)}$ | 85% | 14.7 mol/L |
| Nitric acid | $HNO_{3(aq)}$ | 69% | 15.4 mol/L |
| Acetic acid | $CH_3COOH_{(aq)}$ | 99.5% | 17.4 mol/L |
| Sulfuric acid | $H_2SO_{4(aq)}$ | 94% | 17.6 mol/L |
| Ammonia | $NH_{3(aq)}$ | 28% | 14.8 mol/L |
| Sodium Hydroxide | $NaOH_{(aq)}$ | 50% | 19.1 mol/L |

**FIGURE J3**
**Solubilities of Several Common Acids and Bases**

## Challenges: Try to solve these on your own.

1. One of the uses of methanol, $CH_3OH$ (also known as methyl alcohol, wood alcohol and methyl hydrate), in diluted form is a windshield washer antifreeze. In pure form methanol has a molar concentration of 24.7 mol/L. Using a table from the *CRC Handbook of Chemistry and Physics*, a student prepared 8.0 L of 10.0 mol/L aqueous methanol as windshield washer antifreeze good for –30°C. What volume of methanol was necessary to prepare the antifreeze solution?

2. A concentrated (19.1 mol/L) sodium hydroxide solution (also known as caustic soda), when diluted, has widespread use as a cleaner and disinfectant. What is the molar concentration of a bottle and jar cleaner used by a commercial film if 10. L of concentrated caustic soda solution is diluted to 400. L?

3. Concentrated ammonia ($NH_3(aq)$) solution is prepared by dissolving ammonia gas in water. The molar concentration of concentrated ammonia is 14.8 mol/L. What volume of concentrated aqueous ammonia (Caution!) is required by a consumer to prepare 5.0 L of 0.70 mol/L household ammonia?

4. Pure $C_2H_5OH$, ethanol, is 17.2 mol/L. In diluted form, ethanol is present in all alcoholic beverages and in many cleaners. To what volume must 10.0 mL of pure ethanol be diluted in order to prepare 10.3 mol/L ethanol-type cleaning solution?

**LAB ...**

# J.9 Preparation of a Standard Solution and Dilution of a Known Solution

**Purpose:**
✔ To accurately prepare a solution of known concentration.
✔ To dilute the prepared solution.

**Prelab Exercise:**
Calculate the mass of $CuSO_4 \cdot 5H_2O(s)$ required to prepare 100.0 mL of a 0.200 mol/L solution.

**Materials:**
- centigram balance
- vial of $CuSO_4 \cdot 5H_2O$
- funnel
- 100-mL volumetric flask
- medicine dropper
- wash bottle containing distilled water
- 250-mL beaker
- stirring rod
- scoopula
- 10-mL pipet
- meniscus finder

**Lab Safety:**
- Wear goggles
- Tie back long hair
- Wash hands after completing lab

**Procedure:**
Part A: Refer to the five general steps to be followed in preparing solutions given earlier.

1. Determine and record the mass of a clean, dry, 250-mL beaker. Add $CuSO_4 \cdot 5H_2O$ into the beaker until the calculated amount of chemical is measured.

2. Add 40 - 60 mL of distilled water to the $CuSO_4 \cdot 5H_2O$ in the beaker. Stir the solution with a clean stirring rod until the $CuSO_4 \cdot 5H_2O$ is all dissolved.

3. Using a clean funnel, transfer the solution from the beaker into a clean, 100-mL volumetric flask. Use the wash bottle to rinse any solution from the stirring rod, the beaker, and then the funnel into the volumetric flask.

4. Use a medicine dropper to carefully bring the bottom of the solution meniscus to the 100.0-mL mark on the volumetric flask. (A meniscus finder is useful here.) Stopper the volumetric flask and invert several times.

Part B: Proceed with the following steps to dilute the $CuSO_4$ solution from Part A.

1. Pour the 0.200 mol/L $CuSO_4$ from Part A into a clean, dry, 250-mL beaker.

2. Use a 10-mL pipet to transfer 10.0 mL of the 0.200 mol/L $CuSO_4$ into a clean 100-mL volumetric flask.

3. Add distilled water to the 10.0 mL of $CuSO_4$ solution in the volumetric flask until the bottom of the solution meniscus finder reaches the 100.0-mL mark.

4. Stopper the volumetric flask. Invert several times.

5. Take the final solution to the teacher, who will check it for color intensity or conductivity against a set of standard solutions.

**Data:**

Mass of empty 250-mL beaker _____

Mass of $CuSO_4 \cdot 5H_2O$ required _____

Mass of 250-mL beaker plus required $CuSO_4 \cdot 5H_2O$

_____

**Observations:**

_____

_____

**Results:**

Calculate the concentration of the solution after dilution. (Hint: What was the concentration of the original solution? What of the original solution did you pipet and dilute?)

**Questions:**

1. What property of the $CuSO_4$ solution changed noticeably upon dilution?

_____

2. The original and diluted solutions will react with zinc metal. Predict which solution would react with zinc at a faster rate. Why?

_____

_____

_____

3. Which solution would contain a greater number of moles of solute, 8.00 mL of the concentrated $CuSO_4$ solution or 40.0 mL of the diluted solution? Show calculations.

4. (Optional) Can a 0.2000 mol/L $CuSO_4$ solution (note precision) be prepared using the equipment employed in this lab? Explain.

_____

_____

_____

_____

**Conclusions:**

What did you learn in this lab?

_____

_____

_____

_____

_____

_____

What kinds of errors are possible in this lab procedure, and what kinds of things could you do to avoid these errors?

_____

_____

_____

Comment on the value of careful analytical techniques in chemistry.

_____

_____

_____

_____

## Mini DEMO ...

# J.10 Solute-Solvent Interactions

**Purpose:**
✔ To identify some of the interactions in solute-solvent systems.

**Lab Safety:**
• Wear goggles
• Tie back long hair
• Methanol and hexane produce toxic vapors
• Wash hands after completing lab

**Procedure:**
Almost fill three large (25 × 200-mm) test tubes with water, methanol, and hexane, respectively. Add approximately the same small amount of iodine crystals into each test tube and record observations a) initially, b) after two 10-minute intervals and c) after one day. Stopper the test tubes to avoid evaporation.

Initial state    20 min. later    One day later

**Safety Note: Use caution in the use of methanol (poisonous), hexane and iodine (harmful vapors).**

| Observations | 1. Water ($H_2O$) | 2. Methanol ($CH_3OH$) | 3. Hexane ($C_6H_{14}$) |
|---|---|---|---|
| Initially | | | |
| After 20 min | | | |
| One day later | | | |

undissolved solute     solvent          dissolved solute

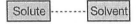

$I_2 \cdots\cdots I_2$ (NP - NP)
*moderate attractions*
moderate collisions will separate molecules

$H_2O \cdots\cdots H_2O$ (SP - SP)
*extremely strong attractions*
vigorous collisions needed to separate molecules

$CH_3OH \cdots\cdots CH_3OH$ (NP/P - NP/P)
*strong attractions*
fairly strong collisions will separate molecules

$C_6H_{14} \cdots\cdots C_6H_{14}$ (NP - NP)
*moderate attractions*
moderate collisions will separate molecules

$I_2 \cdots\cdots H_2O$ (NP - SP)
*weak attractions*
gentle collisions will separate molecules

$I_2 \cdots\cdots CH_3OH$ (NP - NP/P)
*moderate attractions*
moderate collisions will separate molecules

$I_2 \cdots\cdots C_6H_{14}$ (NP - NP)
*moderate attractions*
moderate collisions will separate molecules

**Questions:**

1. Use intermolecular bonding to explain some of the observations. (Use the molecular modeling chart above.)

_____

_____

## J.11 The Process of Dissolving

When a solute dissolves in a solvent, it does so without any extra input from the person making the solution. That is, the solution forms **spontaneously**. There are two factors that "drive" a spontaneous change: 1) the loss of energy (an exothermic change) and/or 2) the tendency to become more spread out (become more disorganized). Energy changes are the result of energy absorbed by breaking solute-solute attractions and solvent-solvent attractions, and energy released by forming bonds between the solute and solvent. Organizational changes result from the solute particles becoming more or less spread out as a result of the dissolving process.

FIGURE J4    The Process of Dissolving

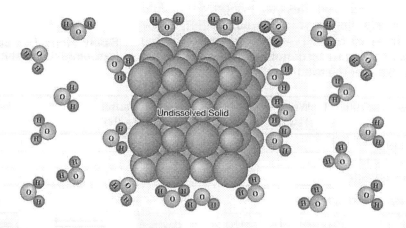

Consider NaCl dissolving in water:

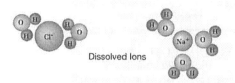

$$NaCl(s) \underset{crystallizing}{\overset{dissolving}{\rightleftharpoons}} Na^+(aq) + Cl^-(aq)$$

Dissolved Ions

The attractions between the sodium ($Na^+$) ions and chloride ($Cl^-$) ions are very strong (ionic bonds), as are the attractions between water molecules (hydrogen bonds). It will require a large amount of energy to break these bonds. There are also attractions between these ions and water molecules: 1) There is an attraction between the negative (oxygen) end of the water molecule and the $Na^+$ ion and 2) a similar attraction between the positive (hydrogen) end of the water molecule and the $Cl^-$ ion. With multiple water molecules attracted to a single ion, the strong interionic attractions are reduced. While the attractions between the ions and water molecules are relatively strong, only a small amount of energy is released when these bonds form. Hence, overall, the dissolving process is **endothermic**. That is, *more (heat) energy is absorbed than is released.* Therefore a solution would not be expected to form. Yet everyone knows that table salt does indeed dissolve in water. This is because of the natural tendency of matter to go from organized to scattered. For this solution, the dissolved particles are much more scattered than the undissolved solid. In this case, the "disorganization" driving force is sufficient to overcome the "energy factor" and allow the dissolving to occur. Adding heat increases the vibration within the crystal and helps break it up, allowing more salt to dissolve at higher temperatures.

For a gas, such as $CO_2(g)$, dissolving in a liquid, such as $H_2O(l)$, the situation is quite the opposite:

$$CO_2(g) \; + \; H_2O(l) \; \underset{\text{bubbling}}{\overset{\text{dissolving}}{\rightleftharpoons}} \; H_2CO_3(aq)$$

In this case, the attractions between $CO_2(g)$ are extremely weak, but the bonds in $H_2CO_3(aq)$ are strong, making the dissolving process exothermic (releasing heat), an obvious driving force. To counter this, the scattered gas molecules become more organized during dissolving, thereby opposing the dissolving process. Keeping a gas dissolved depends on keeping it cold and in a closed container so the gas does not escape.

# J.12 Reversibility, Saturated Solutions and Equilibrium

Some liquids dissolve in each other in all proportions. No matter how much solute is put into solution, the solute always dissolves. Examples are water and antifreeze, or gasoline and kerosene. Such substances are said to be **miscible**. A few liquids, such as water and oil, do not dissolve at all. They are said to be **immiscible**. Most other substances are partially soluble, that is, one dissolves in the other to a concentration that reaches a *definite limiting value*. At this point, the solution is said to be **saturated**. When a solid solute is stirred in water at 20°C for example, the solute dissolves rapidly at first, then apparently more and more slowly. Eventually, dissolving appears to stop and the concentration of solute dissolved in the water no longer increases but remains constant. The solution is now saturated with solute.

Chemists believe that dissolving does not stop when the saturation point is reached. There is evidence to suggest that molecules of the solute continue to leave the solid and pass into the solution, while other molecules of the solute, previously dissolved, return to the solid state from the solution. To explain the constant macroscopic properties, the rate of these two opposing processes must be exactly equal at saturation. The number of particles of solute leaving the solid and *dissolving* in the solution in a specific amount of time is equal to the number of solute particles leaving the solution and *crystallizing* out on the solid in the same amount of time. The solution process at saturation is an example of a **dynamic equilibrium.**

A saturated solution may be defined as a solution in which *the solute dissolves as quickly as the undissolved solute crystallizes again at a specific temperature.* That is, the solution is at equilibrium.

$$\text{undissolved solute} \; \underset{\text{crystallizing}}{\overset{\text{dissolving}}{\rightleftharpoons}} \; \text{dissolved solute}$$

Anytime the amount of dissolved solute is less than the maximum equilibrium amount at that temperature, the solution is **unsaturated**. There is room for more solute to be dissolved and the solution is *not at equilibrium*. A solute crystal added to the solution will dissolve.

Sometimes a saturated solution, prepared at a high temperature, is cooled, and the solute remains dissolved even though the solution would normally not hold that much solute at the lower temperature. Such a solution is said to be **supersaturated** and is *not at equilibrium*. The solution is unstable and the excess solute may crystallize spontaneously, by the addition of a "seed crystal," or even by shaking the solution. Honey is an example of a supersaturated solution. You may have seen honey go "sugary" if it has been sitting around too long. It can be dissolved again by heating in the microwave or in a hot water bath.

## Mini DEMO

## J.13 Supersaturated Solutions

There is a flask containing a sodium acetate solution on the demonstration desk. Feel the temperature of the flask. Your instructor will add a single crystal of sodium acetate to the contents. Observe the change. Feel the flask again.

$$\begin{pmatrix} \text{Solution} \\ \text{separated} \\ \text{particles} \end{pmatrix} \underset{\text{endothermic}}{\overset{\text{exothermic}}{\rightleftarrows}} \begin{pmatrix} \text{Solid} \\ \text{bonded} \\ \text{particles} \end{pmatrix} + \textbf{energy}$$

1. What did you observe?

_____

_____

_____

_____

2. Is the change endothermic or exothermic? How do you know?

_____

_____

_____

3. Are bonds being formed or broken during this change? Explain.

_____

_____

_____

# J.14 Exercises  Reversibility, Saturated Solutions and Equilibrium

1. Solution equilibrium is said to be "dynamic." What is meant by the term *dynamic equilibrium*?

_____

_____

_____

_____

_____

_____

_____

2. How does a system at equilibrium, such as a saturated solution, appear at the macroscopic level?

_____

_____

_____

_____

3. Copper(II) sulfate dissolved in water yields a blue solution. What is the effect, if any, upon color intensity if additional copper(II) sulfate is added to a solution that is already saturated with copper(II) sulfate? Explain your prediction.

_____

_____

_____

_____

_____

_____

# J.15  Solubility

The term solubility is used in two senses — qualitatively and quantitatively. Qualitatively, solubility is often used in a relative way when substances are classed as being **soluble, slightly soluble** or **insoluble**. At extremely low solubilities, the solute may be regarded as having negligible solubility or as being insoluble. FIGURE J5 lists the solubilities generally associated with the qualitative terms. (See the solubility table on the _Periodic Table of Ions_ in the Appendix.)

The qualitative use of solubility is often too imprecise. The quantitative definition of solubility has a definite meaning. In the quantitative sense, **solubility** refers to _the quantity of solute required to produce a saturated solution at a given temperature_. Solubility is the concentration of solute in a saturated solution at a given temperature. Thus **molar solubility** would be the _number of moles of solute required to form one liter of saturated solution at a specific temperature_; i.e., the maximum molar concentration of a solute.

$$\text{molar solubility} = C_{\text{saturated solution}} = \frac{n}{v}$$

$$= \frac{\text{number of moles required to saturate the solution}}{\text{1 liter of solution}}$$

In other words, molar solubility calculations are done just like other concentration problems. The only difference is that the final solution is saturated. The Table of Solubility in the Appendix lists the molar solubilities and percent concentrations for several compounds.

FIGURE J5    Solubility

| Examples (see Solubility Table in Appendix) | Qualitative Description | Quantitative Description |
|---|---|---|
| NaCl(aq)  s=5.3 mol/L | soluble | $s \geq 0.1$ mol/L |
| CaCO$_3$(aq)  s=6.9×10$^{-5}$ mol/L | low solubility | $s < 0.1$ mol/L |
| Hexane(l) — H$_2$O(l) | insoluble | extremely low |

s = molar solubility = the concentration of a saturation solution

## Example:

A saturated solution produced by dissolving hydrogen chloride gas in water is called _concentrated hydrochloric acid_. If 45.2 g of hydrogen chloride gas is required to prepare 100 mL of concentrated hydrochloric acid at 25°C, what is the molar solubility of hydrogen chloride at 25°C?                    _Example continued on next page._

$$\text{Method 1: } n_{HCl} \frac{m}{M} = \frac{45.2 \text{ g}}{36.46 \text{ g/mol}} = 1.24 \text{ mol}$$

$$C_{HCl} = \frac{n}{v} = \frac{1.24 \text{ mol}}{0.100 \text{ L}} = 12.4 \frac{mol}{L}$$

$$\text{Method 2: } \quad C_{HCl} = 45.2 \text{ g HCl} \times \frac{1 \text{ mol HCl}}{36.46 \text{ g HCl}} \times \frac{1}{0.100 \text{ L}} = 12.4 \frac{mol}{L} \text{ HCl}$$

The molar solubility of hydrogen chloride at 25°C is 12.4 mol/L.

# J.16 Exercises Solubility

1. Salt (sodium chloride) is mined by pressurized water from depths of about 1 km below the earth's surface. The mining is done to obtain salt solutions (brine) for chlor-alkali plants (factories designed to produce chlorine and sodium hydroxide), and to produce underground caverns for storage of hydrocarbons.

   The salt plant and the underground caverns employ saturated solutions of sodium chloride at points in their operation. If 35.7 g of sodium chloride dissolves to make 100 mL of a saturated solution at 30°C, what is the molar solubility of sodium chloride at 30°C? Compare your answer with the Table of Solubility in the Appendix.

2. Nitric acid is produced at fertilizer plants by reacting nitrogen dioxide gas with water to produce nitric acid and nitrogen monoxide. Concentrated nitric acid may be prepared by evaporating excess water to obtain a saturated solution.

   If $1.06 \times 10^3$ kg of nitrogen dioxide are reacted to produce 1.00 kL of concentrated nitric acid, what is the molar solubility of nitric acid at 20°C? (Two moles of nitric acid are produced from every three moles of nitrogen dioxide reacted.) Compare your answer with the value for nitric acid found in the Table of Solubility in the Appendix.

# J.17 Factors that Affect Solubility

The prediction of solubilities involves many variables such as relative size and relative charge of solute and solvent particles, interaction between solute and solvent particles, temperature and pressure. In spite of the complexity of factors that affect solubility, some general rules apply to many of the compounds first encountered in the study of chemistry. These general rules are not laws and are therefore subject to exceptions. Below is a discussion of the four factors affecting solubility followed by some relevant general rules.

## The Nature of Solute and Solvent

The rule *"like dissolves in like,"* where *like* refers to similarities in polarities of substances, has useful application for predicting solubilities. In general, polar and ionic solutes tend to be more soluble in polar solvents and nonpolar solutes tend to be more soluble in nonpolar solvents. Thus, inorganic acids (which are polar) and bases and salts (which are ionic) tend to be much more soluble in water (which is highly polar). Solutes such as carbon tetrachloride ($CCl_4$), hexane ($C_6H_{14}$) and benzene ($C_6H_6$), which are nonpolar, are not soluble in (polar) water. Sodium chloride, an ionic substance, is highly soluble in polar water, slightly soluble in weakly polar ethyl alcohol and insoluble in nonpolar carbon tetrachloride. Gasoline, a nonpolar substance, is only very slightly soluble in polar water but highly soluble in nonpolar carbon tetrachloride.

## General Rules:
1. Polar and ionic solutes are soluble in polar solvents.
2. Nonpolar solutes are soluble in nonpolar solvents.

## The Effect of Temperature

Generally there is a limit to the amount of solute that can dissolve in a given amount of solvent at a fixed temperature. The temperature of the solvent generally has a strong effect on the amount of solute that will dissolve. For most solids dissolved in liquids, the dissolving process is endothermic and an increase in temperature results in an increase in solubility. The effect of increased solubility of solids in liquids upon heating is illustrated in everyday experiences. For example, the solubility of soap and dirt in hot wash water is greater than in cold wash water. As for most gases, the dissolving process is exothermic and a decrease in temperature results in an increase in solubility. For example, when water in a kettle is heated but not boiled, dissolved air escapes as it becomes less soluble at higher temperatures. For the dissolving of liquids in liquids, the effect is too variable for any useful generalizations to be made. In every case, a new solubility under a new temperature condition is gradually established.

## General Rules:
3. An increase in temperature generally increases the solubility of solids in liquids.
4. An increase in temperature generally decreases the solubility of gases in liquids.

### FIGURE J6
**Solubility of Several Solids and Gases in Water, as a Function of Temperature**

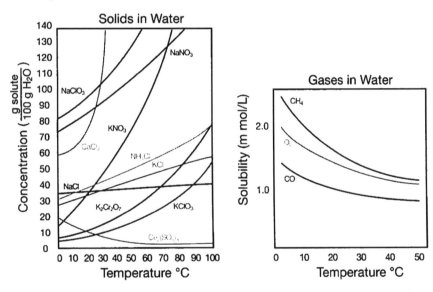

## The Effect of Pressure

Changes in pressure have very little effect on the solubility of solids and liquids. However, changes in pressure have a marked effect on the solubility of gases. The solubility of a gas in a liquid is directly proportional to the pressure of that gas above the liquid. For example, when a bottle of carbonated soft drink is opened, the pressure is reduced and dissolved carbon dioxide bubbles out of the solution. A new solubility under the new pressure conditions is gradually established.

## General Rules:
5. Changes in pressures have no appreciable effect upon the solubility of solids and liquids in a liquid solvent. Rules continue on next page.

6. The solubility of gases in liquids is directly proportional to the pressure above the liquid solvent (i.e., more gas dissolves at higher pressure).

# J.18  Exercises  Factors that Affect Solubility

1. List the three major factors that determine the solubility of a substance.

_____

2. Briefly explain the idea: "Like dissolves in like." Fill in the third column.

_____

_____

| Solute | Solvent | Does it Dissolve? |
|--------|---------|-------------------|
| Polar | Polar | |
| Ionic | Polar | |
| Nonpolar | Polar | |
| Polar | Nonpolar | |
| Ionic | Nonpolar | |
| Nonpolar | Nonpolar | |

3. Why does an increase in temperature usually increase the solubility of a solid in a liquid?

_____

_____

4. What effect does an increase in temperature have on the solubility of gas in a liquid?

_____

_____

The next three questions in this exercise require a limited knowledge of polarity of molecules:

5. Why are water and 2,2,4-trimethylpentane ($C_8H_{18}$, a component of gasoline) mutually insoluble?

_____

_____

6. Explain why $I_2(s)$ has low solubility in water but high solubility in ethanol ($C_2H_5OH$) and cyclohexane ($C_6H_{12}$).

_____

_____

_____

7. From the list given below, decide which substances have good solubility in tetrachloroethene and which dissolve best in water. (Tetrachloroethene, $C_2Cl_4$, is a commonly used solvent in the dry-cleaning process.) One solute dissolves in both.

$KMnO_4(s)$, $Cl_2(g)$, $CH_3OH(l)$, $C_6H_{14}(l)$ $NH_3(g)$, $Br_2(l)$, $HCl(g)$, $Na_2CO_3(s)$

Good solubility in tetrachloroethene:

_____

Good solubility in water:

_____

8. How does solubility of $CO_2(g)$ in $H_2O$ (as in soft drinks) vary with:
   a. an increase in pressure of $CO_2(g)$? Explain.

   _____
   _____

   _____

   b. an increase in temperature? Explain.

   _____
   _____

   _____

9. How does solubility of washing soda, $Na_2CO_3(s)$, in water vary with:
   a. an increase in pressure?

   _____
   _____
   _____
   _____

   b. an increase in temperature?

   _____
   _____
   _____
   _____

10. Will stirring a solution increase the solubility of the solute in the solution? Explain.

   _____
   _____
   _____
   _____

11. All fish need oxygen to survive. Trout require fairly high amounts of dissolved oxygen (DO) and generally live in cold, fast-moving streams while catfish and carp require less oxygen and are capable of living in warm, murky, slow-moving water. How does the temperature of the water relate to the survival of these fish?

   _____
   _____
   _____

# J.19 Solutions and Conductivity

Water is often called the "universal solvent." This is not because of the large amount of it on earth or its presence throughout the universe, but because it can dissolve so many substances. Some substances dissolve in water to produce a solution that conducts electricity, while other substances dissolve, but do not form a conducting solution. This demonstration will attempt to classify substances by the ability of their solution to conduct electricity.

**Purpose:**
✔ To classify solutions of compounds as electrolytes or nonelectrolytes.

**Safety:**
Wear chemical-splash goggles and wash hands after completing.

**Predemo Information:**
Solutes can be classified into two categories:

1. **Electrolytes**, which, upon dissolving, yield solutions that conduct electricity.

2. **Nonelectrolytes**, which, upon dissolving, yield solutions that do not conduct electricity.

**Materials:**
- 1 electrical conductivity apparatus
- 1 400-mL waste beaker
- 1 wash bottle

(All of the solutions listed below will be 0.10 mol/L unless otherwise specified.)
- distilled water
- tap water
- sodium chloride
- hydrochloric acid
- methanol
- sodium hydroxide
- ammonium acetate
- 1-butanol, $C_4H_9OH$
- sulfuric acid
- sucrose, $C_{12}H_{22}O_{11}$
- potassium dichromate
- nitric acid
- potassium hydroxide
- glucose, $C_6H_{12}O_6$
- acetone, $(CH_3)_2CO$
- glycerol, $C_3H_5(OH)_3$
- sodium bicarbonate
- potassium permanganate
- calcium hydroxide (saturated)
- copper(II) sulfate pentahydrate

Testing for Electrolytes (large scale)

Testing for Electrolytes (small scale)

**Procedure:**
Use an electrical conductivity apparatus to determine whether the substances in the materials list are electrolytes or nonelectrolytes. Rinse the electrodes with distilled water after each test.

**Observations:**
Summarize the results of the electrical conductivity tests in the following table.

| Substances that Are Nonelectrolytes | Substances that Are Electrolytes |
|---|---|
|  |  |
|  |  |
|  |  |
|  |  |
|  |  |

**Questions:**

1. Identify the general categories of compounds that are electrolytes. Which type of compound forms nonelectrolyte solutions?

_____

_____

2. Recall from Unit I (Section I.25) that conductivity is a result of charges that are able to move freely. Propose a hypothesis to explain why some substances are electrolytes while others are nonelectrolytes.

_____

_____

_____

_____

_____

_____

_____

_____

# J.20  Explaining Conductivity of Solutions

## Nonelectrolytes

Nonelectrolytes generally include molecular elements and molecular compounds. Solutions of nonelectrolytes are called nonelectrolytic solutions. When *nonelectrolytes* dissolve, they *separate into* individual *neutral molecules* that are free to move throughout the solution.

Equations showing the dissolving process for nonelectrolytes simply show the solutes changing from their pure state to their dissolved state.

For example, when sugar dissolves in water:

$$C_{12}H_{22}O_{11}(s) \rightarrow C_{12}H_{22}O_{11}(aq)$$

## Electrolytes

Electrolytes generally include ionic compounds, acids, and bases. Solutions of electrolytes are called **electrolytic** solutions. When *electrolytes* dissolve and *separate into ions*, they are said to **dissociate** and the process is known as **dissociation**. Although electrolytic solutions may contain billions of ions, the solutions as a whole are always neutral because the solutions always contain equal quantities of positive and negative charge.

Equations that show the dissolving of electrolytes must show the solute in its pure state changing to aqueous ions. Dissociation equations must:

- Be *balanced*
- Show correct *ionic charges*
- Show *physical states*

The following are examples of dissociation equations.

$$KCl(s) \rightarrow K^+(aq) + Cl^-(aq)$$
$$Al_2(SO_4)_3(s) \rightarrow 2\,Al^{3+}(aq) + 3\,SO_4^{2-}(aq)$$
$$Cu(NO_3)_2(s) \rightarrow Cu^{2+}(aq) + 2\,NO_3^-(aq)$$
$$CuSO_4 \cdot 5H_2O(s) \rightarrow Cu^{2+}(aq) + SO_4^{2-}(aq) + 5\,H_2O(l)$$

## Hydrogen Compounds

Hydrogen compounds are a special case. All hydrogen compounds dissolve, but only some hydrogen compounds (e.g., the six listed below) are essentially 100% changed into ions. Most hydrogen compounds only change slightly after dissolving and should be shown in molecular form in solution.

The following acids change 100% of their molecules to ions when they dissolve:

| | | |
|---|---|---|
| Perchloric | $HClO_4(aq)$ | $\rightarrow H^+(aq) + ClO_4^-(aq)$ |
| Hydroiodic | $HI(aq)$ | $\rightarrow H^+(aq) + I^-(aq)$ |
| Hydrobromic | $HBr(aq)$ | $\rightarrow H^+(aq) + Br^-(aq)$ |
| Hydrochloric | $HCl(aq)$ | $\rightarrow H^+(aq) + Cl^-(aq)$ |
| Nitric | $HNO_3(aq)$ | $\rightarrow H^+(aq) + NO_3^-(aq)$ |
| Sulfuric | $H_2SO_4(aq)$ | $\rightarrow H^+(aq) + HSO_4^-(aq)$ |

Note that the hydrogen compound is usually shown as first dissolving in water to form an acid and then "dissociating," hence the $HCl(aq)$ in the equation above rather than $HCl(g)$.

Technically hydrogen compounds do not dissociate. Dissociation is a term reserved for ionic compounds only. Hydrogen compounds are molecular and must react with water to form ions.

## J.21 Exercises Dissociation Equations

1. What types of compounds are nonelectrolytes in aqueous solution?

   _____

2. What types of compounds are electrolytes when dissolved in water?

   _____

3. Why is a solution containing a dissolved electrolyte always neutral overall?

   _____

4. Explain the term dissociation as it applies to ionic compounds.

   _____

   _____

Write dissociation equations for the following electrolytes. Show the physical state of each ion involved. The electrolytes are those tested in the J.19 Demo.

5. sodium chloride _____

6. hydrochloric acid _____

7. sodium hydroxide _____

8. ammonium acetate _____

9. potassium hydroxide _____

10. sulfuric acid _____

11. potassium dichromate _____

12. nitric acid _____

13. copper(II) sulfate pentahydrate _____

14. potassium permanganate _____

15. sodium bicarbonate _____

## J.22 Ionic Concentrations in Electrolytic Solutions

### Importance of Ionic Concentrations

Consider a solution made by dissolving 0.46 mol of $Al_2(SO_4)_3(s)$ to make 2.00 L of aqueous solution. Although it is common to refer to such a solution as 0.23 mol/L $Al_2(SO_4)_3$ (aluminum sulfate), this is technically imprecise. In solution the compound exists as free, separate $Al^{3+}(aq)$ ions and $SO_4^{2-}(aq)$ ions. In chemical reactions involving such a solution, the ions usually react independently of each other. Often, rather than referring to the concentration of a compound in solution, the concentration of each ion present is stated. This system is always more correct and often more convenient.

## Example 1:

In a 0.23 mol/L $Al_2(SO_4)_3(aq)$ solution, what is the molar concentration of each ion?

*Step 1:* Write a balanced dissociation equation.

$$Al_2(SO_4)_3(s) \rightarrow 2\,Al^{3+}(aq) + 3\,SO_4^{2-}(aq)$$

Each mole of compound dissolved yields two moles of cations and three moles of anions.

*Step 2:* Use a mole ratio to determine the ion concentrations.

$$C_{Al^{3+}} = \frac{0.23 \text{ mol } Al_2(SO_4)_3}{1\,L} \times \frac{2 \text{ mol } Al^{3+}}{1 \text{ mol } Al_2(SO_4)_3} = 0.46 \text{ mol/L } Al^{3+}$$

$$C_{SO_4^{2-}} = \frac{0.23 \text{ mol } Al_2(SO_4)_3}{1\,L} \times \frac{3 \text{ mol } SO_4^{2-}}{1 \text{ mol } Al_2(SO_4)_3} = 0.69 \text{ mol/L } SO_4^{2-}$$

## Example 2:

A solution contains 9.61 g of $(NH_4)_2CO_3$ dissolved in water to form 400 mL of solution. What is the concentration of each ion in solution?

*Step 1:* Write the balanced dissociation equation.

$$(NH_4)_2CO_3(s) \rightarrow 2\,NH_4^+(aq) + CO_3^{2-}(aq)$$

*Step 2:* Calculate the concentration of the $(NH_4)_2CO_3$.

$$n_{(NH4)2CO3} = \frac{m}{M} = \frac{9.61 \text{ g } (NH_4)_2CO_3}{96.11 \text{ g/mol } (NH_4)_2CO_3} = 0.100 \text{ mol } (NH_4)_2CO_3$$

$$C_{(NH4)2CO3} = \frac{n}{v} = \frac{0.100 \text{ mol } (NH_4)_2CO_3}{0.400 \text{ L}} = 0.250 \text{ mol/L } (NH_4)_2CO_3$$

*Step 3:* Calculate the concentrations of the ions.

$$C_{NH_4^+} = \frac{0.250 \text{ mol}}{1\,L} \times \frac{2 \text{ mol } NH_4^+}{1 \text{ mol } (NH_4)_2CO_3} = 0.500 \text{ mol/L } NH_4^+$$

$$C_{CO_3^{2-}} = \frac{0.250 \text{ mol}}{1\,L} \times \frac{1 \text{ mol } CO_3^{2-}}{1 \text{ mol } (NH_4)_2CO_3} = 0.250 \text{ mol/L } CO_3^{2-}$$

Or combine all the steps together:

$$C_{NH_4^+} = \frac{9.61 \text{ g } (NH_4)_2CO_3}{0.400 \text{ L}} \times \frac{1 \text{ mol } (NH_4)_2CO_3}{96.11 \text{ g } (NH_4)_2CO_3} \times \frac{2 \text{ mol } NH_4^+}{1 \text{ mol } (NH_4)_2CO_3} = 0.500 \text{ mol/L } NH_4^+$$

$$C_{CO_3^{2-}} = \frac{9.61 \text{ g } (NH_4)_2CO_3}{0.400 \text{ L}} \times \frac{1 \text{ mol } (NH_4)_2CO_3}{96.11 \text{ g } (NH_4)_2CO_3} \times \frac{1 \text{ mol } CO_3^{2-}}{1 \text{ mol } (NH_4)_2CO_3} = 0.250 \text{ mol/L } CO_3^{2-}$$

## Example 3:

In an ammonium dichromate solution where the concentration of the ammonium ion is 0.0466 mol/L, what is the concentration of the solute?

$$(NH_4)_2Cr_2O_7(s) \rightarrow 2\,NH_4^+(aq) + Cr_2O_7^{2-}(aq)$$

$$C_{(NH4)2Cr2O7} = \frac{0.0466 \text{ mol } NH_4^+}{1\,L} \times \frac{1 \text{ mol } (NH_4)_2Cr_2O_7}{2 \text{ mol } NH_4^+}$$

$$= 0.0233 \text{ mol/L } (NH_4)_2Cr_2O_7$$

# J.23 Exercises Ionic Concentrations in Electrolytic Solutions

For each of questions 1–4:
    a. Write the dissociation equation.
    b. Calculate the concentration of each ion.

1. 0.090 mol/L $Na_3PO_4$ tile and household cleaner.

2. 0.00135 mol/L $Ca(OH)_2$ solution in a water treatment plant.

3. A fence post preservative solution is prepared by dissolving 800. g of zinc chloride in enough water to make 4.50 L of solution.

4. A solution formed by dissolving 7.50 mg of $Al_2(SO_4)_3$ in each 1.00 L of water processed by a water treatment plant.

For each of questions 5–7:
    a. Write the dissociation equation.
    b. Calculate the concentration of dissolved electrolyte necessary to give the stated cation or anion concentration.

5. $Na_2CO_3$ to give 0.500 mol/L $CO_3^{2-}(aq)$ concentration.

6. $(NH_4)_2SO_4$ to give 1.20 mol/L $NH_4^+(aq)$ concentration.

7. What mass of calcium chloride is required to prepare 2.000 L of 0.120 mol/L $Cl^-(aq)$ solution.

**DEMO ...**

# J.24  Some Properties of Mixtures

**Purpose:**
✔ To observe several different mixtures and explain their properties.

**Materials:**
- 3 50-mL beakers
- sucrose
- 3 stirring rods
- coffee creamer
- 3 scoopulas
- calcium carbonate
- overhead projector
- water
- laser (optional)

**Procedure:**
1. Add a small amount of sucrose into the first beaker, some calcium carbonate powder into the second beaker, and a tiny amount of coffee creamer to the third beaker (just enough to make the color noticeable). Half-fill each beaker with water and stir. Place these on the overhead projector.
2. Record your observations in the chart below:

**Questions:**
To be discussed with the teacher.
1. Based on your observations, which mixture has the largest particles? smallest particles? How do you know? (Consider the settling and visibility of solute particles.)

_____

_____

_____

_____

_____

_____

_____

2. In the coffee creamer/water mixture the white light from the projector allowed the reds, yellows and oranges to be transmitted to the screen while the blue colors were scattered from the beaker. Light scattering is caused when molecules and colloidal-sized particles first absorb, then re-radiate light.

| Observations | Examples of Mixtures | | |
|---|---|---|---|
| | Sugar and Water | Calcium Carbonate and Water | Coffee Creamer and Water |
| Color of mixture | | | |
| Color of projected light | | | |
| Evidence of settling | | | |
| Result of shining laser light through the mixture (Is beam visible?) | | Before Stirring:<br><br>After Stirring: | |

How does this explain why the sun appears yellow during the day, orange at sunrise and sunset, and the sky looks blue?

_____

_____

_____

_____

_____

_____

_____

3. Explain the results of the laser light.

_____

_____

_____

_____

_____

_____

_____

_____

_____

_____

_____

# J.25 Solutions, Suspensions and Colloidal Dispersions

Thus far in this unit, you have only looked at *solutions*—homogeneous mixtures that have a uniform distribution of solute particles throughout. That is, there is a single visible **phase** or state of matter present in the mixture. The particles are small enough that they are invisible even under a microscope. Mixtures can also be heterogeneous. In this case, two or more visible phases are present in the mixture of which there are two types: **suspensions** and **colloidal dispersions** or **colloids**. Suspensions contain relatively large particles that are easy to see and that settle upon standing. Colloids have particles that are large enough to scatter light—thus often appearing cloudy—but small enough to be invisible to the naked eye and remain suspended in the mixture. Consider the results from the J.24 Demo.

Colloids are actually quite common in nature and include such things as gelatin, blood, milk, mayonnaise, pumice and fog, to name a few. One unique characteristic of colloids occurs as a light beam passes through it, producing a visible beam called the **Tyndall Effect**. This effect can be seen on a partly sunny day as a cloud passes in front of the sun, producing the sunbeams caused by sunlight scattered by colloidal-sized particles in the atmosphere.

FIGURE J7   Examples of Mixtures

|  | Sugar and Water | Calcium Carbonate and Water | Coffee Creamer and Water |
|---|---|---|---|
| Observations | Clear; no settling; no particles visible | Cloudiness; clears on standing; solid particles visible on bottom | Cloudiness; no settling; particles visible with a microscope |
|  | Color of projected light is the same as the mixture | Projected light is blocked | Blue light is scattered; reds and yellows are transmitted |
|  | Laser light not affected | Laser light is blocked after mixing | Laser beam is visible (**Tyndall effect**) |
| Particle Size | Smallest | Largest | Intermediate |
| Type of Mixture | Homogeneous mixture (***solution***) | Heterogeneous mixture (***suspension***) | Heterogeneous mixture (*microscopic view*) Homogeneous mixture (*macroscopic view*) (***colloid***) |

# J.26 Two Colloidal Systems

## Purpose:
✔ To observe the formation of a gel.
✔ To illustrate one way to remove colloidal-sized aerosol particles from a system.

## Materials:
Part 1:
- 1 250-mL beaker
- 1 10-mL graduated cylinder
- 1 50-mL graduated cylinder
- saturated calcium acetate solution
- ethanol
- ceramic gauze pad
- jumper wire w/alligator clips
- matches or lighter

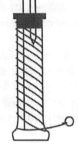

**Electrostatic Precipitator**

Part 2:
- Beral pipet
- 1 100-mL graduated cylinder
- 2-hole rubber stopper to fit cylinder
- copper wire
- 6.0 mol/L NH$_3$
- 6.0 mol/L HCl
- Tesla coil
- jumper wire w/alligator clips
- Beral pipet

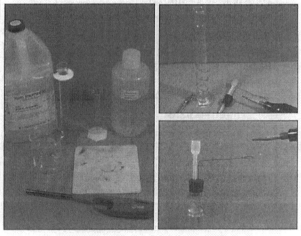

Two Colloidal Systems
Part One              Part Two

## Procedure:
Part 1:
1. Measure 5 mL of calcium acetate and 45 mL of ethanol.
2. Simultaneously mix both into the 250-mL beaker. Record your observations.
3. Place some of the "new substance" on the gauze pad and ignite the mixture. Record your observations.

Part 2:
1. Set up the apparatus as shown above.
2. Place 2 to 3 drops of 6.0 mol/L NH$_3$ at the bottom of the graduated cylinder.
3. Carefully add just enough 6.0 mol/L HCl to form a drop at the end of the funnel. Record your observations.
4. Now come near the center wire with the Tesla coil so that a spark discharge is visible. Record your observations.

## Observations:

| Part 1 |
|---|
|  |

| Part 2 |
|---|
|  |

## Comments:
1. The first colloid is a result of the ethanol being dispersed throughout the mixture by the calcium acetate. This gel is similar to the "canned heat" used in cafeterias to keep food warm.
2. Colloidal-sized particles are often electrically charged. When the copper wire is highly charged by the Tesla coil, the aerosol particles inside are attracted to the wire and the cylinder. This process, called **electrostatic precipitation**, is similar to that used to remove smoke particles from a smokestack or dust from the air passing through a furnace or air conditioner.

# J.27 <u>Exercises</u> Solutions, Suspensions and Colloidal Dispersions

1. Fill in the table below showing the differences between solutions, colloids and suspensions.

|  | **Solutions** | **Colloids** | **Suspensions** |
|---|---|---|---|
| Evidence of settling |  |  |  |
| Separated by filtration |  |  |  |
| Clarity |  |  |  |
| Effect of light |  |  |  |
| Particle size |  |  |  |

2. Identify the following mixtures as solutions, colloids or suspensions:

   a. mayonnaise _____

   b. wine _____

   c. air _____

   d. gasoline _____

   e. grape jelly _____

   f. medicine that says,
   "Shake well before using." _____

3. When car headlights are shone in fog, the headlights become visible. What is this called and how does this work?

   _____

   _____

   _____

# J.28 Colligative Properties

Certain properties of solutions such as color and solubility depend on the kinds of particles that are dissolved. Other properties of solutions, called **colligative properties**, depend only on the concentration of solute particles in the solution, not on the type of particle. Colligative properties include vapor pressure, boiling point, freezing point and osmotic pressure.

**FIGURE J8 Comparing Colligative Properties — Pure Sovents vs. Solutions**

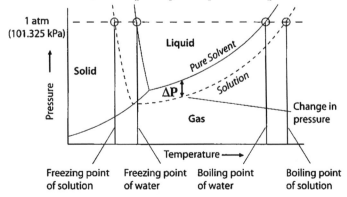

- The vapor pressure of a solution is lower than the vapor pressure of a pure solvent.

- The boiling point of a solution is higher than the boiling point of a pure solvent.

- The freezing point of a solution is lower than the freezing point of a pure solvent.

## Vapor Pressure

In a pure solvent, 100% of the molecules at the surface of the liquid belong to the solvent. In a closed system, there is evaporation and an equal rate of condensation. When a solute is added to the solvent to make a solution, some of the surface positions are now occupied by solute. As a result, there are fewer solvent molecules evaporating; *a lower vapor pressure results.* (See FIGURE J8) What is important here is that it does not depend on what kind of particle it is, only that it is taking up room on the surface of the liquid. Ionic compounds are more effective than molecular compounds due to dissociation:

Molecular : $C_{12}H_{22}O_{11}(s)$         $\rightarrow C_{12}H_{22}O_{11}(aq)$

          1 mol of solid sucrose (table sugar) $\rightarrow$ 1 mol of dissolved sucrose molecules

One mole of molecular solute produces one mole of dissolved particles.

Ionic :       $KCl(s)$           $\rightarrow K^+(aq) + Cl^-(aq)$

          1 mol of solid potassium chloride $\rightarrow$ 2 mol of dissolved ions

One mole of ionic solute produces two moles of particles. A 1 mol/L KCl solution will have a lower vapor pressure than a 1 mol/L $C_{12}H_{22}O_{11}$ solution.

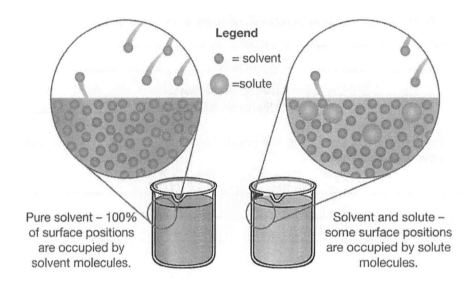

Legend

● = solvent

⬤ =solute

Pure solvent – 100% of surface positions are occupied by solvent molecules.

Solvent and solute – some surface positions are occupied by solute molecules.

## Boiling Point

Recall from Unit I that boiling will occur when the vapor pressure of a liquid is greater than or equal to the external pressure applied to it. If a **nonvolatile** (not easily vaporized) solute is added to the solvent, the vapor pressure is lowered. With a lower vapor pressure the solution must be heated to a higher temperature before the vapor pressure equals the external pressure. That is, *the boiling point of a solution is higher than that of the pure solvent.* (See FIGURE J8)

This can be applied to the coolant system of a car. Ethylene glycol is mixed with water to produce a solution that has a higher boiling point than water alone. This allows the engine to operate more efficiently at higher temperatures without the risk of having the coolant boil away. This also applies to cooking: if salt or sugar is added to the cooking water the food cooks at a higher temperature, reducing the cooking time.

## Freezing Point

When salt is added to icy sidewalks in the wintertime, the mixture melts even though the temperature is still below freezing. As the salt dissolves in the ice, it interferes with the ability of the ice to freeze. This is, again, directly related to vapor pressure, because freezing occurs when the vapor pressure of the liquid is equal to the vapor pressure of the solid. The ice that eventually freezes is almost always pure water. Since the vapor pressure of the solution is lower than the solid, the temperature must be decreased until the vapor pressure of the solid reaches the vapor pressure of the solution. *The freezing point of a solution is lower than that of the pure solvent.* (See Figure J8)

There is a limit to how much the freezing point is lowered; if the temperature gets below the **freezing point depression**, the salt will not work. Two substances commonly used for melting ice are table salt (NaCl) and calcium chloride (CaCl$_2$):

$$NaCl(s) \rightarrow Na^+(aq) + Cl^-(aq) \quad \left( \begin{array}{c} 2 \text{ moles of} \\ \text{dissolved particles} \end{array} \right)$$
$$\quad 1 \text{ mol} \qquad 1 \text{ mol} \qquad 1 \text{ mol}$$

$$CaCl_2(s) \rightarrow Ca^{2+}(aq) + 2\,Cl^-(aq) \quad \left( \begin{array}{c} 3 \text{ moles of} \\ \text{dissolved particles} \end{array} \right)$$
$$\quad 1 \text{ mol} \qquad 1 \text{ mol} \qquad 2 \text{ mol}$$

Calcium chloride is more effective in melting the ice than sodium chloride because it produces three moles of particles per mole of solute rather than just two moles of particles.

Freezing point depression can also be used to protect the coolant in a car from freezing in the winter. The same ethylene glycol added to prevent "boil over" in the summer will lower the freezing point of the coolant to prevent it from freezing in the engine block—a definite problem due to the expansion of water during freezing!

## Osmotic Pressure

In biology class, you studied the process known as **osmosis**, the passage of solvent molecules through a **semipermeable membrane** (See FIGURE J9). The semipermeable membrane is a thin layer of material that acts as a kind of filter paper with holes so small only the solvent can pass through in either direction. Earlier you learned that spontaneous processes occur either due to a decrease in energy or to an increase in the disorganization of the system. In this case, the solvent has a net flow in the direction of the more concentrated solution, that is, the solvent will dilute the solution and make it more disorganized.

FIGURE J9    **Solvent Passing Through a Semipermeable Membrane**

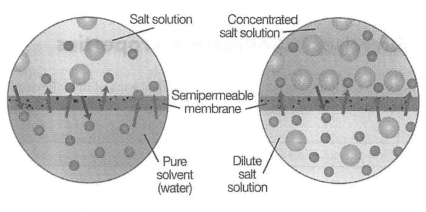

More water molecules move into the salt solution from the pure solvent than vice versa.

More water molecules move into the concentrated salt solution from the dilute salt solution than vice versa.

In the apparatus shown, as the water flows into the tube to dilute the solution, the level of the liquid rises. The liquid will continue to rise until the concentration of the solution inside the tube is equal to the concentration in the beaker. **Osmotic pressure** is the amount of pressure needed to prevent the net flow of solvent into the tube. Since this property depends on the concentration of the particles in the solution, it is also considered to be a colligative property.

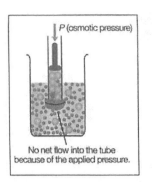

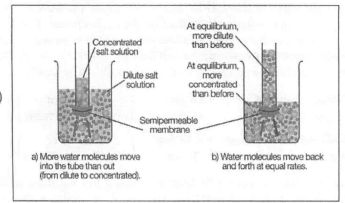

Reverse osmosis is used to purify ocean water and also in many home water purifying systems. Pressure greater than osmotic pressure is applied on the salt water side of the membrane. Pure water is forced through the membrane and collected for later use. Periodically the membrane must be replaced as it becomes contaminated with various substances and no longer functions efficiently.

Cell membranes are semipermeable in nature so osmotic-type processes occur frequently in biological systems and often allow not only the passage of water, but also small molecules such as nutrients and waste products. Consider, for example, carrots and celery that have become limp because they have lost water; they can once again give that satisfying "crunch" after being soaked in water for a time. Cucumbers are made into pickles by soaking them in a salt water brine; the water in the cucumber flows out by osmosis and it shrivels to become a pickle. In the human body, solution concentrations are critical to survival. Any solution injected into the body must have the *same concentration* as the blood serum, that is, it must be **isotonic**. If a less concentrated solution, a **hypotonic solution**, is used, there will be a net flow of water into the cells and the cells may burst from the added pressure. If a more concentrated solution, a **hypertonic solution**, is injected, the cells will lose water, begin to shrivel, and may even die.

# J.29 <u>Exercises</u>   Colligative Properties

1. How does the addition of a nonvolatile solute affect each of the following?
   a. vapor pressure

   _____

   _____

   _____

   b. boiling point

   _____

   _____

   _____

   c. freezing point

   _____

   _____

   _____

   _____

d. osmotic pressure

_____

_____

_____

2. Put the following solutions in order of increasing boiling point:
   0.10 mol/L KCl, 0.10 mol/L $(NH_4)_2SO_4$, 0.10 mol/L $Na_3PO_4$, 0.10 mol/L $C_6H_{12}O_6$

3. Which evaporates faster under the same conditions, 100 mL of ocean water or 100 mL of distilled water? Explain.

_____

_____

_____

_____

4. Explain how drinking salt water can actually make you dehydrated.

_____

_____

_____

_____

# Unit K
# Organic Chemistry

## K.1 What Is Organic Chemistry?

The terms *organic* and *inorganic* are used to distinguish between two different groups of substances. **Organic substances** are considered to *include all compounds of carbon except oxides of carbon, carbonates, carbides and cyanides.* These exceptions plus the substances of the remaining elements are considered to be **inorganic**. Organic substances include those derived from living organisms as well as numerous synthetic substances. Examples of organic materials include, but are not limited to, the following:

- foodstuffs, proteins, carbohydrates
- fuels of many kinds
- greases and lubricating oils
- wood and paper products
- antibiotics and vitamins
- perfumes and flavors
- fabrics
- paints, varnishes and lacquers

- plastics and elastomers (e.g., polystyrene and rubber)
- dyes and pigments
- soaps and detergents
- cosmetics
- some explosives
- some agricultural chemicals (some fertilizers, insecticides and pesticides)

Knowledge of organic substances has grown to the extent that presently between three and four million organic compounds are known. By contrast, known inorganic compounds number about 50 000. To establish coherence among the vast array of organic compounds, chemists use the technique of simplification by classification. Organic compounds are usually classified into two main groups—hydrocarbons and derivatives of hydrocarbons.

Smaller families or series of compounds are established according to their representative structure and properties. Such a general scheme of classification is used in approaching the study of organic compounds in this unit. However, since this is only intended to be a brief introduction to organic chemistry, the scope in this unit is being limited to a consideration of only some of the simpler hydrocarbons and their derivatives.

## K.2 Hydrocarbons

**Hydrocarbons** are *organic compounds composed solely of carbon and hydrogen atoms.* The atoms are bonded to each other by covalent bonds. The vast number and wide range of complexity of hydrocarbons necessitates their further subdivision into two general classes—**aliphatic** compounds and **aromatic** compounds.

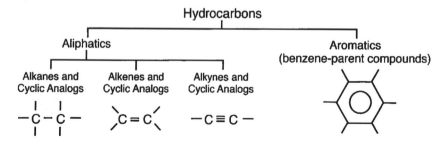

# K.3 Alkanes

The **alkane hydrocarbon series** (the simplest class of organic compounds) has the *general formula* $C_nH_{2n+2}$ (where n = the number of carbon atoms in the hydrocarbon molecule). These hydrocarbons are like other organic compounds in that *each carbon atom shares four pairs of electrons to form four covalent bonds.* All members of this series are called saturated compounds. The term **saturated** is used to describe any organic molecule that contains only single bonds between carbon atoms.

FIGURE K1   Straight-Chain Alkanes

| Name | Molecular Formula | Structural Formula | Phase at Room Temp | Uses or Sources |
|------|------|------|------|------|
| methane | $CH_4$ | | gas | |
| ethane | $C_2H_6$ | | gas | |
| propane | $C_3H_8$ | | gas | natural gas ($C_1$ to $C_4$) |
| butane | $C_4H_{10}$ | | gas | |
| pentane | $C_5H_{12}$ | | liquid | high-grade naphtha |
| hexane | $C_6H_{14}$ | | liquid | |
| heptane | $C_7H_{16}$ | | liquid | gasoline ($C_5$ to $C_{12}$) |
| octane | $C_8H_{18}$ | | liquid | |
| nonane | $C_9H_{20}$ | | liquid | |
| decane | $C_{10}H_{22}$ | | liquid | |
| | $C_{16}H_{34}$ | | liquid | kerosene ($C_{12}$ to $C_{16}$) |
| | $C_{17}H_{36}$ | | solid | Diesel fuel ($C_{15}$ to $C_{18}$) |
| | | | | Lubricants ($C_{16}$ to $C_{20}$) |
| **Note:** Chemists and chemistry students find it very useful to learn the names (more specifically the root words) of the first ten alkanes. | | | | Paraffin, Asphalt ($C_{20}$ or more carbons) |

## Isomerism in Alkanes

Consider the following structural formulas for butane, $C_4H_{10}$.

$$H-\overset{\overset{\displaystyle H}{|}}{\underset{\underset{\displaystyle H}{|}}{C}}-\overset{\overset{\displaystyle H}{|}}{\underset{\underset{\displaystyle H}{|}}{C}}-\overset{\overset{\displaystyle H}{|}}{\underset{\underset{\displaystyle H}{|}}{C}}-\overset{\overset{\displaystyle H}{|}}{\underset{\underset{\displaystyle H}{|}}{C}}-H$$

$$H-\overset{\overset{\displaystyle H}{|}}{\underset{\underset{\displaystyle H}{|}}{C}}-\overset{\overset{\displaystyle H}{|}}{\underset{\underset{\displaystyle H-\overset{\overset{\displaystyle H}{|}}{\underset{\underset{\displaystyle H}{|}}{C}}-H}{|}}{C}}-\overset{\overset{\displaystyle H}{|}}{\underset{\underset{\displaystyle H}{|}}{C}}-H$$

expanded structural formulas

$$CH_3-CH_2-CH_2-CH_3$$

$$CH_3-\underset{\underset{\displaystyle CH_3}{|}}{CH}-CH_3$$

condensed structural formulas

Note that these two compounds have the same molecular formula, $C_4H_{10}$, but different structural formulas. *Compounds with the same formula but different structural formulas are often called* **structural isomers**. The two butanes, for which the structural formulas are given above, are isomers of each other. The structural formula containing the *straight-chain sequence of carbon atoms* is called a **normal alkane**; the other isomer with *side chains off the straight-chain sequence*, is referred to as a **branched-chain alkane**.

The number of possible isomers increases rapidly as the number of carbon atoms is increased. For example, three isomers are possible for $C_5H_{12}$, five for $C_6H_{14}$, 75 for $C_{10}H_{22}$, 366 319 for $C_{20}H_{42}$ and 4 111 846 763 for $C_{30}H_{62}$. Quite obviously, all these isomeric forms, though theoretically possible, have not been prepared. In fact the total number of known organic compounds is less than the number of possible isomers for $C_{30}H_{62}$.

# K.4 Nomenclature of Alkanes

The large number of isomers poses a major problem when naming organic compounds. This problem is overcome by using a systematic method of nomenclature. (In some instances a common name is retained.) Chemists throughout the world use the systematic names developed by the International Union of Pure and Applied Chemistry (IUPAC). The beginning rules for nomenclature of alkanes using the IUPAC systems are listed below.

### Nomenclature of Straight-Chain Alkanes

Straight-chain alkanes are given the names listed in FIGURE K1. Each straight-chain alkane is named according to the stem plus the ending **-ane**. The first four members retain the common name of the stem. All subsequent stems use the Greek or Latin (e.g., *oct-*) numerical prefixes:

### Nomenclature of Branched Chain Alkanes

The following steps are used in naming branched chain hydrocarbons:

1. Determine the longest continuous chain of carbon atoms in the molecule.

2. Number the carbon atoms of the continuous chain consecutively starting at the end closest to the branching.

3. Locate the branch by the number of the carbon atom to which it is attached on the continuous chain.

4. Name the branch. The branches are called alkyl groups ($C_nH_{2n+1}$ groups) and are named by using the stem of the parent alkane plus the ending **-yl**. The position and name of alkyl branches are given first in the overall name.

5. If more than one of the same alkyl groups are present as branches, the number of these branches is indicated by using prefixes: *di, tri, tetra, penta*, etc. A number is used to locate each of these alkyl groups, using the lowest numbers possible (see FIGURE K2).

Example:

$$CH_3 - CH - CH_2 - CH - CH_2 - CH_3$$

with $CH_3$ branch above the fourth carbon and $CH_3$ branch below the second carbon

2,4-dimethylhexane

6. If different alkyl groups are present as branches, assign the lowest numbers possible to locate each branch. The order of the branches is alphabetical regardless of the numbers.

Example:

$$CH_3 - CH_2 - CH - CH - CH_2 - CH_2 - CH - CH_2 - CH_2 - CH_3$$

with $CH_3$–$CH_2$ branch above the third carbon, $CH_3$ below the fourth carbon, and $CH_3$ above the seventh carbon

3-ethyl-4, 7-dimethyldecane (alphabetical order)

FIGURE K2    Naming Alkyl Groups

| Examples | | Alkyl Groups $(C_nH_{2n+1})$ |
|---|---|---|
| $\overset{5}{C}H_3 - \overset{4}{C}H_2 - \overset{3}{C}H_2 - \overset{2}{C}H - \overset{1}{C}H_3$ with $(CH_3)$ branch<br><br>2-methylpentane<br><br>location of branch on chain → branch → longest chain | 1 $CH_3$<br>2 $CH_2$<br>3 $CH - \overset{4}{C}H_2 - \overset{5}{C}H_2 - \overset{6}{C}H_2 - \overset{7}{C}H_3$ with $(CH_2$ $CH_3)$<br><br>3-ethylheptane | methyl, $CH_3-$<br><br>ethyl, $C_2H_5-$ or $(CH_3-CH_2-)$<br><br>propyl, $C_3H_7-$ or $(CH_3-CH_2-CH_2-)$<br><br>butyl, $C_4H_9-$ or $(CH_3-CH_2-CH_2-CH_2-)$<br><br>pentyl, $C_5H_{11}-$ or $(CH_3-CH_2-CH_2-CH_2-CH_2-)$ |

# K.5 <u>Exercises</u> Nomenclature of Alkanes

1. Draw structural formulas and give the names for the five possible noncyclic isomers of $C_6H_{14}$.

2. Why is the name 2-ethyl-2,4-dimethylhexane unsuitable for the following compound?

$$CH_3 - \underset{\underset{\underset{CH_3}{|}}{\overset{\overset{CH_2}{|}}{\underset{|}{C}}}}{\overset{\overset{CH_3}{|}}{}} - CH_2 - \underset{\overset{CH_3}{|}}{CH} - CH_2 - CH_3$$

_____

_____

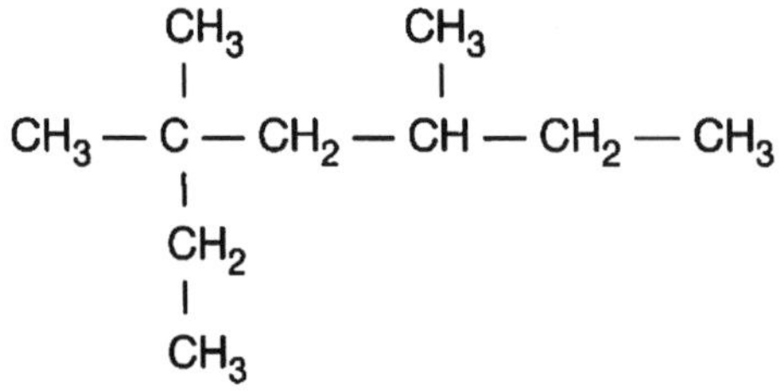

Name each of the following compounds.

3. 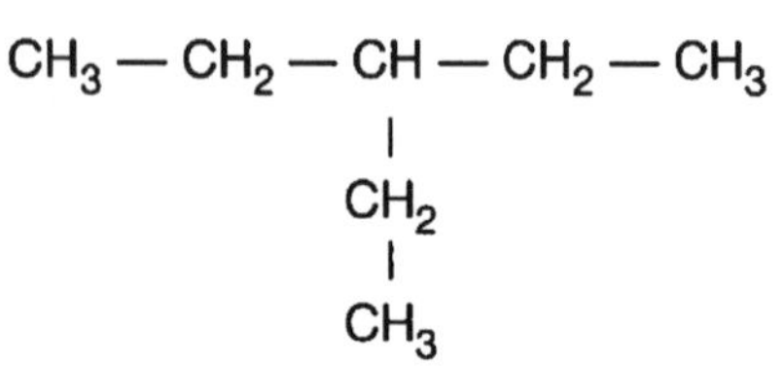 $CH_3 - CH_2 - \underset{\underset{\underset{CH_3}{|}}{\overset{CH_2}{|}}}{CH} - CH_2 - CH_3$

4. 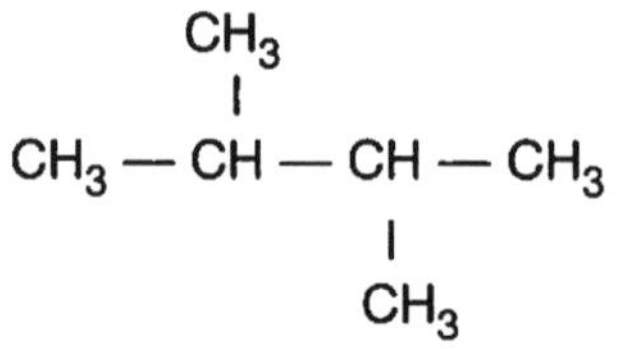 $CH_3 - \overset{\overset{CH_3}{|}}{CH} - \underset{\underset{CH_3}{|}}{CH} - CH_3$

_____          _____

Write structural formulas for the following compounds.

5. 3-ethylhexane

6. 3, 4-diethyl-3-methylhexane

# K.6 Properties of Alkanes

### Physical Properties of Alkanes

The alkanes form a set of compounds called a homologous series. This is a name applied to any series in which each successive member differs by a $CH_2$ unit. Within a homologous series (e.g., alkanes) the boiling points (and hence the melting points) increase as the carbon content increases as illustrated in FIGURE K1. This trend is predictable. Molecules of hydrocarbons are nonpolar and it should be expected that London dispersion forces should increase as the number of electrons in the molecule increases. Alkanes containing up to four carbons are gases. The straight-chain alkanes from five to sixteen carbon atoms are liquids. Beyond that the compounds are wax-like solids. Further, because alkane intermolecular attractions involve only London dispersion forces, alkanes have relatively low melting and boiling points compared to inorganic compounds of similar molar mass. Since alkanes are nonpolar, they are not soluble in polar solvents such as water. Liquid alkanes are good solvents for other hydrocarbons.

### Chemical Properties of Alkanes

Alkanes are relatively unreactive under normal conditions. However, some reactions of alkanes are common at higher temperatures.

1. Alkanes *react with oxygen* (burn or undergo combustion) at high temperatures *to produce primarily $CO_2$, $H_2O$ and heat.* This reaction is called **combustion**. *Alkanes used in this manner are called* **fuels**. For example, the burning of propane is represented by the equation

$$C_3H_{8(g)} + 5 O_{2(g)} \rightarrow 3 CO_{2(g)} + 4 H_2O_{(g)}$$

Gasoline used as a fuel has an **octane rating**. This rating, commonly 87, 89 and 92, is used to match burning qualities with engine performance. The higher the octane number, the more the fuel can be compressed without premature explosion (known as engine knocking).

Branched chain hydrocarbons tend to have a higher octane rating than straight-chain hydrocarbons. Diesel fuel, composed primarily of straight-chain hydrocarbons, explodes when it is compressed. That is why a diesel engine does not need spark plugs.

2. In the absence of air, alkanes can be **cracked** (*broken into smaller fragments*) at high temperatures or in the presence of catalysts. This process is called thermal or catalytic cracking. The cracking reaction is commonly used to convert high-molar-mass hydrocarbons ($C_{15}$ to $C_{18}$) to gasoline hydrocarbons ($C_5$ to $C_{12}$).

3. Alkanes can undergo **substitution reactions** in which *another atom or group of atoms is substituted for a hydrogen atom.* For example, the chloro substitutions of methane can be represented by the equation

$$\text{H}-\underset{\underset{\text{H}}{|}}{\overset{\overset{\text{H}}{|}}{\text{C}}}-\text{H}_{(g)} + \text{Cl}_{2(g)} + \text{light} \rightarrow \text{H}-\underset{\underset{\text{H}}{|}}{\overset{\overset{\text{H}}{|}}{\text{C}}}-\text{Cl}_{(g)} + \text{HCl}_{(g)}$$

Substitution reactions of alkanes usually occur very slowly and only in the presence of light.

# K.7 <u>Exercises</u> Properties of Alkanes

For each of the following questions write a balanced chemical equation using structural formulas for all organic substances. (The nomenclature of the halogen-substituted alkanes will be covered later in the unit.)

1. The combustion of 2, 2, 4-trimethylpentane, one component of gasoline.

Complete the following equations. Use <u>structural formulas</u> for the organic compounds.

2. $CH_3 - CH - CH_2 - CH_3 + O_2 \rightarrow$
   $\qquad\quad |$
   $\qquad\; CH_3$

3. decane + hydrogen $\xrightarrow[\text{catalyst}]{\text{heat or}}$ butane + ???

# K.8 Some Common Sources and Uses for Alkanes

The main source of hydrocarbons is petroleum (also known as *crude oil*). However, the various hydrocarbon components of crude petroleum must be separated before they can be used. *The processes involved in separation, purification and increasing of the yield of the desirable components of crude petroleum* is called **petroleum refining**.

Since crude petroleum is a complex mixture of hydrocarbons, it has no fixed boiling point. The mixture has a boiling or distillation range, which may start as low as 20°C and end above 400°C. The difference in the volatility (as indicated by boiling point) of components in the mixture makes possible the initial *rough separation of crude petroleum* by **fractional distillation** (*also called fractionation*). In general, the smaller the molecule the lower its boiling point (recall the variation of London dispersion forces with number of electrons in the molecule). As a result, fractional distillation sorts the crude petroleum into its main constituents according to size of molecules.

The separation of crude petroleum by fractional distillation is carried out in vertical columns containing series of horizontal plates or trays (see FIGURE K3). Each tray contains *molecules with a similar boiling point,* often referred to as a **fraction** since it is *a portion of the total crude oil molecules.* The crude petroleum is heated to about 400°C and the vapors pass into the fractionation tower.

FIGURE K3
**Schematic Diagram of a Typical Modern Fractionation Tower**

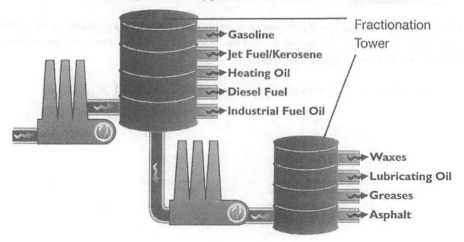

As the vapors pass through the openings in the trays they condense to the liquid phase. The more volatile portion of the liquid revaporizes and rises to the next tray. The less volatile portion remains on the tray, where it serves to condense new vapors rising from below. Thus, the various fractions of crude oil distribute themselves among the trays according to boiling temperature ranges. In this way, the extremely light gases are taken off at the top of the tower, gasoline from the top tray, the kerosene and gas oils in the middle, and the fuel oils, lubricants and waxes at the bottom. Residue drawn off at the bottom may be burned as fuel, pressed into asphalt, or heated further to produce other hydrocarbons and a residue of coke (see FIGURE K4).

Fractional distillation is a physical process, and does not alter the chemical composition of the hydrocarbon molecules. To bring about chemical changes, other refining methods are used, generally called cracking or reforming processes.

The first cracking processes, because of the use of high temperatures, were called **thermal cracking**. These have been largely replaced by methods called **catalytic cracking** in which the molecular breakdown is brought about by catalysts. *The cracking process breaks down large molecules into smaller molecules.* For example, heavier fractions (containing larger molecules) are broken down into more useful fractions (containing smaller molecules) such as gasoline and kerosene.

**Thermal and catalytic reforming** *uses heat or catalysts respectively to convert lighter molecules into heavier fractions.* Reforming is commonly used to convert low-grade gasoline into higher-grade fuels, and to produce larger hydrocarbons for chemical use.

By using fractional distillation and various other processes, the end products from refining can be varied within fairly wide limits. Generally, the main factors that affect the end product are the kinds of crude petroleum available (crudes from different sources may vary in their constituents) and the economic demands for specific products.

FIGURE K4
**Fractions from Fractional Distillation of Petroleum**

| Range of Carbon Atoms | Boiling Point Range (C) | Fraction | Some Typical Uses |
|---|---|---|---|
| $C_1$ to $C_5$* | −164 to 30 | gas | gaseous fuels; e.g., heating homes |
| $C_5$ to $C_6$ | 30 to 90 | petroleum ether | solvent, dry cleaning, naphtha |
| $C_5$ to $C_{12}$ | 30 to 200 | straight-run gasoline | motor gasoline |
| $C_{12}$ to $C_{16}$ | 175 to 275 | kerosene | fuel for stoves, diesel and jet engines; cracking stock |
| $C_{15}$ to $C_{18}$ | up to 375 | light gas oil or fuel oil | furnace oil; cracking stock |
| $C_{16}$ to $C_{20}$ | 350 and up | heavy gas oil | lubricating oils; cracking stock |
| $C_{18}$ and up | (semi-solid) | greases | lubricating; cracking stock |
| $C_{20}$ and up | melt at 52 to 57 | paraffin (wax) | candles, waxed paper, cosmetics, polishes; cracking stock |
| $C_{26}$ and up | to 515 | residue in boiler | asphalts and tars (roofing and paving; wax; residue oils) |

* These are also available from natural gas.

# K.9 <u>Exercises</u> Some Common Sources and Uses for Alkanes

1. What physical property is used to separate different compounds in a petroleum fractionization tower?

2. How does the average number of carbon atoms per molecule vary for the fractionization products shown in FIGURE K4? Explain this order.

_____

_____

_____

_____

3. What chemical processes may be used to convert the petroleum distillation residue into gasoline or naphtha ($C_6 - C_7$, boiling range 60 to 100°C)?

_____

4. Compare catalytic cracking to catalytic reforming.

_____

_____

_____

_____

---

**DEMO ...**

# K.10 Fractional Distillation

**Purpose:**

✔ To separate a two-component mixture by the method of fractional distillation.

**Materials:**
- 2 ring stands
- 2 ring clamps
- boiling chips
- 2-propanol/water mixture
- 2 utility clamps
- graph paper (or graphing program)
- 500-mL round bottom flask
- Liebig condenser
- distilling column
- rubber tubing
- thermometer (−10 to 150°C)
- hot plate (or electric heating mantle)

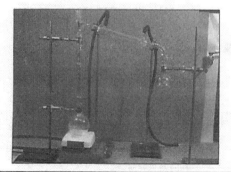

**Procedure:**
1. Assemble the apparatus as pictured.
2. Place 50 mL of the mixture in the distillation flask. Add several boiling chips.
3. Ensure that all connections are tight.
4. Heat the mixture slowly.
5. When the temperature starts to rise, record the temperature every 30 s.

   *Note:* The leveling-off of temperature indicates that one of the components of the mixture is boiling. At this temperature liquid will begin to collect in the collection flask. Remember that the thermometer is measuring the temperature of the vapor and not the temperature of the liquid in the flask.

6. Once the temperature begins to rise again, change the collection flask to collect the next component that distills.
7. Continue heating until the temperature levels off again. Change the collection flask again to collect the last component. Continue the procedure only until a few milliliters remain in the heating flask. Do not heat to dryness.
8. Use the 25-mL graduated cylinder to measure the volume of the first fraction collected. Record this volume in the data table provided and calculate the volume of the second fraction by subtraction.

9. Plot a graph of temperature versus time.
10. From the graph plotted, determine the temperature that most likely represents the boiling point of each component. Record these temperatures in the data table provided.
11. Test the flammability of each fraction by pouring some of each liquid into an evaporating dish and igniting.

| Time (min.) | (°C) | Time (min.) | (°C) |
|---|---|---|---|
| 0 | | 10.5 | |
| 0.5 | | 11 | |
| 1 | | 11.5 | |
| 1.5 | | 12 | |
| 2 | | 12.5 | |
| 2.5 | | 13 | |
| 3 | | 13.5 | |
| 3.5 | | 14 | |
| 4 | | 14.5 | |
| 4.5 | | 15 | |
| 5 | | 15.5 | |
| 5.5 | | 16 | |
| 6 | | 16.5 | |
| 6.5 | | 17 | |
| 7 | | 17.5 | |
| 7.5 | | 18 | |
| 8 | | 18.5 | |
| 8.5 | | 19 | |
| 9 | | 19.5 | |
| 9.5 | | 20 | |
| 10 | | 20.5 | |

| Fraction | Boiling Point (°C) | Flammability |
|---|---|---|
| 1 | | |
| In between | | |
| 2 | | |

**Today's Air Pressure:** _____

**Questions:**

1. On the graph, label the different parts of the curve:
   - pure water boils
   - 2-propanol boils
   - vapor reaches thermometer
   - vapor has not yet reached the thermometer
   - mixture of 2-propanol and water boils

2. Explain what happens during the process of distillation.

_____

_____

_____

3. How does the "scrubber" help to improve separation of the two components?

_____

_____

4. How does the boiling point relate to the air pressure of the day? Did the boiling points match the literature values for the components? Explain.

_____

_____

_____

_____

5. Explain how intermolecular forces relate to differences in boiling point.

_____

_____

_____

_____

**Conclusions:**

1. What did you learn in this lab? Discuss at least 3 or 4 things you learned including something regarding the statement given in the Purpose.

_____

_____

2. Can you identify any errors that actually occurred or are possible in the procedure?

3. General comments: e.g., "I liked/disliked this lab because..." and "My favorite part was..."

## K.11 Bonding in Alkenes

The **alkenes** (*general formula*, $C_nH_{2n}$) contain two less hydrogen atoms than the alkanes with the same number of carbon atoms. Since each carbon must have four covalent bonds, the lower H-to-C ratio necessitates that a double bond be placed between one pair of carbon atoms. Because of the presence of a double bond, the term **unsaturated** is applied to the compounds in this series. In this sense, unsaturated means that *there is room for more hydrogen atoms to bond onto the carbon atoms.* Each carbon atom that is part of the double bond in an alkene is bonded to two other atoms. For example, the bonding in the simplest alkene, $C_2H_4$, can be represented as follows:

$$\cdot \overset{\circ}{\underset{\circ}{C}} \cdot + \cdot \overset{}{\underset{\circ}{C}} \cdot \quad \text{and} \quad \begin{matrix} H \circ \\ H \circ \\ H \circ \\ H \circ \end{matrix} \rightarrow \overset{H \cdot}{\underset{H \circ}{{}_{\circ}C}} \overset{\cdot H}{::} \overset{\cdot H}{\underset{\circ H}{C_{\circ}}} \qquad \overset{H}{\underset{H}{}} C = C \overset{H}{\underset{H}{}}$$

### Nomenclature of Alkenes

The IUPAC system of nomenclature for the alkanes applies to the alkenes with the following additions (IUPAC Section 3.1):

1. The ending *-ene* is used (instead of *-ane*) to indicate the presence of one carbon double bond.

2. The longest continuous chain of carbon atoms containing the double bond determines the stem for the name.

3. The longest continuous chain is numbered so that the carbon atoms of the double bond have the lowest possible numbers, and next so that the branches have the lowest possible numbers.

## Examples:

The only alkene common to high school chemistry for which a common (nonsystematic) name is retained by the IUPAC is ethylene for $C_2H_4$.

$CH_2 = CH_2$
ethene (ethylene)

$CH_2 = CH-CH_3$
propene

$CH_2 = CH-CH_2-CH_3$
1-butene

$CH_3-CH = CH-CH_3$
2-butene

$$CH_3-CH_2-\overset{\overset{\displaystyle CH_3}{|}}{C} = CH_2$$

2-methyl-1-butene

$$CH_3-CH_2-\overset{\overset{\displaystyle CH_3}{|}}{\underset{\underset{\displaystyle CH_3}{\underset{|}{CH_2}}}{C}} = \overset{}{\underset{\underset{\displaystyle CH_3}{\underset{|}{CH_2}}}{C}}-CH_2-CH_3$$

3,4-diethyl-3-hexene

# K.12 Exercises Bonding in Alkenes

Provide the name for each of the following compounds.

1. $CH_3 - CH = C - CH_3$
                $|$
               $CH_3$

2. $CH_2 = CH - C - CH_2 - CH_3$
                    $CH_3$ (above)
                    $|$
                    $CH_3$ (below)

_____          _____

Write a structural formula for each of the following compounds.

3. 2,4-dimethyl-2-pentene    4. 4-ethyl-3-methyl-2-hexene    5. methylpropene

---

# K.13 Molecular Models of Alkanes and Alkenes

**Purpose:**

✔ To construct models for some alkanes and alkenes.

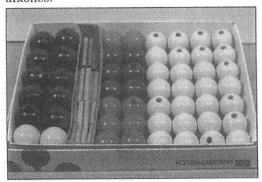

**Prelab Exercise:**

If the teacher so instructs, complete the following tables before going into the laboratory.

**Procedure:**

1. Use a molecular model kit to construct the following alkanes and alkenes.

2. If using ball and spring kits, assemble and disassemble by turning clockwise. (Turning counter clockwise will unravel the springs.)

3. Construct as many structures as possible before disassembling to construct other ones.

4. Check with the teacher if uncertain whether a model is correct.

**Observations:**

## Part A: Alkanes

| Member | Molecular Formula | Structural Formula | Name |
|--------|-------------------|--------------------|------|
| First | | | |
| Second | | | |
| Third | | | |
| Fourth | | | |
| | | | |
| Fifth | | | |
| | | | |
| | | | |

## Part B: Alkenes

| Member | Molecular Formula | Structural Formula | Name |
|--------|-------------------|--------------------|------|
| First  |                   |                    |      |
| Second |                   |                    |      |
| Third  |                   |                    |      |
|        |                   |                    |      |
|        |                   |                    |      |

# K.14 The Properties of Alkenes

**Physical Properties of Alkenes**  The physical properties of alkenes roughly correspond to the physical properties of alkanes with the same number of carbons.  Refer back to the physical properties of alkanes discussed earlier.

### Chemical Properties of Alkenes

1. Alkenes (like alkanes) react with oxygen (burn to undergo combustion) at high temperatures to produce primarily $CO_2$ and $H_2O$.

2. Oxidizing agents such as $KMnO_4$ and $K_2Cr_2O_7$ readily react with alkenes by attacking at the site of the double bond.  For example, when potassium permanganate is added to an unsaturated hydrocarbon, the violet color of permanganate fades.  This reaction, as well as the reaction with bromine, is used as a test for the presence of unsaturation in hydrocarbons.  The reactions of alkenes with $KMnO_4$ are too complex to consider here.

3. Alkenes are chemically more reactive than alkanes because of their ability to undergo addition reactions at the site of the double bond.  Only a single bond is necessary to hold the molecule together.  The second pair of electrons in the double bond of the alkene is available for reaction under the right conditions.  For example:

The reaction is called an addition reaction because atoms of some substance can be added to the alkene.  Some examples of addition reactions are given below.  Note that in all instances the double bond is eliminated and a saturated compound is formed.

## Examples:

- Addition reactions with hydrogen

• Addition reactions with a halogen

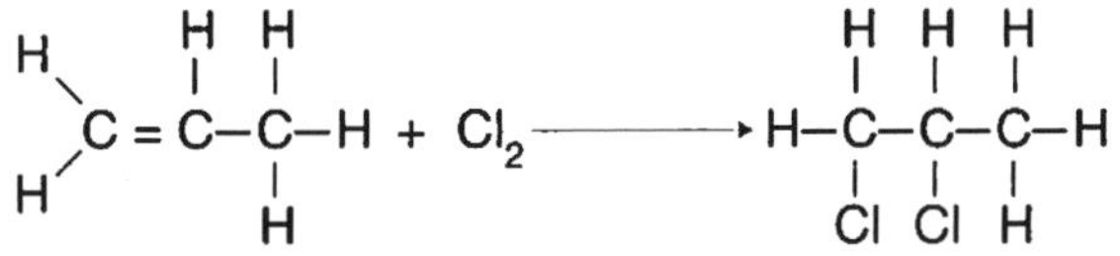

$$H_2C=CH-CH_2-H + Cl_2 \longrightarrow H-CH_2-CHCl-CHCl-CH_3$$

• Addition reactions with a hydrogen halide

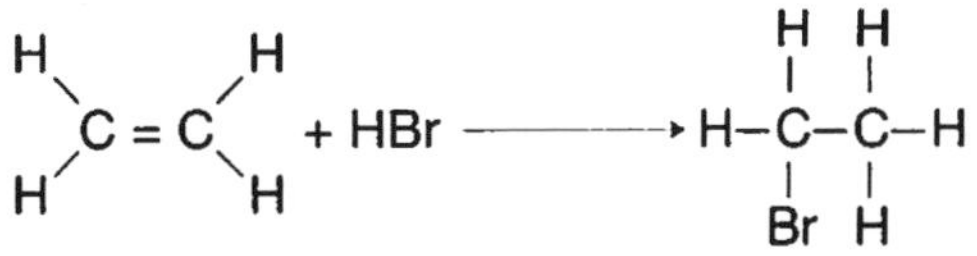

$$H_2C=CH_2 + HBr \longrightarrow H-CH_2-CHBr-H$$

• Addition reactions with water

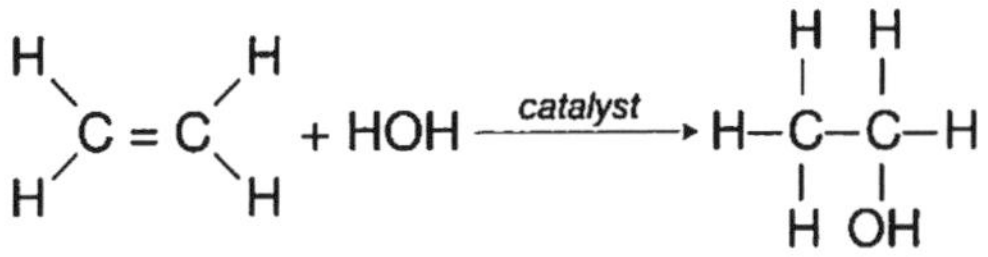

$$H_2C=CH_2 + HOH \xrightarrow{catalyst} H-CH_2-CH(OH)-H$$

# K.15    <u>Exercises</u> The Properties of Alkenes

1. The boiling point of propane is –44.5°C and that of propene is –47.8°C.  Is this consistent with the nature of the intermolecular forces present in both these hydrocarbons?  Explain.

_____

_____

_____

_____

2. Compare the chemical reactivity of alkenes with alkanes.

_____

_____

3. Describe a test that may be used to distinguish between an alkane and an alkene.

_____

_____

_____

_____

_____

4. Discuss the versatility of the compound ethene.

_____

_____

_____

Write balanced equations for the reactions involving the following substances.  Use structural formulas for the organic compounds.    *Exercises continued on next page.*

5. 3-methyl-2-pentene and hydrogen

6. 2,3-dimethyl-2-butene and water

# K.16 Some Sources and Uses of Alkenes

Alkenes are usually obtained in industrial quantities by the catalytic cracking of alkanes. (Recall that catalytic cracking is a process by which larger molecules are broken down into small molecules.) The smaller alkenes (up to five carbons) can be obtained from the fractional distillation of petroleum. Larger alkenes, which are not separated from petroleum by distillation, remain as valuable components of gasoline.

Alkenes, particularly ethene (ethylene), because of their unsaturated and therefore chemically reactive character, serve as starting materials for a vast variety of useful organic compounds.

### Ethylene and Its Derivatives

Natural gas contains compounds other than methane. Sulfur extraction plants remove the hydrogen sulfide in natural gas as elemental sulfur. The liquefied petroleum gases (LPG) are removed by gas liquefaction plants. The LPG gases include butane, propane and ethane. Ethane has been of lesser importance, but now will become the most important of these gases. After the ethane has been removed from natural gas by cooling and compression, it is cracked by heat into ethene—the main building block of the petrochemical industry.

$$-\overset{|}{\underset{|}{C}}-\overset{|}{\underset{|}{C}}- \xrightarrow{\text{heat}} \phantom{x} \overset{\backslash}{\diagup}C=C\overset{\diagup}{\backslash} \phantom{x} + H_2$$

Under proper conditions, ethene can react with itself to form a polymer known as **polyethylene**. Polyethylene is a very long chain of hydrocarbons formed by the joining of 500-700 ethene units.

$$n \phantom{x} CH_2 = CH_2 \longrightarrow \left( CH_2 - CH_2 \right)n$$

Polyethylene has more varied uses than any single substance known. These include chemical equipment, packaging material, industrial protection, clothing and toys. The manufacture of various other plastics and synthetic fibers uses ethylene as a starting material. The usefulness of polyethylene and other polymers is unquestionable. However, at the same time, their use poses an environmental hazard, since most of these plastics are not biodegradable. Thus the utility of plastics and the consequence of their continued use pose a dilemma in modern society.

*The process of forming huge, high-molar-mass molecules from smaller molecules* is called **polymerization**. The *large molecule*, or unit, is called the **polymer** and the *small unit* the **monomer**. The term polymer has its origin from the Greek word *poly*, meaning many, and *meres*, meaning part. For example, ethene is a monomer and polyethylene is a polymer.

Ethylene is used as a starting compound in the manufacture of other common products such as polyesters, ethylene glycol (antifreeze), polyvinyl chloride (tubing, pipe), polystyrene, polyvinyl acetate, paints and drugs.

# K.17 Bonding in Alkynes

**Alkynes** are *hydrocarbons that contain a triple bond between one pair of carbon atoms.* The alkynes contain two less hydrogens than the corresponding alkene (or four less than the corresponding alkane), hence *the general formula for alkynes is $C_nH_{2n-2}$.* The alkynes, like the alkenes, are called unsaturated because they contain at least one multiple bond and are capable of reacting with more hydrogen.

Each carbon atom that is part of the triple bond in an alkyne is bonded to one other atom. The bonding in the simplest alkyne, $C_2H_2$, can be represented as follows:

$$\cdot \overset{\circ}{\underset{\circ}{C}} \cdot \; + \; \cdot \overset{\circ}{\underset{\circ}{C}} \cdot \quad \text{and} \quad \overset{H\; \circ}{\underset{H\; \circ}{}} \; \rightarrow \; H\!:\!C\!:\!:\!:\!C\!:\!H \quad \text{or} \quad H-C \equiv C-H$$

**Nomenclature of Alkynes**

The IUPAC nomenclature for the alkynes is identical to that of the alkenes except the ending **-yne** is used to indicate the presence of a triple bond (IUPAC Section 3.2). The names, including the IUPAC accepted common (nonsystematic) name for the first member, and the structural formulas for some of the representative members of the series are given in the examples following:

$H-C \equiv C-H \quad$ or $\quad CH \equiv CH$  
ethyne (acetylene)

$CH \equiv C-CH_3$  
propyne

$CH \equiv C-CH_2-CH_3$  
1-butyne

$CH_3-C \equiv C-CH_3$  
2-butyne

# K.18 <u>Exercises</u> Bonding in Alkynes

Provide the name for each of the following compounds.

1. $CH \equiv C - \overset{\overset{\displaystyle CH_3}{\displaystyle |}}{CH} - CH_3$

2. $CH_3 - C \equiv C - \overset{\overset{\displaystyle |}{\displaystyle CH}}{\underset{\overset{\displaystyle |}{\displaystyle CH_2}}{}} - CH_3$
   $\quad\quad\quad\quad\quad\quad\quad\; |$
   $\quad\quad\quad\quad\quad\quad\; CH_3$

_____          _____

Write a structural formula for each of the following compounds.

3. 4, 4-diethyl-1-hexyne

4. 5-ethyl-4-propyl-2-heptyne

5. Give the structural formula and names for three noncyclic isomers of $C_5H_8$.

# K.19 The Properties of Alkynes

### Physical Properties of Alkynes

The physical properties of alkynes are quite similar to the physical properties of alkenes and alkanes with corresponding numbers of carbon atoms. Refer back to the discussion of properties of alkanes as a review of the typical physical properties.

### Chemical Properties of Alkynes

1. Alkynes (like alkenes and alkanes) can react with oxygen (burn or undergo combustion) at high temperatures to produce mainly $CO_2$ and $H_2O$. (Acetylene is an important example.)

2. Alkynes are similar to the alkenes in that they can undergo addition reactions. In this respect, the alkynes are even more reactive than the alkenes since they can make available four bonding electrons, as shown below:

$$H:C:::C:H \text{ can become } H:\overset{\circ\;\;\circ}{\underset{\circ\;\;\circ}{C:C}}:H$$

Alkynes can undergo addition at four sites, as illustrated in the following examples:

$$H-C \equiv C-H + 2Br_2 \rightarrow H-\overset{\displaystyle Br}{\underset{\displaystyle Br}{C}}-\overset{\displaystyle Br}{\underset{\displaystyle Br}{C}}-H$$

The addition reaction of alkynes proceeds in two steps, depending upon the availability of added reagent, as the following examples illustrate:

*Step 1:*

$$H-C \equiv C-\overset{\displaystyle H}{\underset{\displaystyle H}{C}}-H + Cl_2 \rightarrow H-C = \overset{\displaystyle H}{C}-\overset{\displaystyle H}{\underset{\displaystyle H}{C}}-H$$
(with Cl, Cl on the double bond carbons)

*Step 2:*

$$H-C = \overset{\displaystyle H}{\underset{\displaystyle Cl\;\;Cl\;\;H}{C}}-C-H + Cl_2 \rightarrow H-\overset{\displaystyle Cl}{\underset{\displaystyle Cl}{C}}-\overset{\displaystyle Cl}{\underset{\displaystyle Cl}{C}}-\overset{\displaystyle H}{\underset{\displaystyle H}{C}}-H$$

Alkynes (like alkenes) may add a variety of reactants such as hydrogen, halogens, hydrogen halides and water. Since alkynes are the most reactive of aliphatic hydrocarbons, the first step of the addition is extremely fast. If the number of moles of the added reagent equals the number of moles of alkyne, then a substituted alkene is formed (Step 1). If two or more moles of reagent are added then a substituted alkane will be produced (Steps 1 and 2).

# K.20 <u>Exercises</u> The Properties of Alkynes

1. Ethyne (acetylene), the most useful alkyne, can be prepared by reacting calcium carbide, $CaC_2(s)$, with water. In addition to acetylene, calcium hydroxide is also produced. Write a balanced equation for this reaction.

2. Ethyne (acetylene) is prepared commercially in large quantities by reacting methane with itself at the high temperatures of an electric arc. Write a balanced equation for this reaction.

Ethyne is so unsaturated that it reacts with many substances, including hydrogen, halogen acids ($HCl(aq)$ and $HClO_3(aq)$), and other alkynes. Thus ethyne is an excellent starting material for the commercial synthesis of more complex organic compounds such as ethanoic acid, ethanol and other alcohols, benzene, synthetic rubber and synthetic fibers such as Orlon, Acrilan and Dynel. The polymerization of ethyne, like that of ethene, represents a typical reaction of unsaturated hydrocarbons.

3. Write a balanced structural equation for the controlled addition of one mole of chlorous acid to one mole of ethyne.

4. Write a balanced structural equation for the addition of excess hydrochloric acid to ethyne.

Ethyne is really the only unsaturated hydrocarbon that is burned as a source of heat. The high heat of combustion of ethyne makes it useful in oxy-acetylene welding.

5. Write a balanced molecular equation for the combustion of ethyne.

# K.21 Bonding in Aromatics

The parent molecule of aromatic compounds is benzene, $C_6H_6$. The six carbon atoms in benzene are arranged in a cyclic structure, with one hydrogen atom attached to each carbon atom. The structure can be represented by the following diagrams, with alternate single and double bonds between carbon atoms. Kekule, the German architect turned chemist, who first popularized the use of structural formulas, proposed the following benzene ring structure in 1865.

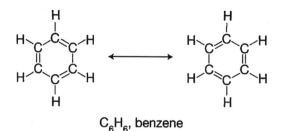

$C_6H_6$, benzene

However, since evidence indicates that all bonds between the carbon atoms are equivalent (in length and strength), neither a single nor a double bond is present. The actual structure is a hybrid of the two structures shown above. The valence electrons are evenly distributed over the entire ring. The benzene structure is conventionally represented as

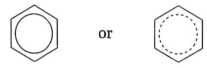

where the circle represents the evenly distributed electrons. It is understood that at each point in the hexagon, there exists a carbon atom with one hydrogen atom bonded to it.

### FIGURE K5
### Some Common Aromatics

| Aromatic Name | Structural Formula | Use |
|---|---|---|
| aniline (aminobenzene) | | production of dyes, perfumes, varnishes, medicines |
| aspirin (acetylsalicylic acid) | | relief of pain |
| benzedrine (2-methyl-1-phenylpropane) | | central nervous system stimulant; decongestant |
| benzocaine | | local anesthetic |
| D.D.T. (dichlorodiphenyl-trichloroethane) | | insecticide (banned in many countries) |
| naphthalene | | moth killer |
| 1, 4-dichlorobenzene (paradichlorobenzene) | | moth repellant |
| benzopyrene | | carcinogen (a compound that may induce cancer) present in cigarette smoke |
| phenol (hydroxybenzene) | | germicides, disinfectants |
| TNT (2,4,6-trinitrotoluene) | | explosive |
| vanillin | | the compound that is responsible for the vanilla flavor |
| DEET N, N-diethyl-$m$-toluamide | | insect repellant |

# K.22 Description of Hydrocarbon Derivatives

Numerous organic compounds are considered derivatives of hydrocarbons. This means that *a single atom, or group of atoms, takes the place of one of the hydrogen atoms in the hydrocarbon.* This atom, or group of atoms, is called a **functional group** and gives the hydrocarbon a completely different set of properties. Functional groups usually contain elements other than carbon and hydrogen. The most common other element is oxygen and comparatively less common are the halogens, nitrogen and sulfur.

When hydrocarbon derivatives react, only the functional group is changed. For this reason, if the behavior of a functional group is known, the products of its reaction can be predicted. For example, 1-propanol and hydrogen chloride react to give 1-chloropropane and water.

$$CH_3-CH_2-CH_2-\boxed{OH}_{(l)} + HCl_{(g)} \xrightarrow{catalyst} CH_3-CH_2-CH_2-\boxed{Cl}_{(l)} + H_2O_{(l)}$$

|          functional group          |          new functional group          |

In the preceding reaction, the alkyl portion of each molecule remained unchanged and only the functional groups changed. Keeping in mind the functional group idea, the following general equation can be written for this reaction where "R" stands for an alkyl group:

$$R-OH + HCl \xrightarrow{catalyst} R-Cl + H_2O$$

The hydrocarbon derivatives that will be considered in this unit include alcohols, carboxylic acids and esters.


# K.23 Alcohols

### Bonding in Alcohols

Alcohols are compounds that have an OH or hydroxyl functional group bonded to a carbon atom or alkyl chain. Their general formula can be represented as ROH, where "R" is an *alkyl group*. Unlike inorganic hydroxides (NaOH, KOH), alcohols are nonionic and do not produce OH⁻ ions in aqueous solution. Generally, only single bonds are present in simple alcohols; thus most alcohols are saturated compounds. All bonds in an alcohol are covalent, but the O–H bond is polar and the shorter chain alcohols involve hydrogen bonding among their molecules.

### Nomenclature of Alcohols

The IUPAC names of alcohols may be obtained by employing the following steps:

*Step 1*: Drop the final *e* from the hydrocarbon name and add the suffix
   *-ol*. (The suffixes *-diol* and *-triol* indicate two and three OH substituents, respectively. For these types of compounds the final *e* of the hydrocarbon name is retained.)

*Step 2*: List any other substituents as prefixes in alphabetical order.

*Step 3*: Use the lowest set of numbers possible to indicate the position of the substituents. The position of the OH functional group is given preference and must have the lowest number possible.

|   |   |   |
|---|---|---|
| CH₃CH₂CH₂OH | CH₃CHCH₃<br>     \|<br>    OH | CH₃<br> \|<br>CH₃CHCH₂OH |
| 1-propanol | 2-propanol<br>(rubbing alcohol) | 2-methyl-1-propanol |
|   | CH₂–OH<br> \|<br>CH₂–OH | CH₂–OH<br> \|<br>CH–OH<br> \|<br>CH₂–OH |
|   | 1,2-ethanediol<br>(ethylene glycol) | 1,2,3-propanetriol<br>(glycerin or glycerol) |

# K.24  Exercises Alcohols

Complete the following table.

| IUPAC Name<br>(Common Name in Brackets) | Structural Formula | Typical Uses |
|---|---|---|
| 1. (methyl alcohol or wood alcohol) | | gas line and windshield washer antifreeze; solvent for varnishes and shellacs; denaturant for ethanol |
| 2. (ethyl alcohol or grain alcohol) | | alcoholic beverages; in pharmaceutical industry as solvent and medicinal ingredients; in industry as solvent and antifreeze |
| 3. | $CH_3 - CH - CH_3$<br>          $\mid$<br>         OH | rubbing alcohol; solvent |
| 4. 1-butanol<br>solvent; hydraulic fluid | | |
| 5. |               $CH_3$<br>              $\mid$<br>$CH_3 - CH_2 - C - CH_3$<br>              $\mid$<br>             OH | solvent |
| 6. phenol (carbolic acid) | | germicide; ingredients of some plastics |
| 7. 1,2-ethanediol (ethylene glycol) | | permanent radiator antifreeze |
| 8. (glycerin or glycerol) | $CH_2 - OH$<br> $\mid$<br>$CH - OH$<br> $\mid$<br>$CH_2 - OH$ | making synthetic resins for paints; manufacture of cellophane; cosmetics and toilet soap; pharmaceutical ingredient; making of nitroglycerin explosives; in food and beverages |

# K.25 The Properties of Alcohols

## Physical Properties of Alcohols

The physical properties of alcohols significantly differ from those of hydrocarbons or organic halides. This difference is due primarily to hydrogen bonding among alcohol molecules. As a result, the melting and boiling points of alcohols are much higher than the melting and boiling points of the corresponding alkanes or organic halides. For example, the boiling point of methanol is 64.5°C, that for methane is −161°C, and that for monochloromethane is −23.7°C.

Because alcohols involve hydrogen bonds, they are more soluble in water than the corresponding hydrocarbons or organic halides. The lower alcohols are completely miscible with water. In these compounds the hydroxyl group comprises an appreciable portion of the molecule. Attraction between the water and alcohol dipoles is significant. As the number of carbon atoms in the alcohol molecules increases, the water solubility decreases because the alcohol is becoming more like a hydrocarbon and less like water. For example, 1-hexanol is only slightly soluble in water but very highly soluble in hexane.

## Chemical Properties of Alcohols

Alcohols exhibit wide versatility in their ability to react with other species. As a result the reactions of alcohols are extensive and varied. For present purposes, the discussion is being limited to two kinds of reactions—combustion and esterification.

Alcohols, like most hydrocarbons, readily burn. In fact, alcohol lamps were common before being replaced by electrical lights because alcohols burn with a clean bright flame. The following reaction illustrates the burning (*combustion*) of alcohols:

$$2\ CH_3OH_{(l)} + 3\ O_{2(g)} \longrightarrow 2\ CO_{2(g)} + 4\ H_2O_{(g)}$$

Ethanol, present in alcoholic beverages, is burned in the body by what is usually called oxidation. The reaction rate for oxidation is slow compared to combustion.

Esterification reactions will be discussed in the section on organic acids.

## The Petrochemical Industry

Using readily available ethene, chemical companies produce ethylene oxide and ethylene glycol according to the following equations:

| ethene | 2-chloroethanol | ethene oxide | 1,2-ethanediol |
| (ethylene) | (1-chloro-2-hydroxyethane) | (ethylene oxide) | (ethylene glycol) |

Ethylene glycol has a variety of uses, but is primarily used as the main ingredient in permanent radiator antifreeze.

## Properties and Preparation of Methanol

Methanol (*methyl alcohol, methyl hydrate or wood alcohol*) is the simplest alcohol. This alcohol had been, and may be in the future, obtained from the destructive distillation of wood during the preparation of charcoal, hence the name wood alcohol.

$$\text{wood (poplar)} \longrightarrow CH_3OH_{(l)}$$

Presently, methanol is usually synthesized by the reaction between carbon monoxide and hydrogen in the presence of appropriate catalysts. The carbon monoxide and hydrogen are obtained from the steam reduction of natural gas.

$$2\ CH_{4(g)} + 3\ H_2O_{(g)} \longrightarrow CO_{2(g)} + CO_{(g)} + 3\ H_{2(g)}$$

$$CO_{(g)} + 2\ H_{2(g)} \xrightarrow{catalyst} CH_3OH_{(g)}$$

Methanol is highly toxic. If taken internally in small quantities, it causes blindness by destroying cells of the optic nerve; large quantities may cause death. Methanol is often used as a medium for organic reactions, as a solvent for varnishes and shellacs, as a gas line antifreeze, and for denaturing ethanol.

### Properties and Preparation of Ethanol

Ethanol (ethyl alcohol or grain alcohol) is the second member of the alcohol series. It is the essential ingredient in alcoholic beverages. Although ethanol has relatively low toxicity, its excessive use can cause various harmful side effects like cirrhosis of the liver. The ethanol that is designated for beverage use is carefully controlled and heavily taxed. Industrially used ethanol is generally tax-free but is **denatured** *to prevent its use as a beverage.* Denaturing is done by the addition of some agent that is disagreeable and probably poisonous such as methanol, benzene or pyridine.

Ethanol destined for beverage use is produced by the **yeast fermentation** of solutions containing simple sugars or other carbohydrates. The reaction involved in the fermentation of glucose is:

$$C_6H_{12}O_{6(aq)} \xrightarrow{yeast} 2\ C_2H_5OH_{(aq)} + 2\ CO_{2(aq\ and\ g)}$$
$$\text{(glucose)}$$

Ethanol destined for industrial uses is generally prepared by hydrating ethene. This method involves the following reaction:

$$CH_2 = CH_{2(g)} + H_2O_{(aq)} \xrightarrow{H_2SO_{4(aq)}} CH_3CH_2OH_{(l)}$$

The product from this reaction yields the fairly pure ethanol (96% ethanol and 4% water) that is required for reagent purposes. For some applications the ethanol can be further purified to 100% (absolute ethanol).

Alcohol beverages produced by the fermentation process consist of two types—undistilled and distilled. The main undistilled beverages are beer, wine and champagne, whereas the distilled beverages include whiskey, gin, rum and brandy (40% ethanol by volume). Undistilled beverages can have a much lower alcohol content than the distilled.

The fermentation of malted (germinated) grain is used to produce beer. Hops, the dried cones of a special vine, are added to beer to give it a bitter taste. The alcoholic content of beer usually varies from 3 to 5%. (It might be noted that an alcohol content of 5% corresponds to a proof value of 10, the proof value being double the alcoholic percentage by volume.)

Wine and champagne are produced by the fermentation of grape juice, although other wines can be prepared from other fruit juices. The natural wines produced by the fermentation process alone have an alcohol content of no higher than 15% since fermentation stops when the ethanol concentration reaches that level. Some wines (fortified wines) contain added alcohol and may have an alcoholic content as high as 20%. Champagne wine is bottled so that it retains natural carbon dioxide, although some cheaper champagnes are artificially carbonated.

# K.26 <u>Exercises</u> The Properties of Alcohols

Complete the following table.

| IUPAC Name | Structural Formula | Melting Point (°C) | Boiling Point (°C) | Solubility in $H_2O$ (g/100 g $H_2O$) |
|---|---|---|---|---|
| 1. methanol | | − 97 | 64 | ∞ |
| 2. | H   H<br> \|   \|<br>H−C−C−OH<br> \|   \|<br>H   H | −115 | 78 | ∞ |
| 3. 1-propanol | | −126 | 97 | ∞ |
| 4. | H  H  H  H<br> \|  \|  \|  \|<br>H−C−C−C−C−OH<br> \|  \|  \|  \|<br>H  H  H  H | −90 | 118 | 7.9 |
| 5. 1-pentanol | | −78 | 138 | 2.3 |
| 6. | H  H  H  H  H  H<br> \|  \|  \|  \|  \|  \|<br>H−C−C−C−C−C−C−OH<br> \|  \|  \|  \|  \|  \|<br>H  H  H  H  H  H | −52 | 156 | 0.6 |
| 7. 1-heptanol | | | | |
| 8. | H  H  H  H  H  H  H  H<br> \|  \|  \|  \|  \|  \|  \|  \|<br>H−C−C−C−C−C−C−C−C−OH<br> \|  \|  \|  \|  \|  \|  \|  \|<br>H  H  H  H  H  H  H  H | −15 | 195 | 0.05 |

# K.27 Bonding of Carboxylic Acids

Organic acids, known as carboxylic acids, are characterized by the functional group called a **carboxyl group**. The carboxyl group (COOH) *consists of a carbonyl group (−C=O) with a hydroxyl group attached to the carbon atom.*

The carboxyl group has a covalent bond with hydrogen in the simplest acid and with a hydrocarbon chain for most of the other organic acids.

**Nomenclature of Carboxyl Acids**

Carboxyl acids are named in the IUPAC system by *dropping the e* and *adding the suffix -oic* to the name of the parent hydrocarbon (containing the same total number of carbon atoms). *The resulting name is then followed by the word **acid**.* Many carboxyl acids are naturally occurring and have common or trivial names that reflect their natural source.

The IUPAC and common names of several organic acids are given in FIGURE K6.

**Sources and Uses of Some Common Carboxylic Acids**

Many carboxylic acids are present in various fruits and impart to them the sour taste characteristic of acids. An important source of longer chain organic (fatty) acids is animal fats and vegetable oils. FIGURE K6 gives the source and use of some common organic acids. (Except for benzoic acid and 2-hydrobenzoic acid, the carboxylic acids extend the nomenclature of carboxylic acids beyond this course.)

FIGURE K6
Sources and Uses of Some Common Carboxylic Acids

| Name (Common Name) | Structural Formula | Sources and Typical Uses |
|---|---|---|
| ethanedioic acid (oxalic acid) | 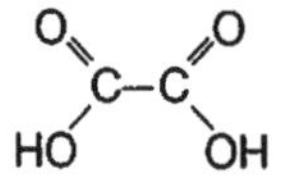 | somewhat toxic material occurring free as calcium salts in spinach, Swiss chard and rhubarb; used as a bleaching agent for wood and as a spot remover where iron(II) ion is involved; oxalate salts used in medical laboratories to prevent coagulation of blood specimens |
| 2-hydroxy-1,2,3,-propanetricarboxylic acid (citric acid) | 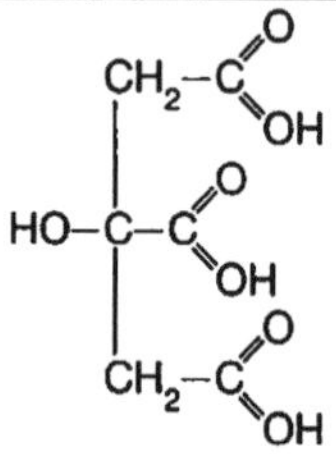 | most widely distributed plant acid; present in citrus fruits; used in soft drinks, sherbet and many other foods to provide a tart flavor; used as a blood anticoagulant; used in effervescing powders and tablets such as Alka-Seltzer |
| benzoic acid or benzene carboxylic acid | 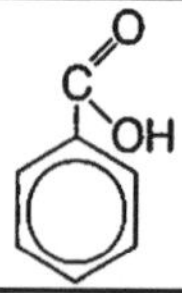 | acid salts used as a common food preservative, especially for soft drinks; benzoate esters used in several perfumes |
| 2-hydroxybenzoic acid (salicylic acid) | 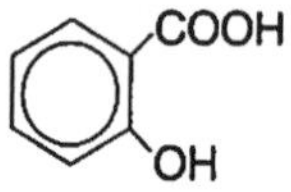 | used as a food preservative and starting material for synthesis of dyes and medicinals |
| 2-acetoxybenzoic acid (acetylsalicylic acid; ASA; also called aspirin) | 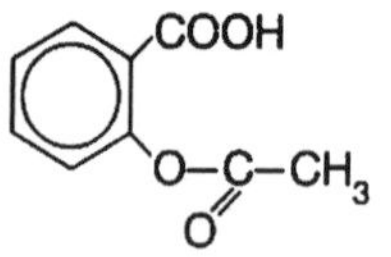 | used as relief of fever, pain and rheumatic conditions |
| octadecenoic acid (oleic acid) | 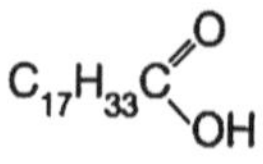 $C_{17}H_{33}C\!\!\diagup^{O}_{OH}$ | found in vegetable oils; sodium and potassium salts used in soaps; zinc salts used in face powders |
| octadecanoic acid (stearic acid) | 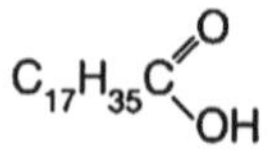 $C_{17}H_{35}C\!\!\diagup^{O}_{OH}$ | found in beef tallow; sodium and potassium salts used in soaps; zinc salts used in face powders |

# K.28 <u>Exercises</u> Bonding of Carboxylic Acids

Complete the following table.

| IUPAC Name (Common Name in Brackets) | Structural Formula | Sources and Typical Uses |
|---|---|---|
| **Example:** methanoic acid (formic acid) | $HC\underset{OH}{\overset{O}{\diagup}}$ | responsible for sensation caused by nettle, bee and ant stings; used in medicine and food preservations; used commercially in the textile industry |
| 1. (acetic acid) | $CH_3-C\underset{OH}{\overset{O}{\diagup}}$ | component of vinegar; used as a solvent; salts of acid used as mordant and in insecticides and fungicides |
| 2. propanoic acid (propionic acid) | | used as antifungal agents in the baking industry and ointments either in salt or acid form |
| 3. (butyric acid) | $CH_3-CH_2-CH_2-C\underset{OH}{\overset{O}{\diagup}}$ | employed as flavoring agent; odor-causing component of rancid butter |
| 4. hexanoic acid (caprioic acid) | | employed as a flavoring agent; has odor characteristic of limburger cheese |

# K.29 The Properties of Carboxylic Acids

**Physical Properties of Carboxylic Acids**

Carboxylic acids have higher melting points than hydrocarbons, organic halides or alcohols with the same number of carbon atoms. The acids containing one to ten carbon atoms are liquids at room temperature; the higher members are wax-like solids. The higher melting and boiling points of the organic acids are due mainly to strong hydrogen bonding. Carboxylic acids have even higher melting points than alcohols because of the special nature of the hydrogen bonding. In organic acids, there is hydrogen bonding to the oxygen of the carbonyl group as well as the oxygen of the hydroxyl group.

$$R-C\underset{OH\ \text{------}\ O}{\overset{O\ \text{------}\ HO}{\diagup \diagdown}}C-R$$

Organic acids containing one to four carbon atoms are completely soluble (miscible) with water. Those acids having six or more carbon atoms are almost insoluble in water. This reflects the interactions between the polar and nonpolar parts of the molecule in determining the properties of substances. The short-chain molecules have small nonpolar portions and are soluble in water. The long-chain molecules have large nonpolar portions and have very low solubility in water but good solubility in nonpolar solvents.

### Chemical Properties of Organic Acids

Organic acids have properties like that of inorganic acids except, in general, they are weaker acids. Like inorganic acids, they similarly affect indicators, react with active metals and carbonates, and are neutralized by bases.

$$2\ RCOOH_{(aq)} + 2\ Na_{(s)} \longrightarrow 2\ RCOONa_{(aq)} + H_{2(g)}$$

$$2\ RCOOH_{(aq)} + Na_2CO_{3(aq)} \longrightarrow 2\ RCOONa_{(aq)} + H_2CO_{3(aq)}$$

$$RCOOH_{(aq)} + NaOH_{(aq)} \longrightarrow RCOONa_{(aq)} + H_2O_{(l)}$$

The most common $RCOO^-$ ion is called the acetate ion, $CH_3COO^-$. Other carboxylate ions found on the polyatomic ion table are benzoate, oxalate and stearate ions. In addition, carboxylic acids react with alcohols, in a reaction comparable to neutralization, to form compounds called esters. The esterification reaction involved will be discussed in the section dealing with esters.

### The Petrochemical Industry

The acetic acid is produced by the catalyzed (with Co or Mn) reaction of butane with oxygen. The butane is obtained by extracting the butane from natural gas. The oxygen is obtained from a liquid air plant.

$$C_4H_{10(l)} + O_{2(g)} \xrightarrow{\text{Co or Mn}} CH_3COOH_{(l)} + HCOOH_{(l)} + C_2H_5OH_{(l)} + CH_3OH_{(l)}$$

$$\text{(mole percents)} \Longrightarrow \quad (72\%) \qquad (7.4\%) \qquad (1.4\%) \qquad (1.1\%)$$

About five percent of the acetic acid made is used to produce vinegar. (By law vinegar is about 5% acetic acid.) Much is used as a solvent. Salts of the acid are used as a mordant, which fixes a dye on a substance, and in insecticides and fungicides.

# K.30 Exercises The Properties of Carboxylic Acids

1. The boiling point of acetic acid is 118.5°C and that of 1-propanol is 97.1°C. Account for this difference in boiling point between acetic acid (with 32 electrons) and 1-propanol (with 34 electrons).

_____

_____

2. Discuss the solubility of carboxylic acids in water and in organic solvents.

_____

_____

_____

_____

Which are the most likely physical properties of the carboxylic acid, $C_5H_{11}COOH$? (Compare to acetic acid above.)

3. solid, liquid or gas? _____

4. boiling point: 95°C, 205°C, or 300°C? _____

5. highly soluble in water, slightly soluble in water or insoluble in water? _____

Write equations for reactions between the following substances and name the products. (Use structural formulas for the organic substances.)

6. magnesium metal and ethanoic acid

7. benzoic acid and a solution of sodium hydroxide

8. potassium carbonate and oxalic acid (ethanedioic acid)

# K.31 Esters

Esters are best studied by considering the esterification reaction first. **Esters** are derivatives of the reactions between carboxylic acids and alcohols.

**Esterification Reaction**

carboxylic acid + alcohol $\xrightarrow{\text{acid catalyst}}$ ester + water

($R_1$ and $R_2$ represent alkyl groups)

Examples:

Polyester (PolyEthylTErephthalate—PETE)

$\eta$ represents 50 to 10,000 molecules.

ethylene glycol + terephthalic acid $\longrightarrow$ PolyEthylTErephthalate + water

*The fact that the OH group comes from the acid, rather than the alcohol, has been proven by radioactive tracing using an isotope.*

**Nomenclature of Esters** A general formula for esters is

$$R_1-\overset{\overset{\textstyle O}{\|}}{C}-O-R_2 \quad \text{or} \quad R_1COOR_2$$

where the RCO part is derived from the acid and O–R is the alkyl part derived from the alcohol. In the naming of an ester, the alkyl (alcohol) name is given first followed by the name of the acid part. In the IUPAC system, when naming the acid part, *drop the ending -ic* and replace it with ***-ate***. Consider the following examples. (*Note that the nomenclature system contradicts the actual origin of the O in the $OR_2$ group.*)

Examples:

$$CH_3-C \overset{O}{\underset{O-CH_3}{\lessgtr}}$$

| For naming purposes, the part considered derived from the organic acid in this case is named *ethanoate*. Full name of ester: ***methyl ethanoate*** | Alkyl part of alcohol, in this case named *methyl*. |

$$CH_3-CH_2-C \overset{O}{\underset{O-CH_2-CH_3}{\lessgtr}}$$
ethyl propanoate

$$\overset{O}{\underset{CH_3-CH_2-O}{\parallel}} C-H$$
ethyl methanoate

$CH_3CH_2CH_2COOCH_2CH_2CH_3$
propyl butanoate

$C_2H_5COOC_4H_9$
butyl propanoate

Esters are a common occurrence in nature and are abundant in animal fats and vegetable oils. Unlike the acids involved in their formation, simple esters usually have pleasant odors and constitute the odors and flavors of fruits.

# K.32   Exercises Esters

Complete the following table.

| IUPAC Name (Common name is given in brackets) | Structural Formula | Sources and Typical Uses |
|---|---|---|
| 1.  ethyl methanoate (ethyl formate) | | rum flavor and odor |
| 2.  (ethyl acetate) | $CH_3-C \overset{O}{\underset{O-CH_2-CH_3}{\lessgtr}}$ | fingernail polish remover, solvent |
| 3.  pentyl propanoate (pentyl propionate) | | apricot flavor and odor |
| 4.  (ethyl butyrate) | $CH_3-CH_2-CH_2-C \overset{O}{\underset{O-CH_2-CH_3}{\lessgtr}}$ | used in artifical peach, pineapple and apricot flavors |

| | | |
|---|---|---|
| 5. octyl ethanoate (octyl acetate) | | orange flavor and odor |
| 6. (n-amyl acetate) | 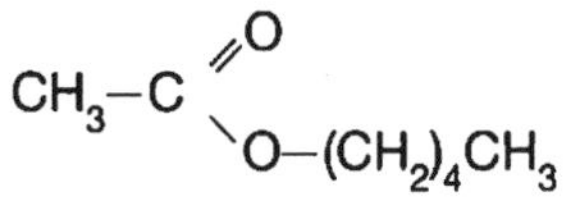 $CH_3-C \begin{smallmatrix} \nearrow O \\ \searrow O-(CH_2)_4CH_3 \end{smallmatrix}$ | pear flavor and odor |
| 7. ethyl benzoate | | cherry flavor and odor |

# K.33 The Preparation of Several Esters

**Purpose:**

✔ To prepare some common esters and to note their characteristic odor.

**Materials:**

- 4 18 × 150 mm test tubes
- 1 #1 one-hole rubber stopper to fit test tube
- 1 50-cm length of 6 mm glass tubing
- 1 250-mL beaker
- 1 utility clamp
- 1 ring stand
- 1 hot plate or heating mantle
- 1 dropper bottle of 2-pentanol (optional)
- 1 dropper bottle of 3-pentanol (optional)
- 1 dropper bottle of concentrated $H_2SO_4$
- 1 dropper bottle of methanol
- 1 dropper bottle of ethanol
- 1 dropper bottle of 1-butanol
- 1 dropper bottle of 1-pentanol
- 1 dropper bottle of glacial ethanoic acid (also called glacial acetic acid)
- 1 bottle of salicylic acid
- 1 dropper bottle of 2-butanol (optional)
- 1 dropper bottle of 2-pentanol (optional)
- 1 dropper bottle of 3-pentanol (optional)

**Prelab Exercise:**

Write equations using structural formulas for the four non-optional esterification reactions for this lab. (See the procedure for the reactions used.)

- salicylic acid + methanol $\xrightarrow{H_2SO_4}$

- ethanoic acid + ethanol $\xrightarrow{H_2SO_4}$

- ethanoic acid + 1-butanol $\xrightarrow{H_2SO_4}$

- ethanoic acid + 1-pentanol $\xrightarrow{H_2SO_4}$

**Procedure:**

*Caution: This procedure uses concentrated acids. Be prepared to immediately wash skin exposed to any solution in this lab.*

*Note: If the laboratory period is short, each of four adjacent groups should do a different esterification.*

1. Set up a 250-mL beaker on a ring stand using a ring and a wire gauze pad. Fill the beaker with water to about the two-thirds level. The beaker of water will serve as a water bath. (See photo.)

2. Use a utility clamp to support an 18 × 150 mm test tube. Lower the test tube into the water bath. (See photo.)

3. Check the odor of salicylic acid (2-hydroxybenzoic acid) and methanol.
   *Precaution: Use your hand to waft the odor toward your nose. Do not smell directly.*

4. Place about 2 mL of salicylic acid into the supporting test tube (to a depth of about 1 cm or 1 fingernail width).

5. Add about 2 mL of methanol to the salicylic acid in the test tube (to an additional depth of about 1 cm or 1 fingernail width).

6. Add about 2 drops of concentrated sulfuric acid catalyst to the mixture in the test tube. **Caution.**

7. Check to see that the glass tubing through the stopper is not plugged. Insert the stopper and glass tubing into the test tube. (See photo.) (*The glass tubing serves as a reflux condenser, which condenses volatile components and returns them into the test tube.*)

8. Heat the water bath until the reaction mixture starts to bubble slowly. Continue moderate boiling for about 5 min.

9. Allow the reaction mixture to cool for several minutes. Remove the condenser and check the odor of the ester formed in the test tube (odor of wintergreen).

10. Repeat procedure steps 1 through 9 for each of the following combinations of glacial (concentrated) ethanoic (acetic) acid with an alcohol. (If the laboratory period is short, share results with other groups.)

    a. glacial ethanoic (acetic) acid and ethanol (odor of sweet fruit; used in some brands of nail polish remover)

    b. glacial ethanoic (acetic) acid and 1-butanol (odor of raspberries)

    c. glacial ethanoic (acetic) acid and 1-pentanol (odor of pears)

    d. (optional) glacial ethanoic (acetic) acid and 2-butanol (odor of strawberries)

    e. (optional) glacial ethanoic (acetic) acid and 3-methyl-1 butanol (*isopentyl alcohol*) (odor of bananas)

**Observations:**

| | Acid | Alcohol | Ester |
|---|---|---|---|
| Station # 1 | Name:<br><br>Odor: | Name:<br><br>Odor: | Name:<br><br>Odor: |
| Station # 2 | Name:<br><br>Odor: | Name:<br><br>Odor: | Name:<br><br>Odor: |
| Station # 3 | Name:<br><br>Odor: | Name:<br><br>Odor: | Name:<br><br>Odor: |
| Station # 4 | Name:<br><br>Odor: | Name:<br><br>Odor: | Name:<br><br>Odor: |

**Questions:**

1. Why is a hot water bath used instead of a Bunsen burner?

_____

_____

2. What is the purpose of the sulfuric acid?

_____

_____

3. A candy wrapper reads, "Artificial flavoring added." What kind of compound has likely been added to the candy. Explain.

_____

_____

4. (Optional) On a separate sheet of paper, write structural equations for the optional esterifications. Name the esters produced.

**FIGURE K7  Summary Table for Some Organic Compounds**

| Group | Structure (R represents H or Carbon Chain) | Nomenclature | General Formula | 1. Physical Properties 2. Chemical Properties | Uses and Occurrences |
|---|---|---|---|---|---|
| alkanes | R–C–C–R | -ane | $C_nH_{2n+2}$ | 1. nonpolar; insoluble; low melting and boiling points 2. substitution; combustion fuels; petrochemical building blocks | fuels; petrochemical building blocks |
| alkenes | R–C = C–R | -ene | $C_nH_{2n}$ | 1. same as alkanes 2. addition of one or two molecules of adding reagent; combustion | starting materials for many polymers first member of the series used in oxyacetylene welding |
| alkynes | R–C ≡ C–R | -yne | $C_nH_{2n-2}$ | 1. same as alkanes 2. addition of one or two molecules of adding reagent; combustion | first member of the series used in oxyacetylene welding |
| aromatics | H or R on each of the six positions | -benzene or phenyl- | $C_6H_nR_{(6-n)}$ (variable) | 1. nonpolar; insoluble in water 2. substitution; combustion | very diverse: solvents, foods, drugs, explosives |
| alcohols | R–OH, R(–OH)$_2$, R(–OH)$_3$ | -ol, -diol, -triol | $C_nH_{2n+1}OH$, $C_nH_{2n}(OH)_2$, $C_nH_{2n-1}(OH)_3$ | 1. higher boiling point; soluble because of hydrogen bonding 2. many reactions; e.g., esterification, combustion | very diverse: antifreeze, alcoholic drinks, cosmetics, foods |
| acids | R–C(=O)OH | -oic acid | $C_nH_{2n+1}COOH$ | 1. high boiling point; first four members soluble 2. all inorganic acid reactions; esterification | commonly occur in foods, waxes |
| esters | R–C(=O)O–R | R-yl R-oate | $C_nH_{2n+}COOC_mH_{2m+1}$ | 1. insoluble in water 2. can react with water to form a carboxylic acid and alcohol | used as solvents and artificial flavors; commonly occur in animal fats and vegetable oils |

# Glossary

**absolute zero** 185, 205 based on Charles' Law, the lowest possible temperature = Celsius + 273.15°; where all particle motion would stop completely.

**accuracy** 117 how close a measurement comes to the true or accepted value; how correct it is.

**acid** 93, 94, 303 turns blue litmus paper red (pH <7); reacts with many metals to produce hydrogen gas; dissolves in water and able to conduct an electric current; neutralizes basic solutions (and produces hydrogen ions).

**actual yield** 153 the amount of product obtained when the experiment is actually performed. It includes errors due to splashes, incomplete reaction, incomplete drying, etc.

**addition and subtraction rule** 129 add or subtract as usual, then round off the answer to the fewest number of decimal places contained in the question.

**adhesion** 207 one substance sticking to another.

**air pollution** 164 anything in the air that causes difficulty to humans.

**alcohols** 299 molecular compounds that have an OH (hydroxyl) functional group bonded to a carbon atom or alkyl chain; names end in "-ol," such as ethylene glycol, ethanol, methanol, and glycerol.

**aliphatic compounds** 280 class of hydrocarbons that includes alkanes, alkenes and alkynes.

**alkane** 281 simplest class of hydrocarbons; each carbon atom shares four pairs of electrons as single bonds; saturated compounds.

**alkene** 290 containing two less hydrogen atoms than an alkane (see alkane) with same number of carbon atoms, necessitating a double bond; more reactive than alkanes; names end in "-ene."

**alkyl (group)** 282 an alkane from which one hydrogen is removed.

**alkynes** 295 hydrocarbons that contain a triple bond between one pair of carbon atoms; two less hydrogen atoms than alkenes, and four less than alkanes; names end in "-yne" to indicate the triple bond; most reactive of hydrocarbons; e.g., ethyne (acetylene).

**allotropes** 240 different forms of the same element in the same state of matter.

**alloy** 6 homogeneous mixture of two or more elements (usually metals).

**altimeter** 177 an aneroid barometer that measures the altitude of a plane above the earth's surface, based on air pressure.

**amorphous solid** 240 a solid whose particles have no orderly structure.

**aneroid barometer** 177 a barometer that uses a vacuum canister that expands or contracts with air pressure, rather than mercury.

**angular** 62, 63, 64 one shape of a polar molecule, where the bond angle is ~105° or ~120° (e.g., sulfur dioxide or water) with two bonding pairs and one or two lone pairs around a central atom.

**anion** 73 a negative ion; if polyatomic (e.g., $MnO_4^-$), may not be nonmetallic.

**aqueous solution** 246 a solution where water is the solvent.

**Archimedes' Principle** 131 a method of finding the volume of a solid, nonsoluble object, whereby the water level rises an amount equal to the volume of an object placed in that water.

**aromatic compounds** 280 class of hydrocarbons that includes benzene($C_6H_6$)-parent compounds; an apparent alternating single-double bond in a cyclic hydrocarbon compound.

**atmosphere (atm)** 164, 177 a unit of standard (sea-level) pressure = 101.325 kPa.

**atom** 25 derived from the Greek word, "atomos,"— indivisible; the basic building blocks of all substances; the smallest particle of matter which will react chemically.

**atomic mass** 29 the actual mass of a single type of isotope; the relative average mass of all naturally occurring isotopes of an element.

**atomic molar mass** 137 the mass of one mole of atoms (vs. molecules or formula units).

**atomic number** 26 the number of protons in the nucleus of an atom or ion of an element, distinguishing various elements on the Periodic Table.

**atomic radius** 41 the distance from the center of the atom to the outside "edge."

**atomic spectra** 23, 34 the lines of color (line spectrum) that are visible when an element is viewed through a diffraction grating.

**atomic symbol notation** 26, 45 used to indicate the number of particles in an atom (mass number above and atomic number below).

**Avogadro's Hypothesis** 191, 194 equal volumes of gases at the same temperature and pressure contain equal numbers of molecules; $V = k_3 n$, where V = Volume (L) and n = number of moles.

**Avogadro's Number** 136 $6.02 \times 10^{23}$ = number of atoms in exactly 12 grams of Carbon-12 isotope.

**balanced equations** 96 equations where the reactants and the products both have the same kind and number of each type of atom in accordance with the Law of Conservation of Matter; atoms, mass and energy are conserved.

**base** 94 turns red litmus paper blue (pH >7); able to conduct an electric current and neutralize acidic solutions (and produce hydroxide ions).

**bends** 182 the result of nitrogen bubbles forming in blood and bodily fluids due to sudden decreased atmospheric pressure after a condition of high pressure (e.g., as experienced by divers).

**binary molecular compound** 87 a compound that consists of only two kinds of nonmetallic atoms.

**Bohr atom model** 23 Orbit model—electrons of specific energies move in orbits around the nucleus, not between orbits.

**boiling** 244 the vaporization of a gas anywhere in a liquid; the vapor pressure is greater than or equal to the external air pressure.

**boiling point** 41, 277 the temperature at which an element boils (changes from a liquid to a gas).

**boiling temperature** 244 temperature at which the vapor within the body of a liquid has enough energy to escape the attractions of the other particles in the liquid state.

**bond dipole** 67 a charge separation within the bond of a polar covalent bond.

**bonding capacity** 54 the maximum number of covalent bonds that each atom forms.

**bonding electrons** 45 unpaired electrons in singly occupied orbitals that are available for sharing with other atoms.

**Boyle's Law** 178, 180, 189, 194 the volume of a quantity of gas at a particular temperature is inversely proportional to the pressure applied to the gas; $PV = k_1$.

**branch chained alkane** 282 structural isomer formula containing side chains off the straight-chain sequence of carbon atoms; names end in "-yl," such as methyl ($CH_3$), ethyl ($C_2H_5$), etc.

**calculated value** 129 only contains one uncertain digit.

**calx** 108 the crumbly residue left when a metal or mineral has been subjected to calcination (high heat) or combustion.

**capillary action** 207 the movement of a liquid up a slender tube.

**carbon dating** 29 a process using the half-life of carbon-14 as the basis for dating an artifact by comparing amounts between the death of the organism and the remaining amount.

**carboxyl group** 303 (COOH) consisting of a carbonyl group (–C=O) with a hydroxyl group (OH) attached to the carbon atom; covalently bonded to a hydrogen atom or a hydrocarbon chain to form an organic acid.

**catalytic cracking** 287 cracking in the presence of a catalyst; see cracking.

**catalytic reforming** 287 uses a catalyst to convert lighter molecules into heavier fractions, e.g., larger hydrocarbons for chemical use.

**cation** 73 a positive ion; if polyatomic (e.g., $NH_4^+$), may not be metallic.

**centrifuging** 6 spinning to separate an insoluble solid from a liquid.

**charge separation** 52 the shift of the bonding electrons toward one of the atoms, so that one of the atoms becomes positively charged while the other becomes negatively charged.

**Charles' Law** 183, 184, 185, 189, 194 for every degree Celsius increase in temperature, the volume of a gas increases by 1/273 of its original volume; $V/T_K = k_2$.

**chemical change** 2, 11 composition or structure of the substance changes (atoms rearrange) to form new substances; a transformation converting one substance into another substance, usually identified by a color change, an energy change, and bubbling or precipitation.

**chemical formula** 71 a mathematical description of the number and kind of each atom bonded together.

**chemical means** 20 various ways of breaking compounds down into their elements—including using heat, acids, electricity, etc.

**chemical nomenclature** 71 the organized system to name substances and write their chemical formulas.

**chemical processes** 4 processes that break down compounds, e.g., heating, reaction with acids, electric current; and form new chemicals.

**chemical properties** 3 characteristics of a substance that require at least an attempt to change the substance to something new.

**chemical reaction** 2 chemical change.

**Classical system** 73, 78, 79 used only with elements that have a Latin symbol for the element; it uses the suffix "-ic" for the larger charge on an ion, and "-ous" for the smaller.

**cohesion** 207 one substance sticking to itself.

**colligative properties** 275 solution properties that depend only on the concentration of solute particles in the solution, not the type of particle.

**colloid (colloidal dispersion)** 6, 273 a mixture that falls between homogeneous and heterogeneous (e.g., milk, gelatin, etc.); a heterogeneous mixture in which particles are large enough to scatter light, but too small to be seen with the naked eye, remaining suspended in the mixture.

**Combined Gas Law** 189 involves simultaneous changes in pressure, volume, and temperature when the number of molecules remains constant. See Charles' Law and Boyle's Law.

**combustion** 285 when a compound (usually organic) reacts with oxygen to produce primarily $CO_2$, $H_2O$ and heat; an exothermic reaction that decreases the potential energy of the system.

**composition** 2 the make-up of the matter—kinds and numbers of particles present in substance.

**compound** 4, 73 formed when two or more different elements have been chemically joined together to create a new substance with different properties from the original elements; a pure substance that contains more than one kind of atom and/or ion.

**concentrated solution** 246 a solution of high concentration.

**molar concentration** 246 the number of moles of solute dissolved in a liter of solution.

**conductivity** 3, 91 the ability of elements or compounds to transmit heat or electricity.

**conversion factor** 126 a fraction, obtained from an equality, which relates one unit to another.

**conversion factor method** 126 factor-label method = unit analysis = dimensional analysis: the method of calculating using a conversion factor.

**covalent bonding** 32, 51, 54 a rearrangement of electrons in a chemical reaction, where electrons of the differing atoms are shared; a force of attraction between two nonmetallic atoms to attain noble-gas electron configurations, by sharing electrons.

**covalent compound** 6 compound formed by the combination of a nonmetal with another nonmetal by sharing electrons.

**cracking** 285 when an alkane (molecule) is broken into smaller fragments (molecules) in the absence of air.

**Dalton model** 21 "Billiard Ball" model (where the atom is a single, indivisible particle)—elements are made up of simple atoms, while compounds contain 'compounded atoms' (now called molecules).

**Dalton's Law of Partial Pressures** 196, 197, 198 in a mixture of gases, the total pressure exerted by the mixture is equal to the sum of the partial pressures exerted by the separate components.

**decanting** 155 to carefully pour off the liquid portion of a liquid-solid mixture.

**delivery pipet** 252 transfer pipet; a pipet that delivers a specific volume only.

**denaturing** 302 the addition of a disagreeable and perhaps poisonous agent (like methanol, benzene or pyridine) to ethanol, to prevent its use as a beverage.

**density** 131, 187 mass/volume; the amount of matter in a certain space.

**deposition** 245 the reverse of sublimation; the change from a gas directly to a solid.

**diatomic** 87 an element whose molecules contain two atoms.

**diatomic molecules** 191 molecules that have only two atoms.

**dilute solution** 246 a solution of low concentration.

**dipole-dipole forces** 214 forces of attraction between polar molecules that result when the partially positive end of one molecule is attracted to the partially negative end of another.

**dissociation** 267 the process of electrolytes dissolving and separating into ions.

**double bond** 58 two pairs of electrons (4 e⁻) between bonded atoms.

**double replacement reaction** 102, 105 a chemical reaction where two compound reactants become two compound products.

**ductile** 16 pulled into wires.

**dynamic equilibrium** 259 when molecules of solute continue to dissolve at the same rate as dissolved molecules of solute continue to return to the solid state; when the rates of these opposing processes are exactly equal at saturation.

**electrolyte** 266, 267 a solute that dissolves, yielding a solution that conducts electricity.

**electromagnetic radiation (EMR)** 32 any kind of energy that is transferred in the form of waves; pure energy without mass nor charge, but ionizing radiation.

**electron** 26, 37, 44 an elementary particle carrying one unit of negative charge, equal in size to the proton; a fundamental negatively charged particle that exists in specific energy levels about the nucleus of atoms and simple ions.

**electron-dot diagram** 45 See Lewis diagram.

**electronegativity** 41, 48, 216 the relative attraction that an atom has for a pair of bonding electrons.

**electrostatic precipitation** 274 when electrically charged particles are attracted to a charged source (e.g., smoke in a smokestack).

**element** 4 composed of a single atom or a group of atoms of the same type; a pure substance containing only atoms of the same atomic number.

**empirical formula** 75 a chemical formula, indicating the simplest whole number ratio of atoms or ions in the compound; empirical—tested by experiment.

**endothermic** 259 a chemical reaction that absorbs energy; when the system absorbs heat from the surroundings, which become cooler; e.g., in bond breaking.

**energy** 2 whatever it takes to generate heat, produce electricity, or move an object (do work).

**energy change** 8 whenever heat and/or light is released or absorbed.

**energy level** 34, 37, 39 a specific and nonchanging energy which is possessed by electrons surrounding a nucleus. The electrons may only possess these specific energies within the atom or simple ion.

**equal sharing** 51 when two atoms have the same electronegativity, the bonding electrons are equidistant between the atoms.

**error** 117 the difference between an observed value and the true value; the smaller the difference, the greater the accuracy.

**ester** 307 a derivative of the reaction between carboxylic acids and alcohols; contains a -C=O(=O) group (where both double-bond O's come from the C).

**ethanol** 302 produced by the yeast fermentation of carbohydrate solutions, when used for beverages; for industrial uses, ethene is hydrated, then denatured to prevent its use as a beverage; an alcohol with the formula $C_2H_5OH$.

**evaporation** 244 the vaporization of a gas at the surface of a liquid; the vapor pressure has not yet reached the external air pressure.

**exact numbers** 119 not uncertain; having an infinite number of significant digits; including defined numbers, and the result of counting objects.

**excess** 160 more than the minimum amount required for a complete reaction.

**excited state** 35 after an atom absorbs energy, and one electron is in a higher than normal energy level.

**exothermic** 258 a chemical reaction that releases energy; when the system loses heat to the surroundings, which become warmer; e.g., in bond formation.

**extranuclear region** 26 the part of the atom that is outside the nucleus; the electron cloud.

**family** 14 a group of elements in the Periodic Table which has similar chemical and physical properties (e.g., alkali metals, halogens, noble gases, etc.).

**formula unit** 75 an imaginary unit which is the expression of the simplest whole-number ratio of cations to anions in an ionic compound.

**fraction** 286 a portion of the total crude oil molecules found in a horizontal tray in the fractionation tower. Heavier fractions contain larger molecules, etc.

**fractional distillation** 164, 286 the process of heating a substance (crude oil or air) until various types of vapors condense into trays that hold mixtures with similar boiling points. See also fractionation.

**fractionation** 286 the physical separation of crude petroleum using the different volatilities (indicated by boiling points) of petroleum's various components.

**freezing point** 243, 277 same temperature as the melting point, but releasing energy; the temperature at which a liquid is changed to a solid.

**freezing point depression** 277 the limit on the freezing point, below which salt will not melt ice.

**frequency** 32 the number of complete waves that pass a given point in one second.

**fuels** 285 when an alkane is used in a combustion reaction to produce energy for transportation, home heating, etc.

**functional group** 299 when an atom or group of atoms takes the place of one of the hydrogen atoms in a hydrocarbon.

**gamma rays** 33 EMR of very short wavelength used by doctors to treat cancer; a type of natural radioactivity.

**gas** 203 a phase where the strength of particle attractions is much less than the disruptions caused by molecular motions; totally random particle movement, with particles able to move rapidly in all directions.

**gas law stoichiometry** 199 the use of a balanced equation and the ideal gas law to predict the mass, moles, or volume of one substance in the equation, when the required information of another is known.

**graduated pipet** 252 a pipet that has a scale to measure incremental volumes of a liquid.

**gram (g)** 122 the standard unit of mass = 1 cm³ = 1 mL of water at 4°C.

**gravimetric** 149 that which measures mass.

**greenhouse effect** 187 the warming effect our atmosphere produces when it traps visible and ultraviolet rays from the sun under a blanket of carbon dioxide and water vapor.

**ground state** 35 when all electrons are in the lowest possible energy levels.

**group** 14 a vertical column in the Periodic Table, corresponding to the number of valence electrons in the atoms of an element.

**heterogeneous mixture** 6 one that is not uniform in its composition, but has distinct phases; when two or more visible phases are present in the mixture.

**homogeneous mixture** 6 one that is completely uniform in its composition (color and concentration); only one phase present.

**hydrate** 84 ionic compound that releases water when heated.

**hydrocarbon** 280 an organic compound composed only of hydrogen and carbon.

**hydrocarbon combustion reaction** 102, 106, 107 a chemical reaction where a hydrocarbon reacts with oxygen to produce carbon dioxide plus water vapor.

**hydrogen bonding** 215, 216 an intermolecular force caused by the attraction of the slightly positive hydrogen atom to an available lone pair of valence electrons in fluorine, oxygen or nitrogen; a very special case of the dipole-dipole force.

**hypertonic** 278 more concentrated than.

**hypothesis** 3 a predicted answer to a problem.

**hypotonic** 278 less concentrated than.

**ideal gas** 201 a hypothetical gas that would obey the Ideal Gas Law; where molecules have no volume and there are no intermolecular forces (IMF).

**Ideal Gas Law** 194, 195 the combination of Boyle's Law, Charles' Law, and Avogadro's Hypothesis: PV = nRT, where P = pressure (kPa); V = volume (L); n = number of moles of gas (mol); T = absolute temperature (K); R = universal gas constant (8.314 kPa•L/mol•K).

**Ideal Gas Model** 169, 170 part of the Kinetic Molecular Theory of Matter, this model makes several assumptions to simplify the explanations of gases.

**immiscible** 259 substances that do not dissolve at all.

**infrared radiation** 33 EMR most commonly known as heat or thermal energy.

**inorganic substances** 280 include exceptions of organic carbon compounds plus compounds of all other elements.

**intermolecular attractions** 209 forces of attraction that one molecule has for another molecule.

**intermolecular forces (IMF)** 206 forces between molecules; bonds.

**interparticle attractions** 209 electrostatic attractions between particles in an atom.

**ionic bonding** 32, 51, 229 a rearrangement of electrons in a chemical reaction, where electrons of the differing atoms are lost and gained; a force of attraction between a cation and an anion.

**ionic compound** 5, 73 a class of compounds where a cation (simple metal ion or positively charged polyatomic ion) combines with an anion (simple nonmetal ion or negatively charged polyatomic ion) (e.g., table salt, Epsom salt, etc.).

**isoelectronic molecules** 219 molecules that contain equal numbers of electrons.

**isotonic** 278 having the same concentration as (e.g., blood serum).

**isotope** 28, 30, 31 an atom or ion with the same atomic number (number of protons) but a different mass number (number of neutrons in the nucleus) of an element.

**IUPAC** 17 International Union of Pure and Applied Chemistry—which sets standards for nomenclature of elements and compounds.

**Kekule** 297 German architect turned chemist, who popularized the use of structural formulas.

**Kelvin temperature** 184, 185 a temperature scale of positive numbers, where absolute zero = 0 K, but degrees = Celsius degrees.

**kinetic energy** 13 the movement of matter (involving mass and velocity).

**Kinetic Molecular Theory of Matter** 169, 180, 203 particles of any substance at any real temperature are in constant motion.

**lattice energy** 229 an energy release where positive and negative ions form a regular three-dimensional arrangement found in ionic crystals.

**Law of conservation of energy** 13 energy is never lost or gained, but can be converted from one form to another (aka first law of thermodynamics).

**Law of conservation of mass** 20 the total mass of a system remains constant during a chemical or physical change.

**leading zeros** 119 zeros in front of a value which only serve to set the decimal place, are not significant digits (e.g., 0.0214).

**Lewis diagram** 45, 54, 55 a method of showing the organization of the valence electrons in an atom; see Lewis structure.

**linear** 60, 61 one shape of a nonpolar molecule, where the bond angle is 180° (e.g., methane), with two bonding pairs and zero lone pairs around a central atom.

**liquid** 203 a phase where the strength of particle attractions is approximately equal to the disruptions caused by molecular motions; semi-organized groups and clusters of particles, fairly tightly packed.

**liter (L)** 122 the standard unit of volume = 1 dm³

**London dispersion forces** 211 a subclassification of van der Waals forces, whereby there exists a temporary dipole caused by a shift in the electron cloud of neighboring atoms or molecules.

**lone pair** 45 See nonbonding electron pair.

**macroscopic** 5, 259 how it appears to the naked eye.

**malleable** 16 capable of being rolled into sheets.

**mass number** 26 the total number of protons and neutrons in a nucleus. See nucleon number.

**matter** 2 anything that has mass and takes up space (has volume).

**measured value** 129 always yields those digits that are certain, plus one uncertain digit.

**measurement** 117 a quantitative observation that includes a number that tells the amount measured, a unit that tells the kind of measurement made, and the possibility of error in the measurement.

**melting point** 41, 242 the temperature at which a crystalline solid begins to break apart, absorbing energy, changing to a liquid.

**mercury barometer** 176, 177 an instrument that measures air/atmospheric pressure; mercury column falls as air pressure drops; measured in terms of "mm Hg."

**metal** 16 an element which gains electrons and forms negative ions; group of elements in the Periodic Table that are shiny and flexible, and good conductors of heat and electricity.

**metallic bonding** 231, 232 chemical bonding where there is a simultaneous attraction of two or more nuclei for the same electrons, giving rise to an array of positive metal ions in a sea of mobile electrons.

**metalloid** 16 groups of elements in the Periodic Table that have some properties of both metals and nonmetals.

**meter (m)** 122 the standard unit of length; now the distance traveled by light in a vacuum in 1/299 792 458 of a second!

**methanol** 257, 301 methyl alcohol, methyl hydrate or wood alcohol; the simplest alcohol, formed during the preparation of charcoal from wood; highly toxic; used as a solvent, antifreeze, organic reactions.

**microwaves** 33 used to transmit signals and cook food (by making water molecules in the food spin faster, producing heat).

**mineral** 5 any element or compound that occurs naturally in the earth.

**miscible** 259 substances that dissolve in each other in all proportions.

**mixture** 6 an impure substance that contains two or more pure substances that are not chemically joined together (e.g., alloy, milk, Jell-O).

**model** 20 picture or diagram to help understand a theory.

**molar mass** 139, 142, 143 an average value of the isotopes of an element, relative to the mass of one mole of carbon-12; of a compound = sum of molar masses of its component atomic elements (in g/mol).

**molar solubility** 261 number of moles of solute required to form one liter of saturated solution at a given temperature.

**molar volume** 192 (of a gas at STP) 22.4 L/mol.

**mole** 135 $6.02 \times 10^{23}$ things.

**mole ratio** 150, 156, 199 a ratio of the coefficient of substance A/coefficient of substance B, based on the balanced chemical equation.

**molecular compound** 74 a compound that consists of more than one kind of nonmetallic atom.

**molecular dipole** 68 a molecule with an asymmetrical overall distribution of the electron charge.

**molecular formula** 75 the chemical formula of a molecule.

**molecular substance** 47, 55 a substance (element or compound) that contains only nonmetallic atoms covalently bonded as molecules.

**molecule** 6, 75 a group of atoms covalently bonded together (e.g., water, ammonia).

**monatomic** 77 having but one atom in a molecule.

**monomer** 294 the small molecules in a polymerization process.

**multiplication and division rules** 130 multiply or divide and then round off to the measurement with the fewest number of significant digits found in the question.

**neutron** 23 a fundamental neutrally charged particle found in the nucleus of atoms and simple ions, with a mass slightly larger than a proton.

**noble gas** 15, 16 the last element in a period of the Periodic Table; characterized by a lack of chemical reactivity.

**nonbonding electron pair** 45 electrons that are paired in an orbital and are not usually available for bonding with other atoms; aka lone pair.

**nonelectrolyte** 266, 267 a solute that dissolves, yielding a solution that does not conduct electricity.

**nonmetal** 16 group of elements in the Periodic Table that are dull and brittle, and poor conductors of heat and electricity.

**nonpolar covalent bonds** 67 covalent bonds in which the bonding electron pair is shared equally and is uniformly distributed between the nuclei of two bonded atoms.

**nonvolatile** 276 not easily vaporized.

**normal alkane** 282 structural isomer formula containing a straight-chain sequence of carbon atoms; names all end in "-ane," including methane ($CH_4$), ethane ($C_2H_6$), propane ($C_3H_8$), butane ($C_4H_{10}$), octane ($C_8H_{18}$), etc.

**normal boiling point** 244 the temperature at which a liquid will boil when the air pressure is at standard atmospheric pressure.

**nuclear change** 2 produces entirely different atoms; nucleus changes; one element is converted into (an)other element(s), absorbing or giving off extremely large amounts of energy.

**nucleon** 26 any particle in the nucleus (both protons and neutrons).

**nucleon number (mass number)** 26 the total number of protons and neutrons in the nucleus of an atom.

**nucleus** 23, 25 the core of the atom, located at the center of the atom, containing all of the positive charge, nearly all of the mass, but only one quadrillionth of the volume.

**octet rule** 45, 54 when four valence orbitals are completely filled with electrons ($8e^-$), the atom assumes the stable electron configuration of a noble gas.

**orbital** 44 the three-dimensional space in which an electron is most often found.

**organic substances** 280 include all compounds of carbon except oxides of carbon, carbonates, carbides and cyanides.

**osmosis** 277 the passage of solvent molecules through a semipermeable membrane.

**osmotic pressure** 277 amount of pressure needed to prevent the net flow of solvent in a tube.

**oxide** 5 a compound composed of oxygen and one other element (e.g., alumina, rust, carbon dioxide).

**pascal** 176 a unit of pressure = force/area = newton/m² = Pa.

**percent composition** 138 a way to express the proportion of elements in a compound by mass.

**percent error** 153 an indication of how close the actual yield is to the theoretical yield; = [(actual yield - theoretical yield)/theoretical yield] × 100; the degree of error in the experiment.

**percent yield** 153 an indication of the amount of product actually obtained compared to the expected amount of product.

**perfect gas** 170 a hypothetical gas in which no intermolecular forces exist between the molecules.

**period** 15 a horizontal row or series in the Periodic Table, corresponding to the energy level number of the valence electrons of the element represented.

**Periodic Table** 14 a device used to organize the elements into groups and periods by properties.

**personal error** 117 error due to personal bias, carelessness, or upon recording the data.

**petroleum refining** 286 the processes involved in separation, purification, and increasing the yield of the desirable components of crude petroleum.

**phase** 273 the physical state of matter (e.g., solid, liquid, gas).

**phase change** 203 change from one state of matter to another (e.g., freezing, melting, boiling, condensing, subliming); change in the state of matter; easily reversible; change in amount of potential energy in that matter.

**photon** 32 a packet or bundle of pure energy.

**physical change** 2 any change that alters the general shape or appearance of a substance; molecules stay the same.

**physical processes** 6 mechanical separation of components of a mixture by filtering, boiling, and centrifuging.

**physical properties** 3 characteristics of a substance that do not involve a change in the internal composition of the substance.

**pipet** 252 an instrument used to deliver small volumes of liquid very precisely.

**plated metal** 6 a metal object that has been covered (coated) with another metal (e.g., dinner utensils, faucets, or steel cans).

**polar covalent bonds** 67 covalent bonds in which the bonding electrons are unequally shared, and thus unsymmetrically distributed between the nuclei of two bonded atoms.

**polar molecule** 68 See molecular dipole.

**polyatomic ion** 81, 82 groups of atoms which are made stable by sharing electrons and gaining or losing electrons; they carry an electric charge but do not exist by themselves.

**polyethylene** 294 a polymer of ethene (also called ethylene) when it reacts with itself, forming a very long chain of hydrocarbons; used in plastics (nonbiodegradable) and synthetic fibers.

**polymer** 294 the large molecule(s) in a polymerization process, formed by linking many short molecules.

**polymerization** 294 process of forming huge, high-molar-mass molecules from smaller molecules (usually linking 50 to 10 000 monomer units).

**polyvinylchloride (PVC)** 295 a polymerization of an unsaturated organic halide.

**potential energy** 12 possibility of causing matter to move; energy stored in matter.

**precipitate** 8, 111 a new, low-solubility solid produced when solutions are mixed.

**precision** 118 the repeatability of a measurement; the closer the spread, the greater the precision; number of digits to the right of a decimal point.

**pressure gauge/sensor** 177 an instrument that measures air/atmospheric pressure, using the movement of steel or foam inside the device to operate a gauge.

**product** 96 the chemical formulas on the right side of a balanced equation; the substances resulting from a chemical change.

**properties** 2 characteristics of matter used to identify the substance—composition + structure.

**proton** 25 a fundamental positively charged particle (2000 times more massive than the electron) that exists in the nucleus of atoms and simple ions.

**pure substance** 4 a category of matter which contains only one kind of matter.

**pyramidal** 63 one shape of a polar molecule, where the bond angle is ~107° (e.g., ammonia), with three bonding pairs and one lone pair around a central atom.

**qualitative observations** 3, 117 descriptive statements of what has been determined by the five senses.

**quanta** 34 packets of light energy, whereby each wavelength corresponds to a single energy of light.

**quantitative observations** 3, 117 generally use measuring instruments to calculate how much has been determined.

**Quantum mechanical model** 24 Cloud model—electrons act as clouds within an energy level, not as particles.

**radio waves** 33 EMR of the longest wavelength, used to transmit signals in the communications field.

**radioisotope** 29 a radioactive isotope of an element; i.e., one that emits radiation.

**random error** 117 error due to unknown and unpredictable variations in experimental situations.

**reactant** 96 the chemical formulae on the left side of a balanced equation; a substance in a chemical change being transformed.

**real gas equation** 201 developed from the ideal gas law, to compensate for molecular volumes (b) and intermolecular forces (a): $(P + n^2a/V^2)(V - nb) = nRT$.

**rounding off (round-off rule)** 120 if the digit following the last significant digit is 5 or more, the last significant digit is increased by one.

**ROY G. BIV** 33 acronym for the colors in the visible spectrum—red, orange, yellow, green, blue, indigo and violet.

**rubber policeman** 153 a rubber scraper that slides onto the end of a stirring rod.

**Rutherford model** 22 "Empty Space" model—an atom has a core or nucleus containing all the positive charge and most of the mass.

**saturated** 259, 281 when a substance dissolves in a solvent to a definite, limiting value, the solution is such.

**saturated solution** 259 a solution in which the solute dissolves as quickly as the undissolved solute crystalizes again, at a specific temperature.

**scientific law** 169 a description of a regularity observed in experiments and tested and retested until accepted as true.

**scientific notation** 120 a method of expressing a number in terms of powers of ten in the form of $D.dd \times 10^n$.

**scientific reductionism** 47 the simplest theory, that explains and predicts within the context of the observations available, is considered to be the "best" theory.

**semipermeable membrane** 277 a thin layer of material filtering solvent.

**SI Rules** 124, 125 includes the use of spaces instead of commas for every 3 digits to the left or right of the decimal point; "mass" replaces "weight."

**SI Unit** 123 International System of Units are base metric units standardized internationally; they include the meter, kilogram (1000 grams), second (time), Kelvin (Temperature), and mole (amount of a substance).

**significant digits** 118 those obtained from a properly taken measurement; all the certain digits from a measurement plus one estimated (uncertain) digit; gives the degree of confidence in a measurement.

**simple composition reaction** 102, 104 a chemical reaction where elemental reactants produce a compound product.

**simple decomposition reaction** 102, 104 a chemical reaction where a compound reactant produces elemental products.

**simple ions** 39 negatively or positively charged version of an atom when it gains or loses electrons to achieve a noble-gas-like electron structure.

**single bond** 58 one pair of electrons (2 e⁻) between bonded atoms.

**single replacement reaction** 102, 105 a chemical reaction where element and compound reactants become different element and compound products.

**smog** 187 smoke + fog, which accumulates in the atmosphere as a result of a temperature inversion.

**solid** 203 a phase where the strength of particle attractions is much greater than the disruptions caused by molecular motions; highly organized, tightly packed particle arrangement with vibrational movement.

**solubility** 91, 261 the ability of compounds to dissolve (in water); concentration of a saturated solution; the quantity of solute required to produce a saturated solution at a given temperature.

**solute** 246 substance that is dissolved; that which dissolves in a solvent to produce a solution.

**solution** 6, 246 a homogeneous mixture; uniform throughout the mixture on a molecular scale.

**solvent** 246 substance that causes the solute to be dissolved; carrier for the solute.

**speed** 32 how fast the waves are actually moving (at the speed of light, $3 \times 10^8$ m/s).

**standard pressure** 176 average pressure of air at sea level = 1 atm = 760 torr = 760 mm Hg = 101.325 kPa.

**state of matter** 102 the condition of being a solid, liquid, or gas, determined by the strength of particle attractions and the degree of molecular motion.

**stereochemistry** 59 the study of the shape of molecules.

**Stock system** 73, 78, 87, 88 IUPAC's preferred naming system for compounds formed by metals that form ions of different charges; it uses the ionic charge as Roman numerals in parentheses.

**stoichiometry** 149 the use of mathematics in chemical equations.

**STP** 192 standard temperature & pressure: 0°C and 101.3 kPa (= 1 atm).

**structural formula** 55 a simple bonding representation of molecules that omits the lone electron pairs and substitutes a dash for each bonding pair of electrons.

**structural isomer** 282 compounds with the same formula but different structural formulas.

**structure** 2 how the particles are bonded together in that substance; the bonding arrangement of atoms in a molecule or ions in a crystal.

**sublimation** 245 the change of a solid directly to the gaseous phase (state) without passing through the liquid phase (said to "sublime"); when the vapor pressure of the solid is greater than or equal to the air pressure acting on the surface of the solid.

**subscript** 71 a number that indicates how many atoms or ions are present in a formula.

**substitution reaction** 285 where another atom or group of atoms is substituted for a hydrogen atom.

**super polar** 216 the enhanced dipole-dipole attraction caused by a hydrogen bond.

**supersaturated solution** 260 as a saturated solution cools, the solute remains dissolved; the solution is not at equilibrium and is unstable (e.g., honey).

**suspension** 273 a heterogeneous mixture in which relatively large particles are visible and settle upon standing.

**systematic error** 117 error due to improperly calibrated instruments, improperly "zeroed" instruments, and human reaction time.

**temperature (thermal) inversion** 187 the situation where denser, cooler air (with pollutants) is trapped under less dense, warmer air.

**tetrahedral** 62, 63 one shape of a nonpolar molecule, where the bond angle is 109.5° (e.g., methane), with four bonding pairs and zero lone pairs around a central atom.

**theoretical yield** 153 the expected amount of product based on the calculations from a balanced chemical equation. It is the amount of product obtained when the conditions are perfect.

**theory** 20 explanation of an observed phenomenon.

**thermal cracking** 287 cracking at high temperatures.

**thermal reforming** 287 uses heat to convert lighter molecules into heavier fractions, e.g., lower to higher grade fuels.

**Thermit** 109, 157 trademark for thermite, a mixture of aluminum powder and a metal oxide that emits high heat when ignited.

**Thomson model** 22 "Raisin Bun" model—an atom is a sphere of positive electricity in which negative electrons are embedded.

**tracer** 29 a radioisotope used in research to follow the progress of molecules through a system (e.g., carbon-14 and phosphorus-32).

**trailing zeros** 119 all zeros following nonzero digits (e.g., 180 000 000 includes 7 trailing zeros).

**transformations** 2 changes in matter involving changes in energy, from one form to another.

**trigonal planar** 62 one shape of a nonpolar molecule, where the bond angle is 120° (e.g., methanal), with three bonding pairs and zero lone pairs around a central atom.

**triple bond** 58 three pairs of electrons (6 e⁻) between bonded atoms.

**Tyndall Effect** 273 when a beam of light is shone through a colloid, it produces a visible beam of light (e.g., sunbeams).

**ultraviolet light** 33 EMR that causes some substances to glow in the dark; called 'black light,' responsible for suntans, sunburns, and skin cancer.

**unequal sharing** 51 a shift of bonding electrons between atoms, due to the inequality of electronegativities between atoms, such that one atom in the bond has a greater share of the electron cloud than another atom.

**universal gas constant** 194 derived from the constants contained in the Laws comprising the Ideal Gas Law; = 8.314 kPa•L•mol⁻¹•K⁻¹.

**universal solvent** 266 water's strong polarity and hydrogen bonding make it dissolve a wide variety of solutes.

**unsaturated compound** 290 compounds that have at least one double bond, enabling more hydrogen atoms to bond onto the carbon atoms.

**unsaturated solution** 259 a solution in which the amount of dissolved solute is less than the maximum equilibrium amount at a specific temperature.

**valence electrons** 37 electrons in the outermost occupied energy level.

**van der Waals forces** 210 forces of attraction between electrically neutral molecules or atoms, which cause a substance to change to a liquid or solid.

**vapor** 244 the gaseous form of a substance that is normally found as a liquid or a solid.

**vapor pressure** 244 the internal pressure of a trapped gas inside a liquid or solid.

**vaporization** 244 the process of changing from a liquid to a gas; includes evaporation, boiling and sublimation.

**viscosity** 208 resistance to flow.

**visible spectrum** 33 the EMR radiation that the eye can see.

**VSEPR Theory** 59 The Valence Shell Electron Pair Repulsion Theory provides a relatively simple and reliable basis for understanding and predicting molecular geometry; says that electron groups around a central atom in a molecule try to push as far away from each other as possible.

**water displacement** 131 a method of finding the volume of a solid, nonsoluble object (aka Archimedes' Principle).

**wavelength** 32 the distance traveled by one complete cycle of a wave (often measured from peak to peak).

**X-rays** 33 high-energy EMR used by doctors to take pictures of one's bones for medical diagnosis.

# Index

# PERIODIC TABLE OF IONS

## TABLE OF POLYATOMIC IONS

| Name | Formula |
|---|---|
| acetate | $CH_3COO^-$ |
| ammonium | $NH_4^+$ |
| benzoate | $C_6H_5COO^-$ |
| borate | $BO_3^{3-}$ |
| tetraborate | $B_4O_7^{2-}$ |
| bromate | $BrO_3^-$ |
| carbonate | $CO_3^{2-}$ |
| hydrogen carbonate or bicarbonate | $HCO_3^-$ |
| chlorate | $ClO_3^-$ |

| Name | Formula |
|---|---|
| perchlorate | $ClO_4^-$ |
| chlorite | $ClO_2^-$ |
| hypochlorite | $ClO^-$ |
| chromate | $CrO_4^{2-}$ |
| dichromate | $Cr_2O_7^{2-}$ |
| cyanate | $OCN^-$ |
| cyanide | $CN^-$ |
| hydroxide | $OH^-$ |
| iodate | $IO_3^-$ |
| nitrate | $NO_3^-$ |
| nitrite | $NO_2^-$ |

| Name | Formula |
|---|---|
| oxalate | $OOCCOO^{2-}$ |
| permanganate | $MnO_4^-$ |
| phosphate | $PO_4^{3-}$ |
| hydrogen phosphate | $HPO_4^{2-}$ |
| dihydrogen phosphate | $H_2PO_4^-$ |
| triphosphate | $P_3O_{10}^{5-}$ |
| silicate | $SiO_3^{2-}$ |
| sulfate | $SO_4^{2-}$ |
| sulfite | $SO_3^{2-}$ |
| hydrogen sulfite or bisulfite | $HSO_3^-$ |

| Name | Formula |
|---|---|
| hydrogen sulfate or bisulfate | $HSO_4^-$ |
| thiocyanate | $SCN^-$ |
| thiosulfate | $S_2O_3^{2-}$ |

- * = used often — should be learned

## NAMING ACIDS
(also see rules for naming ions)

- hydrogen ___ide becomes hydro ___ic acid
- hydrogen ___ate becomes ___ic acid
- hydrogen ___ite becomes ___ous acid

- -ate → -ite : 1 less oxygen
- per- ... -ate : 1 more oxygen
- hypo- ... -ite : 2 less oxygen
- thio- : 1 more sulfur
- bi- : 1 H+ added
- hydrogen + charge decreases

## STRONG ACIDS

| | |
|---|---|
| $HClO_4(aq)$ | $HCl(aq)$ |
| $HI(aq)$ | $HNO_3(aq)$ |
| $HBr(aq)$ | $H_2SO_4(aq)$ |

## Periodic Table (selected ions)

**Group 1A:** $H^+$ hydrogen, $Li^+$ lithium, $Na^+$ sodium, $K^+$ potassium, $Rb^+$ rubidium, $Cs^+$ cesium, $Fr^+$ francium

**Group 2A:** $Be^{2+}$ beryllium, $Mg^{2+}$ magnesium, $Ca^{2+}$ calcium, $Sr^{2+}$ strontium, $Ba^{2+}$ barium, $Ra^{2+}$ radium

**Group 18 / 8A:** He helium, Ne neon, Ar argon, Kr krypton, Xe xenon, Rn radon, Uuo ununoctium

**Group 17 / 7A:** $H^-$ hydride, $F^-$ fluoride, $Cl^-$ chloride, $Br^-$ bromide, $I^-$ iodide, $At^-$ astatide

**Group 16 / 6A:** $O^{2-}$ oxide, $S^{2-}$ sulfide, $Se^{2-}$ selenide, $Te^{2-}$ telluride, $Po^{2+}/Po^{4+}$ polonium, $116$ ununhexium (Uuh)

**Group 15 / 5A:** $N^{3-}$ nitride, $P^{3-}$ phosphide, $As^{3-}$ arsenide, $Sb^{3+}/Sb^{5+}$ antimony, $Bi^{3+}/Bi^{5+}$ bismuth, $115$ ununpentium (Uup)

**Group 14 / 4A:** C carbon, Si silicon, $Ge^{4+}$ germanium, $Sn^{4+}/Sn^{2+}$ tin, $Pb^{2+}/Pb^{4+}$ lead, $114$ ununquadium (Uuq)

**Group 13 / 3A:** B boron, $Al^{3+}$ aluminium, $Ga^{3+}$ gallium, $In^{3+}$ indium, $Tl^+/Tl^{3+}$ thallium, $113$ ununtrium (Uut)

### Transition Elements

- $Sc^{3+}$ scandium, $Y^{3+}$ yttrium, $Lu^{3+}$ lutetium, Lr lawrencium
- $Ti^{4+}/Ti^{3+}$ titanium, Zr zirconium, Hf hafnium, Rf rutherfordium
- $V^{5+}/V^{4+}$ vanadium, Nb niobium, Ta tantalum, Db dubnium
- $Cr^{3+}/Cr^{2+}$ chromium, Mo molybdenum, W tungsten, Sg seaborgium
- $Mn^{2+}/Mn^{4+}$ manganese, Tc technetium, Re rhenium, Bh bohrium
- $Fe^{3+}/Fe^{2+}$ iron (ferric/ferrous), Ru ruthenium, Os osmium, Hs hassium
- $Co^{2+}/Co^{3+}$ cobalt, Rh rhodium, Ir iridium, Mt meitnerium
- $Ni^{2+}/Ni^{3+}$ nickel, $Pd^{2+}/Pd^{4+}$ palladium, $Pt^{4+}/Pt^{2+}$ platinum, Uun ununnilium
- $Cu^{2+}/Cu^+$ copper (cupric/cuprous), $Ag^+$ silver, $Au^{3+}/Au^+$ gold, Uuu unununium
- $Zn^{2+}$ zinc, $Cd^{2+}$ cadmium, $Hg^{2+}/Hg_2^{2+}$ mercury (mercuric/mercurous), Uub ununbium

\*$Hg^+$ or $Hg_2^{2+}$

### Lanthanide Series

$La^{3+}$ lanthanum, $Ce^{3+}$ cerium, $Pr^{3+}$ praseodymium, $Nd^{3+}$ neodymium, $Pm^{3+}$ promethium, $Sm^{3+}$ samarium, $Eu^{3+}/Eu^{2+}$ europium, $Gd^{3+}$ gadolinium, $Tb^{3+}$ terbium, $Dy^{3+}$ dysprosium, $Ho^{3+}$ holmium, $Er^{3+}$ erbium, $Tm^{3+}$ thulium, $Yb^{3+}$ ytterbium, No nobelium

### Actinide Series

$Ac^{3+}$ actinium, $Th^{4+}$ thorium, $Pa^{5+}$ protactinium, $U^{4+}/U^{6+}$ uranium, $Np^{5+}$ neptunium, $Pu^{4+}/Pu^{5+}$ plutonium, $Am^{3+}$ americium, $Cm^{3+}$ curium, $Bk^{3+}$ berkelium, $Cf^{3+}$ californium, Es einsteinium, Fm fermium, Md mendelevium

## Solubility Table

| ION | $H^+$ | $NH_4^+$ | $NO_3^-$ | $CH_3COO^-$ | $Cl^-, Br^-, I^-$ | $SO_4^{2-}$ | $S^{2-}$ | $OH^-$ | $PO_4^{3-}, SO_3^{2-}, CO_3^{2-}$ |
|---|---|---|---|---|---|---|---|---|---|
| SOLUBLE ≥ 0.1 mol/L | all | all | all | all | most | most | Gp 1A and 2A, $NH_4^+$ | Gp 1A, $NH_4^+$, $Sr^{2+}$, $Ba^{2+}$ | Gp 1A, $NH_4^+$ |
| LOW SOLUBILITY s < 0.1 mol/L | none | none | none | none | $Ag^+$, $Pb^{2+}$, $Hg_2^{2+}$ | $Ag^+$, $Pb^{2+}$, $Ca^{2+}$, $Ba^{2+}$, $Sr^{2+}$ | most | most | most |

\*\* s = molar solubility

## KEY

- atomic number, ion charge (most common or most stable ion listed on top), symbol, classical name
- $26$ $Fe^{3+}$ iron(III) ferric (Stock/IUPAC name)
- $26$ $Fe^{2+}$ iron(II) ferrous
- $5$ B boron — Shaded area indicates this element does not form ionic compounds

Inner Transition Elements — Lanthanide Series / Actinide Series

COPYRIGHT © 2009 J.M. LeBel Publishers